THE GEOGRAPHY OF THE OZARK
HIGHLAND OF MISSOURI

THE GEOGRAPHY OF THE OZARK HIGHLAND OF MISSOURI

By

CARL O. SAUER

GREENWOOD PRESS, PUBLISHERS

NEW YORK

THIS BOOK IS INSCRIBED TO THE
GENTLE MEMORY OF MY FATHER, AT
WHOSE SIDE I FORMED MY FIRST
APPRECIATION OF THE THINGS THAT
CONSTITUTE THE LIVING WORLD

PREFACE

This volume is a study in regional geography, the most urgent field of geographic inquiry. Geography is among the youngest of the sciences. It is not ready, therefore, to announce many generalizations, but must concentrate on the systematic and comprehensive scrutiny of individual areas, inquiring into the conditions of the past as well as into those now existing. The collection of facts in this manner, and in this manner only, will lead to the establishment of the principles of geography. Such a study implies the attitude of the judge of conditions rather than of the advocate of theories. It is concerned with the impartial analysis of the conditions of life in a region, not with the enunciation of a theory for which evidence is to be adduced. It does not attempt to make out a case for the potency of any particular element of the environment, but contents itself with asking, What are the advantages and handicaps that are inherent in the region in question? The purposes of such a study are to furnish an adequate explanation of the conditions of life in a given area and to contribute proved statements which will aid in working out fundamental principles.

The preparation of regional monographs, numerously represented in European countries, has hardly commenced in America. A century ago the conditions and resources of various parts of our country engaged the attention of many observant writers. These accounts of early travelers constitute in fact the greater part of our geographic literature to this day. As facilities for observation increased, their number was reduced, until at present there is almost no contemporary geographic literature other than brief papers. If the curiosity which attaches to the unknown has disappeared, the need of correlated information about the parts of our country has increased as its parts have become settled and developed. This it is the province and the duty of the geographer to supply. The present paper considers a single geographic unit. The Ozark Highland of Missouri was selected because of its unusual wealth of geographic responses and because little is known concerning its conditions and possibilities. The size of the area, larger than Scotland and as large as Ireland, has precluded an exhaustive treatment of the subject. It is rather a reconnaissance, which, it is hoped, may lead to more detailed studies.

The topic is treated in three parts. The first is an outline of the environment, that is, a sketch of the region and a statement of the geographic factors. Only those things which are pertinent to an understanding of the conditions under which the people live are introduced. Rock formations are of significance in this connection in so far as they have determined topographic features, soils, and mineral resources, and in so far only. No attempt is made to sketch the physiographic history except as it contributes to the explanation of surface features, drainage conditions, and soils. The mineral resources need discussion only in so far as they have been a factor in the development of the region. Whatever is more than this may be of geologic, physiographic, or mineralogic interest, but is not pertinent to geography. The various factors of the environment differ in importance in different parts of the area. By evaluating them singly and collectively it is possible to establish contrasts between parts of the highland and thus to determine a number of smaller unit areas. Each of these subdivisions has internal unity of geographic conditions, and is set off from its neighbors by important points of contrast. These natural subregions become the units of observation in the sections that follow, in which their past and present utilization is observed and compared.

The second part considers the influences of environment on the settlement and development of the different parts of the highland. Certain portions have had continuous advantages, as others have been permanently retarded in development. In some parts certain geographic opportunities resulted in a period of early growth, soon arrested, whereas other sections, later in securing a start, have forged to the front rapidly. Three racial groups have possessed a part of the area in turn, with curious contrasts in their fortunes under the same environing conditions. This historical portion develops its argument by the fullest possible use of source materials. Wherever possible, statements from original sources are employed to bring out the thread of geographic influences that runs through the history of the region.

Finally, economic conditions are represented as they exist today, together with their explanation in so far as they are not merely the continuation of institutions the beginnings of which were traced in the historical section. In conclusion, a forecast is offered of the lines along which the future of the region will be worked out.

The study here submitted is the outgrowth of long acquaintance with the area and of deep affection for it. It is, in fact, a study in home geography, a study of the old home with its many and vivid associations.

Later residence outside of Missouri has supplied a more objective viewpoint without destroying the old familiarity. Systematic field work in the fall of 1914 and summer of 1915 has supplemented the earlier acquaintance. To consider the region as an outsider has been impossible and will always be. With the increasing distance interposed by time and space there yet remain forever green the scenes of early years. The old white church, astride its rocky point, overtopped by cedars that grow on the warm rock ledges, forever looks forth upon the fairest valley. The lower slopes are abloom with red clover, or golden with wheat. Wide fields of blue-green corn border the shaded stream, where the bass lurk in transparent pools. In the distance forests of oak mantle the hillsides, up which, past spacious farmhouses, the country roads wind. The people who move upon the scene of this account are homefolks one and all. Some have succeeded better than others, some give greater promise than others, but they are all well worth knowing, and in all cases an understanding of their various problems of making a living goes far to explain their contrasted conditions. In this spirit the study is undertaken.

The first draft of the manuscript was presented before the Seminar in Geography at the University of Chicago in 1915 and there subjected to much helpful discussion. The several parts have profited by intensive reading and criticism at the hands of Professors W. S. Tower, H. H. Barrows, and J. Paul Goode. It is difficult for me to express in any adequate way the great debt I owe to my old teacher and friendly counselor, Professor R. D. Salisbury, in the carrying out of this work. From its first planning to its publication his aid has been freely given in many ways. Grateful acknowledgments are due also to the Geographic Society of Chicago for making possible the publication of this volume, a study in a field in which avenues of publication have not yet been established.

TABLE OF CONTENTS

LIST OF ILLUSTRATIONS

PART I

THE ENVIRONMENT

CHAPTER I

INTRODUCTION

LOCATION

The Ozark Highland, locally known as "the Ozarks," lies in five states, Missouri, Arkansas, Oklahoma, Kansas, and Illinois. The boundaries are for the most part ill-defined, and estimates of area therefore may vary considerably: the northern limit is placed usually near Glasgow, Missouri, in Lat. 39° 15′ N.,[1] and the southern limit lies near Van Buren, Arkansas, in Lat. 35° 30′. On the east Shawneetown, Illinois, in Long. 88° 15′ W., may be taken as the extreme limit, and on the west the Neosho River of Oklahoma, in Long. 95° 15′.[2] The highland as thus limited forms a rude parallelogram, the long axis running northeast and southwest. The total area may be estimated at 50,000 square miles, of which about 33,000 are in southern Missouri, 13,000 in northern Arkansas,[3] 3,000 in northeastern Oklahoma, and the remainder in the Shawnee Hills of southern Illinois and in the southeastern corner of Kansas. The highland occupies nearly half of the area of Missouri and all of the state south of the Missouri River, except the Southeastern Lowlands and a triangular area in the Osage Plain on the west (Fig. 1).

The region is a few hundred miles southeast of the center of the United States and constitutes the most centrally located highland of the country. Together with the adjacent Ouachita Mountains, it forms the only extensive tract of elevated land between the Appalachian and the Rocky Mountains. The distance to the Gulf of Mexico is, on the average, little more than five hundred miles.

With regard to lines of communication the location of the area is singular. If the Shawnee Hills are disregarded, the boundaries of the Ozark region are outlined roughly by navigable rivers. These are, on the east the Mississippi, on the north the Missouri, on the south the Arkansas, and on the west the Arkansas, Neosho, and Osage. Great lines of land travel gird the area similarly. The most historic route to

[1] Marbut, *Missouri Geol. Surv.*, X, Plate II; Adams, *U.S. Geol. Surv., Twenty-second Ann. Rept.*, Part II, Plate VIII.

[2] Snider, *Oklahoma Geol. Surv., Bull. 9*, chap. ii.

[3] Estimated from Marbut, *Soil Reconnaissance of the Ozark Region* (Bureau of Soils, 1911), Fig. 2.

the Far West follows the northern margin of the Ozarks. At St. Louis routes from Chicago and the upper Mississippi Valley converge, and thence, skirting the eastern border of the Ozarks, lead to New Orleans and other points in the lower Mississippi Valley. Routes between Kansas City and the South flank the Ozarks on the west. All of these highways are located marginally to the highland, almost irrespective of

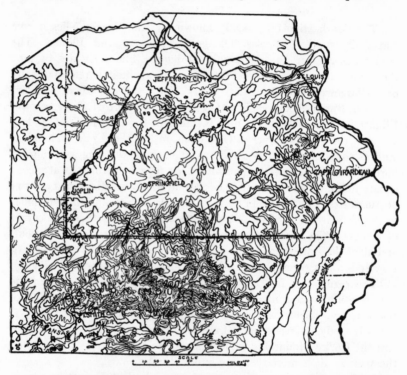

FIG. 1.—Topography of the Ozark Highland. Contour interval, 250 feet (after U.S. Geol. Surv., Folio 119, and Dictionary of Altitudes, Missouri Geol. Surv., VIII). The area of this study is inclosed by a solid black line.

its topographic character. Only two important direct lines of communication extend across the Ozarks, one between St. Louis and the Southwest, the other between Kansas City and the Southeast. One railroad trunk line from St. Louis to the Southwest, the "Frisco," crosses the Ozarks. Due to the fact that the long axis of the Ozarks runs nearly parallel to this line, three other rail routes, which serve the same territory but go around the highland, are almost as direct. From Kansas

City there are two railroads running southeast across the Ozarks. These roads, however, are recent and are not as yet of great commercial importance. The Ozarks occupy, therefore, almost an insular position with reference to great thoroughfares, being closely surrounded, but hardly invaded, by them. This condition is due in part to the obstacles which the region presents to travel, but more largely to its accidental location outside of direct lines of communication between important points.

GENERAL CHARACTER OF THE OZARK HIGHLAND

Because of the complex topography and other readily apparent contrasts between its different parts, the Ozark region has been given various appellations. The term "mountains" is the oldest, and is most employed in the very rugged Arkansas portion, where the name "Ozark" also originated.[1] It is not appropriate to the Missouri part of the Ozarks, has never been in common use there, and is resented by the inhabitants. The term "plateau" properly describes only the western third and is so limited in local usage. For the remainder of the area it is correct only in a technical physiographic sense, and is decidedly misleading otherwise. For certain large but discontinuous tracts the name "hills" is appropriately used. "Dome" and "uplift" are geologic, not geographic, expressions. The name best suited, because not too specific, is "highland." It is applicable to the mountain, plateau, and hill sections, as well as to the gently sloping border areas.

The Ozark Highland has three distinguishing characteristics of surface: (1) elevation generally higher than that of the surrounding regions; (2) greater relief; and (3) general accordance of summit levels.

---

[1] The abbreviation of place-names is common with the French of America. For instance, the old village of Cahokia, across the river from St. Louis, was known as Caho (Stirling [1765], in *Illinois Historical Collections*, XI, 125). Kaskaskia was spoken of occasionally as Cas (Alliott, in Roberts, *Louisiana under Spain, France, and the United States*, p. 133). Many French place-names were proper nouns compounded by means of a preposition with a common descriptive noun, as prairie, river, portage, post, etc. In such cases popular usage not uncommonly retained only the preposition and part of the proper name. The village on the Kaskaskia became shortened to Au Kâ (Monette, *History of the Valley of the Mississippi*, I, 43), the river landing being still known as Okaw. Similarly, the French post on the Arkansas, and the river, were shortened to "aux Arcs" or "Aux-arcs" (Bradbury, in Thwaites, *Early Western Travels*, V, 36). In pioneer days the names "Arkansas" and "Ozark" were used interchangeably, and were applied to the Arkansas River, its drainage basin, the highland north of it, and the post near its mouth (cf. Ashe, *Travels in America*, pp. 273, 275, 276; also Cuming, "Tour of the Western Country," in *Early Western Travels*, IV, 299). It is noteworthy that the region first received a distinctive name in its most rugged portion, although this was not the first part to be explored nor to be settled.

Genetically the highland is an elevated peneplain, developed upon domed rocks, which are for the most part highly resistant to erosion. It has been uplifted very unevenly, and, being composed of different rocks situated at exceedingly varying distances from vigorous drainage lines, its various portions have been modified in different ways and to different degrees by erosion.[1]

The general character of the topography is shown in Fig. 1. The highest elevations are in the Boston Mountains of Arkansas and are about 2,300 feet above sea-level. The average elevation of the Boston Mountains is about 1,800 feet, and the height above the adjoining Arkansas Valley 1,400 to 1,800 feet. This section has been sculptured into truly mountainous forms by the Arkansas and White river systems. The Ozark region proper lies for the most part north of the White River. It forms a broad elliptical shield, the main axis of which extends from the northwestern corner of Arkansas through Springfield and Cedar Gap, Missouri, to the Mississippi River in Ste. Genevieve County. This axis is also the principal watershed. Near its eastern end are several isolated knobs more than 1,700 feet above sea-level, one, Taum Sauk, in Iron County, being approximately 1,800 feet. In the southwestern part of Missouri, in Wright County, are a number of elevations about 1,700 feet above the sea. The average elevation of the crest is estimated at 1,300 feet.[2] The northern slope of the shield is more gentle than the southern, because it is longer and also because the elevation of the glacial prairies, which are adjacent to it on the north, is four to five hundred feet above that of the lowlands of the Mississippi Embayment which lie at its southeastern margin. Most of the eastern crest lies well below the average of the whole western flank.

The western part of the Missouri Ozarks, although highest on the whole, is most remote from drainage lines, and has therefore been eroded only slightly, whereas most of the eastern region is maturely dissected. The western part is still a plateau; the eastern, on the other hand, is principally rough hill country, formed by the intricate dissection of the plateau surface. The borders have in general a less rugged topography than the interior sections, because of lower original elevation, and, excepting the western border, because their erosion is well past the stage of greatest relief.

---

[1] Bradbury, in *Early Western Travels*, V, 244–45, first expressed the true character of the Ozarks. Comparing them to the plains, he said: "Although the surface is more broken and uneven, it is entirely owing to the more powerful action of the streams."

[2] Marbut, *Soil Reconnaissance*, p. 11.

The Ozarks are bounded on all sides by plains. Except on the south and southeast the transition from highland to plain is very gradual. On the southeast the margin of the Mississippi Embayment forms a clear-cut boundary. On the south the Boston Mountains constitute a well-defined escarpment bordering on the Arkansas lowlands. On the basis of elevation the borders on the west, north, and east are transition zones many miles in width. With the aid of additional geographic criteria it is possible to limit these boundaries more narrowly (Figs. 1 and 17). For the state of Missouri they are determined as follows: (1) On the west, from the state line north of Joplin to the Rock Island Railroad north of Warsaw, the boundary is roughly at the contact between the Mississippian and Pennsylvanian rock series and is marked approximately by the courses of the Spring and Sac rivers.[1] (*a*) These rivers occupy a broad, shallow trough, which divides the Ozarks from the high prairies to the west. (*b*) To the east of the two rivers the soil is derived mostly from cherty limestones typical of the Ozarks. To the west it is formed from shales, yielding a type of soil almost unknown in the Ozarks. (*c*) Where dissected the Mississippian limestone gives rise to narrow, steep-sided valleys, whereas the Pennsylvanian shales result in wide, gently sloping valleys. (*d*) The chief mineral wealth of the region included within the western Ozarks is zinc and lead; in the adjacent regions the chief resources are coal, oil, and gas. (2) From the vicinity of Warsaw north to the Missouri River the boundary is drawn chiefly on the basis of contrasts in dissection and in soil, again based partly on differences in geologic formations. (3) Along the Missouri the belt of hills north of the river is included. Their narrow, winding ridges, capped with a heavy clay soil, their many deep valleys with cherty stream beds and numerous cliffs, and their relief stamp these hills as a counterpart of the region south of the river. Their topography is the expression of a well-advanced dissection of rock formations. The country to the north of this belt is smooth glacial prairie.

In the following chapters of Part I the various geographic conditions which give individuality to the Ozark Highland of Missouri and differentiate its parts will be examined. The main thesis is taken up in Parts II and III and consists of an inquiry into the manner and extent of geographic influences in the past development and present utilization of the region by man.

[1] See geological map of Missouri; also soil map, in Marbut, *Soil Reconnaissance.*

CHAPTER II

ROCK FORMATIONS AND THEIR INFLUENCE ON TOPOGRAPHY AND SOIL

STRUCTURE OF THE AREA

Structurally the Ozarks are a broad, asymmetrical dome, whose apex is formed by the igneous rocks outcropping in St. Francois and adjacent counties (Fig. 3).[1] From this crystalline core the rocks dip outward in all directions, well beyond the limits of the area covered in this report (Fig. 2). Over a large part of the Ozark Highland the doming has been so slight that the rocks appear to the eye to be horizontal. On the margins dips in general are steeper than in the central parts (Fig. 3), and faults, minor folds, and fractures have developed.[2] In the uplift is included the complete Paleozoic section of Missouri as well as a number of pre-Cambrian formations. This geologic diversity has expressed itself in extraordinarily varied surface features, soils, and mineral resources. Geologic structure therefore determines the principal geographic contrasts shown by different parts of the highland.

As a result of the doming and of the truncation of the dome by erosion, the rock outcrops are arranged in concentric belts (Fig. 2). Near the margins of the area the belts are most numerous and narrowest, and the contrasts in the resistance of the rock formations are greatest. Here the less resistant rocks have been worn down to lowland strips, whereas in places the more resistant ones form escarpments. Ste. Genevieve County, on the eastern border, has three escarpments and three lowlands, with an almost diagrammatic development of scarp faces, back slopes, and frontal lowlands.[3] On the northern and eastern borders, in spite of the drainage, which is transverse to the strike of the rocks, several scarps are recognizable, and in places these form conspicuous features of the landscape. The largest escarpment of the Ozark region, as well as one of its most striking landmarks, is on the western margin, where the Burlington limestone forms a ridge several

[1] Winslow, *U.S. Geol. Surv., Folio 154,* p. 4.

[2] Haworth, *Bull. Geol. Soc. Amer.,* XI, 240.

[3] Marbut, *Missouri Geol. Surv.,* X, 29–73, gives an extended discussion of these scarps.

hundred feet high, extending from Arkansas northward into Polk County.

In spite of the banded character of the outcrops, the drainage is not adjusted conspicuously to rock structure. This is due to (1) the slope of the surface, (2) the stage of erosion, and (3) the relatively small

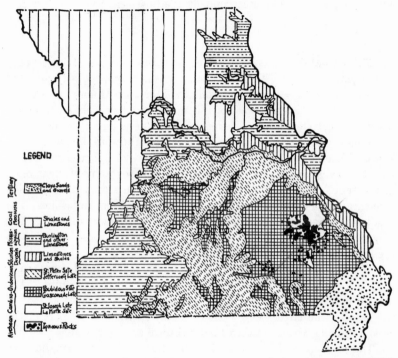

LEGEND

FIG. 2.—Geological formations (after *Missouri Bur. Geol. and Mines* and official handbook of 1904, *The State of Missouri*).

FIG. 3.—Section across Ozark Highland along line *A-A'* of Fig. 1 (after *U.S. Geol. Surv., Folio 119*).

areas of outcrop of weak rocks. The drainage is in large part down the slope of the dome, radial from its center; the larger streams therefore tend to have courses normal to the strike of the rocks. Except on the borders of the Ozarks, the present cycle of erosion is not sufficiently advanced for an extensive adjustment of tributaries to the weaker beds, which, moreover, have small and discontinuous outcrops. In addition to the escarpment areas of the border sections, adjustment of drainage has taken place principally in the apex area of the geologic dome. In the latter, which corresponds to St. Francois County and parts of the adjacent counties, contrasts in resistance of rock formations are greatest and consequently the greatest amount of adjustment has taken place.

CRYSTALLINE CORE

The crystalline rocks of Missouri lie within an area about seventy miles square (Fig. 2).[1]   Their main outcrop is in a compact body, situated south of Bismarck between the two lines of the Iron Mountain Railroad. Chiefly to the south and west of this mass are many isolated outcrops, which are scattered through eleven counties. The largest of these have a diameter of eight to twelve miles, whereas others are but a few rods across. The contact surface of the igneous rocks is irregular, due in part to bowing and folding, but largely to a topography of great relief at the time of their burial beneath the Cambrian sediments.[2]   Erosion is re-excavating this buried mountain mass in very irregular fashion. The smallest outcrops have in general been uncovered most recently. The longer the outcrops of igneous rock have been exposed to erosion the greater are their areas and their relief.

The two kinds of crystalline rocks which are important topographically are rhyolite, locally known as "porphyry," and granite. The area of outcrop of the rhyolite is about three times as great as that of the granite, the latter being dominant only in the eastern part of the crystalline rock areas, between Fredericktown and Doe Run.

The igneous rocks are by far the most resistant formations of the Ozark Highland, the compact porphyry excelling in this respect the coarser-textured granite. As a result, these rocks, and especially the porphyry, form the highest and most conspicuous elevations of the state. It is asserted that their elevation is in part the result of recent local upwarping.[3]   In the St. Francois region the hills of igneous rock rise from 500 to 843 feet above the surrounding plain, which is underlain by sedimentary rocks. The form of these elevations is rather aptly described by the popular name "knob." In principal part they are extraordinarily symmetrical cones with small summit areas. Pilot

[1] Keyes, *Missouri Geol. Surv.*, VIII, 84.

[2] Buckley, *Missouri Bur. Geol. and Mines*, Ser. 2, IX, 17.

[3] Keyes, *Bull. Geol. Soc. Amer.*, VII, 374.

Knob (Plate I *a*) is an excellent example. The granite knobs have larger summit areas and lesser slopes than those of porphyry. The slopes rarely exceed 20°, and in the case of the granite areas are considerably less. The symmetry of the knobs and their low angle of slope are due largely to the accumulation of talus. Jointing along intersecting planes has broken the massive rock into blocks, which are usually large in the case of the granite, small and very angular in that of the porphyry. The blocks of coarse-textured granite readily become rounded by weathering, as in the well-known Elephant Rocks at Graniteville, an aggregation of huge bowlders resulting from spheroidal weathering. The residual sand and clay are washed down slope, and the rounded bowlders in time roll downhill. Blocks of porphyry, on the other hand weather very slowly, and because of their angularity do not roll down slope. There is therefore a greater tendency for the granite knobs to possess a large abutment of talus than is the case with the porphyry. Granite bowlders become lodged in the beds of adjacent streams in considerable numbers, partially blocking them, and thus cause pools and rapids to be formed.

Both sorts of rock give rise to a stiff clay soil, which is thin and infertile. The granite, weathering more rapidly than the porphyry, is concealed for the most part beneath a cover of mantle rock. On the porphyry knobs, however, jagged rock masses protrude conspicuously. Because of the poor soil the areas of igneous rock have remained forested in the main.

Streams which flow over the igneous rocks have eroded valleys not much wider than their channels, and their beds are marked by series of rapids. These gorges are impassable, or nearly so, and with their barren walls and turbulent waters afford some of the wildest scenery of the Ozarks. Many stream courses are in igneous rock for a short distance only, traversing in numerous cases a single ridge. Above such gorges most of the streams of this type flow in broad valleys, floored by limestone or sandstone, their beds worn down to grade (Plate I *b*). The extensive fields and numerous roads and dwellings above the gorge are in striking contrast to the wilderness of the crystalline rocks below. These places, at which streams cross igneous barriers, are called "shut-ins" (Plate II *a*, *b*). The best known is that of the Arcadia Valley, in Iron County, where the "stream cuts directly across a narrow ridge of porphyry, notwithstanding the fact that the ridge terminates less than a mile south of the gap, and is there surrounded by limestone strata in which the creek channel could have been cut with one-tenth of the energy expended in excavating its present course."[1]   Fig. 4 shows the geologic relations of a number of these shut-ins. The streams at such places have cut through the sedimentary rocks into the buried ridges of igneous rock, and are therefore superimposed. Where this has happened a gorge is cut and a local base-level is developed on the sedimentary rock above the narrows. The shut-ins isolate the valley settlements above them very effectively, the inhabitants living in large measure independent of other settlements, but with close social relations among themselves.

▣ Crystalline Rocks

FIG. 4.—Relation of igneous and sedimentary rocks in a portion of the St. Francois region. Arrows indicate the location of gorges in the crystalline rocks, above which lie "shut-ins" (after *Missouri Bur. Geol. and Mines*, Ser. 2, IX, Plate XV).

For each example of superimposition there are several of successful adjustment. To such an extent has adjustment taken place that almost all remnants of sedimentary rock which fill old depressions in the igneous rock have become valleys (Fig. 4, Doe Run, St. Francois River, and Washita Creek). As a result the sedimentary patches are being stripped away rapidly, so that in some cases their removal hardly involves considerations of geologic time.

SEDIMENTARY FORMATIONS

The sedimentary rocks, disposed around the crystalline core, consist of limestones, sandstones, and shales. Predominantly the Ozark Highland is a region of cherty dolomitic limestones. This is true especially of the central Ozarks, in which cherty magnesian limestones determine the surface features over thousands of contiguous square miles. On the margin of the area lithologic conditions are more complex, sandstones and shales are more abundant, the limestones are less cherty[2] and less dolomitic, and the formations outcrop in narrower and more regular belts. These conditions have helped to

[1] *Missouri Geol. Surv., Sheet Report III* (1894), p. 10.

[2] An early soil map of Missouri differentiated the Ozark border soils from those of the center chiefly by chert content. See soil map in *The State of Missouri* (1904).

develop a contrast both in topography and soils between the central and border sections.

The stratigraphy of the central Ozarks and of part of the border region is known very imperfectly. The differentiation of the Cambro-Ordovician, as shown in Fig. 2, is only a rough approximation but indicates important lithologic differences and thus enables the establishment of contrasts in topography and soil.

The crystalline rock area is almost surrounded by a series of sedimentary rocks of very inferior resistance, including the *La Motte sandstone, Bonne Terre limestone*, and *Davis shale*.[1] In the majority of places these formations are not distinguishable from each other by their topography. They form in common a smooth lowland, in striking contrast to the rugged topography of the neighboring igneous masses and to the ridges of the Gasconade and Potosi limestones (Plates I *b* and II *c*). On its eastern margin the La Motte sandstone forms numerous high knolls of almost bare rock, erosion remnants due to a hard local cap. Where the Bonne Terre limestone is being eroded vigorously, steplike slopes of nearly bare rock are developed (Plate III *a*). In most places the La Motte sandstone has a covering of light, sandy soil. The soils of the Bonne Terre and Davis formations are moderately heavy clay loams, commonly red or gray, and are probably the most fertile residual soils of the Ozarks.

A scarp of the *Gasconade* and *Potosi limestones* surrounds the La Motte–Bonne Terre group. In basins of the latter formations these more resistant rocks form numerous conspicuous outliers (Plate II *c*). The Potosi limestone, with the very similar Gasconade formation, dominates the topography from the Meramec River south to the alluvial lowlands of southeast Missouri, including most of the drainage basins of the Meramec, Current, and Black rivers, and those parts of the St. Francois and Castor systems lying south of the crystalline core. The Gasconade limestone is the controlling factor also in the topography of the middle Gasconade Valley and of a large area on the Osage River centering in Camden and Miller counties. The formations consist for the most part of dolomite interbedded with large quantities of chert. Bed rock is rarely seen at the surface, as in most places it has weathered back until it is protected by a casing of chert. The chert, being fine-textured, compact, nearly homogeneous, chemically inert, and in large masses, resists erosion with a high degree of success. In places the apparent resistance of these rocks is due to a capping of hard sandstone. Because

[1] Buckley, *op. cit.*, pp. 20–44.

it fractures into flattish pieces it is not removed readily from the slope on which it has weathered out. After a time, therefore, its loose fragments form a riprap on the hillsides, which checks further erosion.

The region underlain by Gasconade and Potosi limestones has the steepest average slopes of any part of the Ozarks. Although it does not have the greatest relief, it is the most rugged highland country in Missouri, constituting a maze of deep, narrow valleys and almost knife-like ridges. Many of the tributary streams occupy blunt-headed valleys with a depth of one to two hundred feet. Ordinarily these valleys show only obscure traces of a stream channel. They are lacking, therefore, in one of the most important characteristics of stream-cut valleys. Ozark valleys of this type have been assigned to subterranean solution, continued until the roof has caved in.[1] For valley formation by this process the Gasconade limestone affords the proper conditions. Solution is extraordinarily active in it, as is attested by the great number of large caves and springs and by the small amount of surface drainage (Plate III b). Because of the thickness and resistance of the chert beds the intercalated limestones may be removed to considerable depths before the skeleton structure of the chert gives way.

The soils of this area are the least desirable of any in the Ozarks, excepting only the crystalline rock soils. They are not deficient in fertility, but are excessively stony, and with few exceptions the slopes are too steep for ordinary cultivation.

The *Roubidoux sandstone* is the most widely distributed clastic formation. It was named after a tributary of the upper Gasconade, on which it is typically developed. It "occupies the surface of many of the ridges and flat-topped divides throughout the Ozarks."[2] The largest outcrop is in Dent County, south and west of Salem. Here it forms a tract of fairly smooth land, with open, shallow valleys. It is in general not resistant to erosion, but varies greatly in character.[3] The soil derived from it is on the whole poor, thin, and easily eroded, as well as deficient in capacity for retaining moisture and humus materials.

The *Jefferson City limestone* forms a belt around the older formations, unbroken except in southeast Missouri, and broadest on the west and

[1] This origin was suggested by Nason in 1892 (*Missouri Geol. Surv.*, II, 92). Perdue (*Jour. Geol.*, IX, 47–50) accounts for valleys in the Arkansas Ozarks in the same manner. Ball and Smith come to a similar conclusion in Miller County, Missouri (*Missouri Bur. Geol. and Mines*, Ser. 2, I, 6).

[2] Buckley, *Missouri Bur. Geol. and Mines*, Ser. 2, IX, 60.

[3] *Ibid.*

south. The formation contains several beds of soft argillaceous dolomite, or "cotton rock." Chert is represented abundantly, but certain horizons are quite free from it. Where the non-cherty limestone has been subjected to vigorous erosion it forms conspicuous outcrops of bare rock or "balds," as in the White River region.[1] Largely because of the abundance of cotton rock, the formation weathers rapidly and therefore does not form steep slopes as a rule. Because of the lithologic diversity the soil is also of varying quality, but in general above the average of the Ozarks, both as to depth and fertility. It is for the most part heavy clay, some of it chert-free, some mixed abundantly with chert. On exposure much of the chert breaks up into small cubical fragments, and thereby ceases to be a troublesome factor in agriculture.

The remaining formations, younger than Cambro-Ordovician, form for the most part narrow outcrops on the borders of the highland and have varied characteristics.

The *St. Peter sandstone* extends in a narrow, interrupted belt from Callaway to St. Charles County, and thence southward to Cape Girardeau County. The width of outcrop at its maximum is eight miles.[2] The rock is composed uniformly of fine, poorly cemented sand and weathers rapidly, forming a smooth lowland with poor, sandy soil. It is overlain as a rule by a resistant limestone. In combination with its cap rock the St. Peter gives rise to one of the important scarps of the eastern and northern borders, the Crystal Escarpment.[2]

The St. Peter is succeeded by a score of other formations lying within the boundaries of the Ozarks. Most of these are of very limited distribution and inconsiderable thickness, and hence not of significant influence on surface and soil. Only one, the *Burlington limestone* or *Boone chert*, determines to any large extent surface conditions on the margins of the highland. It is one of the thickest and purest limestones of the state, except for its massive beds of chert. The formation resists erosion very well. Streams which have trenched it have for the most part formed narrow valleys with numerous cliffs and barren, cherty slopes.[3] On the western and eastern flanks of the Ozarks the limestone is underlain by much weaker beds and has formed the highest and most persistent escarpment in the state.[4] In southwest Missouri the back slope of the

[1] Marbut, *Soil Reconnaissance*, p. 34.

[2] Marbut, *Missouri Geol. Surv.*, X, 38–40.

[3] Shepard, *U.S. Geol. Surv., Water Supply and Irrigation Paper 195*, p. 21.

[4] Marbut, *Missouri Geol. Surv.*, X, 41–43.

scarp is a broad, gently rolling plain, in which the city of Springfield lies and which has been called the Springfield Structural Plain.[1]   Because of the flat surface a deep soil has been formed, which, although cherty, is very fertile.   On the north and east the formation has been dissected more severely than on the west.   In interstream areas of the White River basin, on the Arkansas border, a number of outliers of the Burlington limestone have been preserved.   They form conspicuous buttes, overtopping by several hundred feet the hills that have been formed by the erosion of older rocks.   They are called "knobs" or "mountains" locally, and because of their striking position in the landscape they have for the most part received individual names, a thing of rare occurrence in the Ozarks.

PHYSIOGRAPHIC SIGNIFICANCE OF THE CHERT

The Ozarks contain probably more chert, or flint, as it is called, than any other similar area.   Over nine-tenths of the surface chert is so abundant that it covers the roads, chokes the stream beds, and in many places all but obliterates the soil (Plate IX a).   The only parts of the highland largely free from it are the sandstone, Bonne Terre limestone, and Davis shale regions, and some of the cotton-rock areas of the Jefferson City limestone.

The chert ranges from small nodules to massive beds.   In most places it has weathered into flattened fragments of conchoidal fracture. Because of this form it is moved with difficulty by the agencies of erosion. Typically the chert consists almost entirely of silica, and is therefore little subject to chemical disintegration.   Because of its hardness, fine texture, and compactness it suffers little from mechanical weathering or from corrasion.   With the possible exception of the porphyry it is the most durable material in the Ozarks.   Consequently, the longer the weathering and erosion of a surface the greater is the quantity of chert found on it, if the underlying formation is chert-bearing.

Chert aids in the accumulation of soil, especially on steep slopes. Under normal conditions there is enough soil on the flint hills for the satisfactory growth of trees and grasses, even where slopes are steepest. Rock exposures are rare.   In the Gasconade, perhaps the chertiest of all formations, it is very difficult to find a rock exposure more than a few feet square, unless the slope is being undercut by a stream.   On the other hand, the chert-free cotton rock of the Jefferson City formation and also the chert-free Bonne Terre limestone abound in bare rock surfaces.

[1] Marbut, *Missouri Geol. Surv.*, pp. 60–65.

These are called "balds" if they form the tops of hills, otherwise "glades" (Plate III a). The upper White River and its tributaries east of McDonald County form a region of many balds and glades, where the chert-free cotton rock of the Jefferson City limestone outcrops (Plate VI b).[1] Here the gleaming white limestone shelves are interrupted horizontally by thin lines of cedar (Plate III a) and of scrub pine which have found a footing on the narrow ledges. Scenically this region is most unlike the uniformly tree-clad slopes of the flint hills. On a smaller scale the Big Niangua Valley reproduces these conditions. In the flint-free sections the weathered material may be washed down the steep slopes approximately as fast as it is formed. The flint fragments, on the other hand, cling to the slopes on which they have weathered out, and between them soil accumulates. They also tend to keep the soil porous, and as a result there is remarkably little soil erosion, considering the angle of slope.

The characteristic stream bed of the Ozarks is floored with a thick bed of chert fragments, which extend the width of the channel. These fragments are little smaller and little less angular than the chert on the hillsides. Except in the large streams there is little rounded gravel and less sand. The floor of such a stream is therefore much more resistant than are the margins of its bed. Consequently even swiftly flowing streams show a strong tendency to accomplish much lateral erosion (Plate IV a). The first result is that the bed develops a prodigious width, in many instances twenty times the width of the stream at ordinary water stages. A diagrammatic cross-section of such a bed would show a strikingly convex surface, with the stream flowing at one side of its bed, and at low water an irregular staggard line of pools along the margins. Adjacent to the water is a wide strip or "bar" of chert. In places the stream crosses this bar to the opposite margin of its gravelly bed. At such crossings wide shoals or "riffles" are developed. It is characteristic of Ozark drainage to find a rapid succession of riffles and pools, with the pools flanked by wide, white "gravel bars." This tendency to cut laterally, which is imposed by the chert, may also help to account for (1) the relatively great width of Ozark valley floors and (2) the extraordinary degree to which Ozark streams have developed meandering habits, although of rapid flow.

One of the early Missouri geologists pointed out that the Ozark region is largely lacking in the brooks so familiar to every eastern landscape.[2] Perennial surface streams are usually large enough to be called

---

[1] Marbut, *Soil Reconnaissance*, p. 35.   [2] Nason, *Missouri Geol. Surv.*, II, 90.

rivers. Valleys a quarter of a mile wide may hold in dry seasons only a few detached pools. This is not due to any dryness of climate, but is rather the result of the large quantity of chert fragments in the valleys. These provide underdrainage, and through the spaces between them the water moves freely. A valley bed, therefore, which appears dry may have a moderate amount of water beneath its surface. Shallow pits dug in the bed of a creek usually fill with water in a short time. The absence of water in the smaller valleys is also partly a result of cavernous drainage.

SOLUBILITY AS AFFECTING UNDERGROUND DRAINAGE AND TOPOGRAPHIC FORMS

Because the Ozarks are made up largely of limestone, solution has been an important factor in the removal of rock materials.[1] It is impossible to evaluate the relative importance of corrasion and of solution in developing the present surface. The fact, however, that limestone pebbles are rare on many Ozark streams, although limestone is the most common rock of the region, indicates the great importance of solution in the erosive process. The extreme clearness of Ozark streams is due in part to the fact that much of their water has come from underground sources, and has not had the opportunity to gather débris. Solution is retarded in some sections by (1) the presence of massive beds of chert underground, blocking the passage of water, and (2) by the extensive dissection of parts of the region, which has destroyed the continuity of many underground drainage channels and lowered the water table. The large undissected areas of the central Ozarks and of the western flank furnish the best conditions for the collection of underground water and for solution.[2]

The ground water dissolves passageways for itself through the limestone, forming numerous caves (Plate V a). In this way an underground drainage net is formed, which may be nearly as complicated and extensive as the drainage aboveground. Some of the underground passages collect water from a wide area. They form small subterranean rivers, as the one in Marble or Marvel Cave, Stone County, and finally issue at the surface in huge springs, such as Bryce's in Dallas, or Hahatonka in Camden County. On the western margin of the Ozarks the Burlington is the most important water-bearing formation, and is

[1] A popular account of Ozark caves and other solution features is in Stevens, *Missouri, the Center State*, I, chap. x.

[2] Shepard, *op. cit.*, p. 15.

described as having a "marvelous system of underground drainage."[1] In virtually all of the other limestones springs abound to a similar or less degree. With increasing dissection of the surface the underground drainage suffers readjustment and former channels are abandoned, appearing here and there on hillsides as dry caves (Plate III *b*). The Gasconade limestone especially is honeycombed by such abandoned passages. At lower levels this formation contains a remarkable wealth of springs issuing from solution channels of the present cycle (Plate III *b*).[2]

If solution continues long enough, part of the roof of an underground passage may collapse. In this way many of the numerous sink holes were formed, especially those in the little dissected central districts and in the Springfield Plain. Their origin is indicated by their linear distribution, outlining the course of the underground drainage line, and by the fact that in places streams still flow beneath the sink hole.[3] Many of the sinks are several hundred feet across and fifty to a hundred feet deep. They are most numerous in undissected limestone regions, although many square miles of such land are entirely without sink holes. Rarely more than two or three are found within a single section of land. On the eastern margin the limestone belt between Ste. Genevieve and Cape Girardeau is marvelously pitted with sinks, which are on the average much smaller but also much more numerous than those of the central or western portions. South of Ste. Genevieve there is scarcely a field without several. Many are sufficiently shallow to be cultivated. Their number is so great and their average size so small as to give to the upland an irregularly rolling character similar to that of a terminal moraine. Brackenridge explained them more than a century ago as "formed by the washing of the earth into fissures of the limestone rock,"[4] and Weller similarly ascribes them to solution along joints.[5]

Solution may continue underground until the roof of a cavern collapses over considerable distances. An example of this is the "Panther's Den," in Green County, really a sink of immense size.[6] Similarly, on the crest of the uplift, east of the Big Piney River, there are small solution basins, which contain much of the agricultural land of that

[1] Shepard, *Missouri Geol. Surv.*, XII, 19.
[2] Shepard, *U.S. Geol. Surv., Water Supply and Irrigation Paper 114*, p. 217.
[3] Shepard, *Missouri Geol. Surv.*, XII, 19.
[4] *Views of Louisiana* (ed. of 1817), p. 201.
[5] Personal statement.
[6] Shepard, *Missouri Geol. Surv.*, XII, 40.

region.[1] Two well-known solution basins have been thus described:
"Near Thayer, in Oregon County, is a place known as Grand Gulf. Here
there is a large underground stream visible for a short distance, and this
is generally believed to be, and probably is, the feeder of the Mammoth
spring in Arkansas. Sinking Creek, in Shannon County, flows as a surface stream for a long distance. A few miles from where it empties
into Jack's Fork it runs into a *cul de sac* formed by a crescent-shaped
mountain . . . . and reappears a mile away on the other side of the
mountain in the form of a large spring."[2] It is stated that boats can be
taken through this subterranean passage.[3] Sinking Valley is formed by
solution; the "mountain" is the initial stage of a huge natural bridge.
A number of these arches are known in various parts of the Ozarks, as at
Hahatonka and in Miller County.[4] In time the entire roof of a
cavernous passage may collapse, and a continuous valley may be formed.

[1] Marbut, *Missouri Geol. Surv.*, X, 92.

[2] Nason, *Missouri Geol. Surv.*, II, 91–92.

[3] Stevens, *Missouri, the Center State*, I, 194.

[4] Ball and Smith, *Missouri Bur. Geol. and Mines*, Ser. 2, I, 13.

CHAPTER III

EROSION CYCLES AND THEIR TOPOGRAPHIC RESULTS

GRADE-LEVELS

One of the most remarkable things about Ozark' topography is that on the upland the horizon is level nearly everywhere, even in the roughest hill sections. In other words, uniform summit-levels are characteristic of almost the entire highland area (Plate V *b*) irrespective of stratigraphic conditions, and thereby indicate an elevated peneplain. Corroborative evidence is found in high-level gravels.[1] The region has been subjected to subaerial degradation for an extremely long period, and has a complicated erosion history,[2] in which the two elements of geographic importance are (1) the general upland peneplain and (2) the valleys and their terraces. A peneplain was developed over nearly the whole of the Missouri Ozarks, the two important exceptions being the larger knobs of crystalline rocks (Plate I *a*) and those of the Burlington limestone in southwest Missouri. In both cases the monadnocks are formed by highly resistant rock. In the eastern region some of the porphyry knobs rise 600 to 800 feet above the old peneplain.[3] In southwest Missouri remoteness from streams aided in the preservation of the limestone monadnocks.

Subsequent to the general peneplanation the region was upwarped unevenly and constituted a plateau. It was raised most along the present line of highest elevation, the amount of uplift decreasing from this axis in all directions.[4] Thus a flattened, elliptical dome was formed, with its main watershed approximately where the principal divide now is. One of the first stages of subsequent uplift had its maximum development in the White River country, which was raised about 300 feet. On the middle Osage at this time the uplift was about 75 feet,[5] and still farther north, in Morgan County, it is recognizable only on careful examination.[6] The resulting rejuvenation of the streams caused the

[1] Marbut, *Missouri Bur. Geol. and Mines*, Ser. 2, VII, 10.

[2] Hershey, in *Amer. Geol.*, XXVII, 25–41, gives an extended analysis.

[3] See Buckley, *Missouri Bur. Geol. and Mines*, Ser. 2, IX, 9, and accompanying map.

[4] Marbut, *Missouri Geol. Surv.*, p. 29.   [5] Hershey, *Amer. Geol.*, XXVII, 35.

[6] Marbut, *Missouri Bur. Geol. and Mines*, Ser. 2, VII, 8–9.

incision of the White River system to a depth of several hundred feet and the development of wide alluvial floors at the new base-level. Later uplift again rejuvenated the drainage and caused the grade-level just referred to to be trenched and its remnants to be left as terraces 50 to 75 feet above the present valley floors of the White River system.

The terraces are locally called "benches," and furnish the most desired lands of the White River country (Plate VII a). The bench lands are underlain by rock at a depth of one to ten feet. Their soils are characteristically a deep red and contain much oxidized gravel and sand. Terraces are well distributed along all the larger tributaries of the White, and form a favorite location not only for farms but also for the community centers of this much-dissected area. Many of the other Ozark valleys contain less conspicuous benches, especially on the northern border. Here almost every valley has several well-defined terraces or "second bottoms," as valley lands above the level of ordinary floods are designated locally. These terraces are *par excellence* the small-grain lands of the valleys and are also suited for corn if the crops are rotated properly. They do not, however, permit continuous cropping in corn, as do the flood plains or "first bottoms."

PRESENT STAGE OF DISSECTION

Since its elevation the peneplain has been redissected so thoroughly as to have lost its plateau character to a large degree. The western part of the highland forms an exception to this statement. The difference in dissection of the various parts of the area is a function of (1) difference in elevation of the peneplained surface after uplift, (2) difference in resistance of the rocks, and (3) difference in position relative to eroding streams.

An economic interpretation of the dissection is shown in Fig. 28, which represents by shaded lines the land too rough for cultivation. As shown in this map the rough land lies mostly in the eastern and central portions, forming a crescentic belt intermediate between the borders and the central region. This dissected belt is the result of (1) elevation greater than that of the margins of the area, (2) outcrops of the Gasconade limestone, and (3) a very close drainage pattern in certain parts, as where the Osage and Gasconade rivers approach each other, with two smaller streams, the Maries and Tavern, crowded between them. In this intermediate area erosion has nearly destroyed the plateau, the remnants being knifelike ridges, in many cases having room scarcely for a wagon trace. Here the land suited to agriculture is confined almost entirely to the larger valleys.

In the northern and eastern border zones lowlands are largest and most numerous because the drainage is most mature. Because in some parts erosion is well past the stage of greatest relief and also because of the lesser original elevation, the contrast between uplands and valleys is less in these border regions than in other parts of the Ozarks. The upland here is for the most part rolling and is largely suited to agriculture. This region is typically a foreland to the higher country at the south and west.

The west central region has been affected but little by erosion. The characteristic landscape is a monotonous plain, beneath which the larger streams have cut a few steep-sided valleys with narrow bottoms. East of the Springfield Plain the plateau is cut into large strips by sub-parallel valleys, most of which run north and south. These plateau remnants are usually designated prairies (Plate VI *a*). Many have individual names, and each forms to a considerable degree a social and economic unit. The western border of the Ozarks, the Springfield Plain, is so remote from the larger streams that in spite of its high elevation it has been least dissected of any part of the highland. Here prairie conditions prevail.

The Ozark Highland therefore shows strong contrasts in topography, because of which it is divided into three main sections: (1) the eastern and northern borders of moderate relief, (2) the intermediate, rough hill belts on the north, east, and south, and (3) the smooth central and western plateaus (Figs. 1 and 18).

CHARACTERISTICS OF STREAMS AND THEIR VALLEYS

Ozark streams have not formed symmetrical drainage basins. The streams which are consequent to the original slope of the dome have enlarged their courses more rapidly than those which flow against it. North of the crest the northward flowing tributaries are much more numerous and have developed longer courses and larger basins than the southward flowing ones. South of the crest the converse is true. From the one side, therefore, the descent into a typical Ozark stream basin is gradual; from the other, abrupt.

Most of the large streams, and many of the small ones, have sinuous courses. The Osage, Gasconade, Meramec, and White rivers and their principal tributaries consist of extraordinarily large meanders incised into the upland. Fig. 5 illustrates a typical case. These meanders are inherited from a peneplained condition of the region, when sluggish streams wandered widely over the smooth surface. On rejuvenation the streams cut down their channels, in many instances 200 feet or more. During incision the stream channels continued to shift laterally at the same time that they were being sunk vertically.[1] As a result the meanders have grown to extraordinary size, the valleys have become unusually wide, and there have developed the gentle

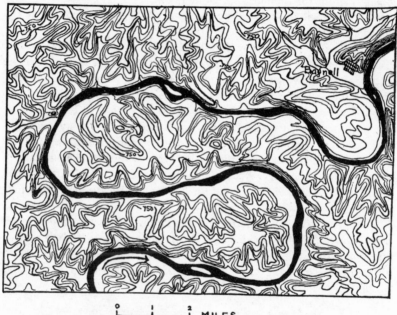

MILES

FIG. 5.—Intrenched course of the Osage River above Bagnell. Three meander loops are shown with slip-off slopes on their inner sides and cliffs on the opposite bank (*U.S. Geol. Surv.*, Versailles Topographic Sheet).

"slip-off" slopes so characteristic of the inner side of all Ozark meanders (*D* in Fig. 6). These slopes provide not merely access from valley to upland, but are invariably the sites of the choicest farms, the lower slopes being farmed, the upper ones utilized as grasslands (Plate VII). Fig. 6 represents in block diagram a typical meander. At *A* the river cuts into the upland very sharply and develops in most cases a sheer bluff on the right bank. At *B*, on the outer edge of the meander, the current is

[1] Hershey, *op. cit.*, XVI, 347–49.

directed against the left bank and there forms a bluff. The bluffs shown in Plate VIII are at the apex of meanders. At C there may or may not be bluffs.

Because of the severity of the attack at A (Fig. 6) the meander may be cut off, as in an alluvial valley. The likelihood is less in this case because the stream is attacking strata of hard rock. Also, so long as the downstream component of the current is much more vigorous than the lateral motion, there may be no undercutting at the downstream side of the neck. Rather, C may shift downstream as rapidly as A, or

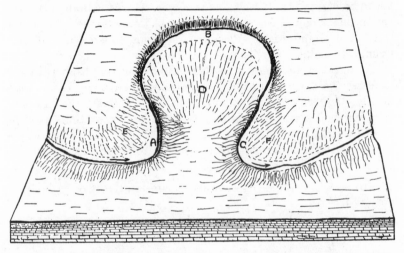

FIG. 6.—Block diagram of an intrenched meander. The stream undercuts the valley sides especially at A and B, and, unless its gradient is high, also at C. Combined down-cutting and lateral shifting give rise to gentle slopes on the inner sides of the meander loops (especially at D, but also at E and F), called "slip-off" slopes. On these the best farms of such valleys are located.

nearly so. Cut-offs are to be found, therefore, principally in the border regions, where the streams are less rapid, and where sapping takes place on both sides of the neck. This is the case on the lower Osage, Gasconade, Pomme de Terre, Whitewater, and other rivers.[1] The cut-off at Richfountain, in Osage County, is nearly diagrammatic (Fig. 12). The length of the abandoned part of the valley is almost ten miles, and forms one of the best farming sections in the country. At the apex of the old meander was an oxbow lake, drained a few years since. At the cut-off

[1] Ball and Smith, *Missouri Bur. Geol. and Mines*, Ser. 2, I, 3; Marbut, *ibid.*, VII, 12–13, and Plate VI.

the stream still flows in a narrow, rocky channel, which indicates that the shortening of the stream course at this place has been very recent. A local name for the detached portion of the upland, remaining after the neck is cut through, is "lost hill," because to the inhabitant of the Ozarks a hill is part of a continuous ridge and an isolated hill is an anomaly. These "lost hills" may be formed in another way: "A short distance upstream from the fork of two streams the widening of their graded valley floors occasionally results in the lateral abstraction of the smaller by the larger one. An isolated hill is then left. An example which bids fair to become typical for this country occurs where the town of Warsaw lies on the margin of one of these hill groups in the (former) fork of the Osage and Grand River valleys."[1] Côte sans Dessein, in Callaway County, is another example.

A secondary topographic result of the meandering habit is that it increases the opportunity for dissection of the adjoining region enormously. Instead of having a normal, linear valley a fraction of a mile in width, such a stream wanders about in a belt many times as wide, within which and adjacent to which tributaries as a rule dissect the upland in intricate patterns. These river hill belts are serious obstacles to communication in any direction.

[1] Davis, *Science*, VII, 273; see also Marbut, *Missouri Geol. Surv.*, X, and *Amer. Geol.*, XXI, 86–90.

CHAPTER IV

CLIMATE

The climate of the Ozark Highland is determined primarily by its mid-continental location in intermediate latitudes. The relief is not sufficient to affect seriously the climate of the region as a whole, and it therefore does not form a climatic province. The areal extent of the highland results in a noticeable contrast in temperature conditions between its northern and southern extremities and a slight contrast in rainfall between the eastern and western parts.

WINDS AND STORMS

The winds are largely cyclonic and the weather is variable. The region is too far south to have its temperatures much affected ordinarily by the strong winter anticyclones of the north central states, which have their origin in the far Northwest. Lesser cyclones and anticyclones, however, moving southeastward from the Rocky Mountain region cross the Ozarks frequently.[1]

The wind of maximum frequency is southerly or southeasterly.[2] From 1912 to 1914 inclusive there were only three months in which the prevailing winds at Springfield were not from the south or southeast. In the same period the prevailing wind at Columbia, just beyond the northern border, was from the south, southeast, or southwest during twenty-eight months.[3] There is a slight increase in the frequency of northerly winds with increase of latitude. Storm winds are prevailingly from the northwest.[4]

Wind velocities are lower on the average than in the northern part of the state. At Springfield the mean velocity is 10.1 miles per hour, being highest in March (12.4) and lowest in August (7.4).[5] From 1912 to 1914 there were twenty-two months in which the maximum velocity at Springfield did not exceed 25 miles.[6]

[1] Taylor, summary of nineteen years' record, *Monthly Weather Review*, XXXV, 265–67; *U.S. Weather Bur., Bull. W.*

[2] *Ibid.*

[3] Summarized from *Climatological Data*, I–III.

[4] Taylor, *op. cit.*

[5] *Monthly Weather Rev.*, XXXV, 267.   [6] *Climatological Data*, I–III.

27

Tornadoes are of almost annual occurrence in the region, although the likelihood of visitation for any one locality is very slight. Many of these storms invade the area from Kansas, and the western border is therefore most subject to them. The vicinity of Springfield is said to have been visited by a tornado three times since its settlement, in 1880, in 1883, and in 1915. The first destroyed the town of Mansfield and resulted in the death of at least a hundred persons.[1] In 1909 there were two tornadoes in the Ozarks. On April 29 one killed twenty people at Golden, Barry County, several persons at Viola, Stone County, and the city of Alton, Oregon County, was nearly destroyed, with the loss of six lives.[2] Two months later Monett and Aurora were swept by a tornado.[3]

TEMPERATURE CONDITIONS

The average annual temperature of the Ozark Highland is a little less than 55° F., which is the average for the city of Springfield. Fig. 7 represents the average January isotherms. This is the coldest month and also the one in which the temperature contrasts between different parts of the region are greatest, amounting to a maximum of 10° between the extreme north and south. In April there is only 3½° difference between north and south, and in the three summer months none. In September the maximum difference is 4½°, and in November 8°. The winters, therefore, are somewhat colder and longer in the north than in the south, whereas there is no appreciable difference in the summers. Autumn, and to a lesser extent spring, are of greatest duration in the southern sections.[4]

Fig. 8 shows the mean monthly changes of temperature for Springfield, which approximate the averages for the region as a whole. During the three summer months the mean daily maximum exceeds 80°, and in none of the winter months does it drop below 40°. In the three winter months the mean daily minimum temperatures are below 30°, and in January and February below 25°. If these average conditions were realized, therefore, in any one year, each day would have frost at night and thawing during the day. Not uncommonly in midwinter this condition does exist for weeks at a time. Periods of more than three or

[1] Taylor, op. cit.

[2] Monthly Weather Rev., XXXVII, 207.

[3] Ibid., p. 225.

[4] Summarized from averages given in Climatological Data, March, 1914, to February, 1915.

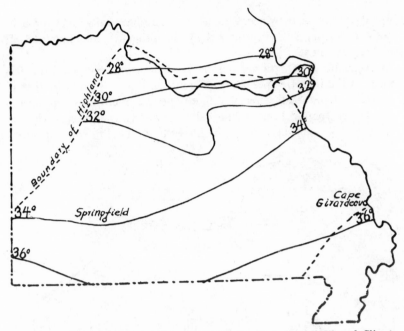

FIG. 7.—January isotherms (after *U.S. Weather Bureau, Bull. W*, and *Climatological Data*).

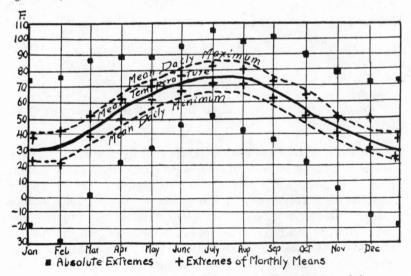

■ Absolute Extremes   + Extremes of Monthly Means

FIG. 8.—Temperature record for Springfield for nineteen-year period

four days without thawing are not usual.   The mean daily range throughout the year is 18.2°, in winter 16.8°, in spring 19°, in summer 18.3°,
and in autumn 18.8°.[1]

Available frost data are too meager to warrant any detailed statement of the frost-free period in different localities.   It appears that in
general the southeastern region is first to be free from frost in spring and
the western border last.   In the fall the west is again first subject to
frost.   This would agree with the increase of humidity southeastward.

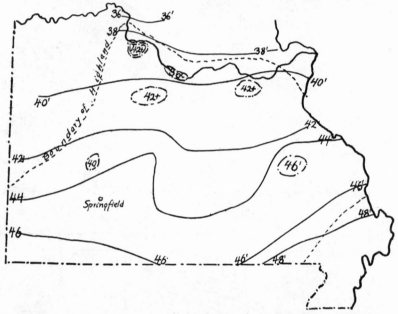

FIG. 9.—Average annual precipitation (after *U.S. Weather Bureau, Bull. W*, and
Climatological Data).

Poplar Bluff, on the east, has an average frost-free season of 193 days;
Mount Vernon, on the west, of 166.   The average length of the growing
season for the region as a whole is nearly six months.[2]   The likelihood of
unseasonable frosts depends much more largely on topographic location
than on latitude or longitude.   As a rule frosts occur in the valleys several
weeks later in spring and earlier in fall than they do on the uplands,
especially in the case of the larger valleys lying in the hill regions.   The
margins of the uplands have the best air drainage and are least subject

---

[1] Taylor, *op. cit.*   [2] *U.S. Weather Bur., Bull. W.*

to frosts. This factor has been important in determining the location of orchards and gardens. On the plateau remnants, at some distance from their margins, the frost danger again increases.

The temperature conditions described are averages, and extremes depart therefrom considerably. The highest temperature ever recorded in Missouri was 116°, at Marble Hill in 1901. Springfield has recorded an absolute range of 135° (see Fig. 9), with such anomalous temperatures as 74° in January and 22° in October and April. The variability of temperatures is greatest in winter. The cold waves may be so severe as to level all climatic distinctions within the state,[1] and not infrequently bring temperatures of −10° to −20°. They are less numerous, however, than farther north, and are of short duration, being followed usually by thawing weather within a few days. Severe winters which have been remembered in local history are those of 1834–35 and 1855–56. In the former "cattle had their horns frozen, pigs and fowls perished in great numbers, and much damage was done to fruit trees. The snow drifted to extraordinary depths, lying on the ground from December to March."[2] Protracted hot "spells" are of greater duration and effect much greater injuries because they are usually associated with droughts.

HUMIDITY AND PRECIPITATION

The nineteen-year average (1888–1906) of relative humidity at Springfield is 73, 77 during the winter months, 75 in summer, and 70 in spring. During the same period the average number of clear days per year was 150, partly cloudy 127, and cloudy 88. The months with the greatest number of clear days were October, 18, September and August, each 16; those with the most cloudy days were December and January, each 11. May has an average of 12 rainy days, whereas October has only 7.[3] In the eastern part of the Ozarks the humidity is slightly greater than at Springfield. On the whole the region is one of abundant sunshine, especially in fall, and of moderately high evaporation. The maximum frequency of rains in spring, and of sunny weather in late summer, is favorable for the production of most crops, especially corn (see Fig. 10).

Precipitation is largely in the form of rain. The average snowfall at Springfield is only 15.9 inches, or about $3\frac{1}{2}$ per cent of the total precipitation. This is less than half the snowfall at Chicago or New

---

[1] Taylor, *op. cit.*   [2] *Ibid.*

[3] Taylor, *Monthly Weather Rev.*, XXXV, 265–67; *U.S. Weather Bur., Bull. W.*

York. In January, 1914, Jefferson City and Glasgow, both on the northern border, had no snowfall. In January, 1915, widely separated stations in Bollinger, Shannon, Iron, and Laclede counties reported no snow. On the other hand, in February, 1914, 27 inches of snow fell in Phelps County and 31 in Franklin.[1] Even on the northern border snow rarely remains on the ground more than a week, and in the south a snow cover of twenty-four days in January is reported as an extraordinary

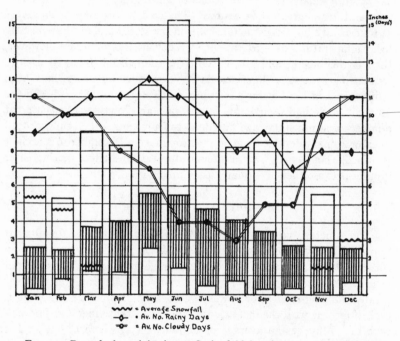

= Average Snowfall
= Av. No. Rainy Days
= Av. No. Cloudy Days

FIG. 10.—Record of precipitation at Springfield for nineteen-year period, 1888–1906. Each column represents maximum, mean, and minimum precipitation for the month.

condition.[2] The latitude position of the region favors occasional sleet storms. In April, 1914, one such storm was reported from the Ozark region; in December sleet fell seven times, and in the following month six times.[3] Not infrequently sleet does considerable damage to trees

[1] Climatological Data, March, 1914, to February, 1915.

[2] Monthly Weather Rev., XL, 403.

[3] Climatological Data, March, 1914, to February, 1915.

and wires and makes travel almost impossible for a day or two. In November, 1848, the southwestern portion witnessed a "big sleet," which was extraordinarily destructive.[1] Hail is most frequent in the western part of the area. In the entire region the Weather Bureau reported fourteen hailstorms from May to September, 1914.[2]

The annual precipitation ranges from a minimum average of 36 inches along the Missouri River valley to a maximum of 48 on the margin of the Southwestern Lowlands, as shown in Fig. 9. Fig. 10 shows the average distribution by months at Springfield, which is fairly typical of the region. The rainfall of the growing season, April to September, is on the average considerably more than half the annual precipitation. In a majority of localities the maximum rainfall is in May, with June in second place. At a few stations June has slightly more rain than May. The normal distribution therefore is very favorable to the growth of crops, the May-June maximum and the high rainfall in July being especially desirable for corn.

Unfortunately, the amount of rainfall in any one year may depart widely from the average. In Fig. 10 the extreme maximum and minimum monthly rainfall at Springfield from 1888 to 1906 is shown. The maximum annual rainfall during this time was 61 inches, the minimum 31.7. June and July, the most critical months for most crops, have the greatest variability of rainfall. According to oral accounts the greatest rain that ever occurred in this section was in July, 1876.[3] June and August, 1915, broke all monthly records in parts of the Ozarks. In August of this year there were seven widely scattered stations at which the rainfall was more than 10 inches above the monthly average. Rain fell in great quantity almost every day, grain rotted in the fields, streams were in flood repeatedly and in a number of instances reached stages never before known, and the wheat crop on almost all bottom lands, as well as a large part of the corn, was lost.

Periods of drought have done more damage than periods of excessive rain. (1) Most droughts are of greater areal extent than heavy or protracted rains. (2) They affect unfavorably a larger proportion of the land area, as they involve both the uplands and small bottoms, whereas in this region damage done by rains is limited mostly to the flooding of valleys. (3) Droughts do permanent injury to field crops during any part of the period of growth. Rains, on the other hand, do direct

[1] Taylor, *op. cit.*

[2] *Climatological Data*, March, 1914, to February, 1915.

[3] Taylor, *op. cit.*

damage only at certain seasons.   (4) Most droughts are of much longer duration than rainy periods.   In 1881 no rain fell from the middle of July to September 10, and the corn crop was nearly a failure.[1]   The great drought of 1901 caused nearly a total failure of crops.   More recently the years 1911, 1913, 1914 were very deficient in rain.   The three dry years and one very wet one (1915) out of five consecutive years were a severe ordeal to almost all rural sections.

In 1911 it was reported from Springfield that "the period of 60 days, from May 1 to June 30, almost without rain, breaks all records in this locality for continued dry weather at this season of the year.   Hay, oats, gardens, berries, and pastures are failures . . . . live stock is being fed full winter rations, water is lower than it has been for years, and the city water company is extending its mains to a new source of supply."[2]

The drought of 1913 commenced in April and lasted through August. In that period the deficiency of rainfall at Springfield was 12.04 inches, at Wheatland, Hickory County, 11.49, at Boonville 11.42, at Ironton 8.37.[3]   During this time there was accumulated an excess temperature at Springfield of 450°.   As a result, it was said, "wells have failed and springs and streams never before known to go dry are absolutely devoid of water.   The danger of fire has become a serious menace, and fire patrols have been established.   Thousands of trees have died and many more will succumb.   The leaves in many localities are dried and withered. . . . . Grass is as dry as in midwinter.   Stock is entirely on dry feed, and there is no prospect for any fall pasture."[4]   Wheat and oats alone, because they mature early, yielded fair crops.   The production of corn for the state was reduced about half,[5] and in the southern portion more than half.   Apple orchards yielded only a third of a crop.[6]

The year 1914 began with deficient precipitation generally, and so continued with few exceptions through July.   This drought was more severe in the eastern than in the western sections.   Ironton had a deficiency of 16.5 inches in the first seven months, Marble Hill of 15, Boonville of 14.1, and Springfield of 8.75.[7]   The severity of the drought

[1] Taylor, *op. cit.*

[2] *Monthly Weather Rev.*, XXXIX, 896.

[3] Summarized from *Climatological Data*, 1913.

[4] Hazen, Springfield, Mo., *Monthly Weather Rev.*, XLI, 1211; see also *ibid.*, pp. 1443–44.

[5] Department of Agriculture, *Farmers' Bulletin No. 570*, p. 24.

[6] *Ibid., No. 563*, p. 13.

[7] Summarized from *Climatological Data*, 1914.

was mitigated in places by heavy but very local rains. The dry weather also "broke" a month earlier than in the previous year. Wheat was better than average, but oats and corn suffered badly. Hay was virtually a failure and the pastures were as brown in midsummer as in late fall.

These are exceptional conditions. The area, being mid-continental, is subject to large variations of weather. In most years, however, the rainfall is ample. The losses from droughts are less than in the states adjoining Missouri on the west and no greater than in many other parts of the Middle West. The damage from excessively wet seasons is less than in the Great Lakes region and the more southerly states. All things considered, the Ozarks have a very desirable, well-moderated climate of the continental type, pleasant and healthful, and very well suited to a large variety of crops.

CHAPTER V

MATERIAL RESOURCES

SOILS[1]

Residual soils.—Most of the soil of the Ozarks was formed by the decay of the local rock formations. On upland flats and gentle slopes the surface materials are mostly derived from the underlying rock, and contacts of rock formations commonly are marked by sharp differences in soils. On steep slopes, however, the more resistant beds of rock dominate the soils, as they do the topography. Because of their resistance they form the summit elevations, and accordingly their weathered products mantle in large part the lower slopes, which are occupied by weaker rocks. This fact, added to their extensive distribution, makes the soils derived from cherty limestones by far the largest group of the region.

Cherty limestone soils: In the cherty limestone soils residual chert is the most conspicuous feature. It is present in the soil, in subsoil, at the surface, or in all of these positions. In nearly all of the soil types of this group are small areas which are free from chert. All of the limestone soils are clays or clay loams.

Because of its area and fertility the *Springfield soil* (see Fig. 11), largely derived from the Burlington limestone, is the most valuable single upland soil type of the Ozarks. It covers most of the western border, whence its name is derived, and also a strip in Cape Girardeau and Ste. Genevieve counties. Its chert content varies greatly but on the whole is high. In places there is a surface concentration which at first sight makes the land appear too stony for cultivation. In the vicinity of Springfield fences are built of cherts that have been taken from the fields. The chert, however, aids the soil in catching and storing moisture, and so helps to make it drought-resistant.[2] For the most part this soil is in the least-dissected portions of the Ozarks and therefore has good depth. It contains the mineral elements necessary for plant growth in proper proportions and ranks high in fertility. This combination of good qualities expresses itself in some of the best farms of the Ozarks.

---

[1] Marbut (Bureau of Soils, 1911), *A Soil Reconnaissance of the Ozark Region*, contains an extended discussion of soils. The nomenclature of this report has been followed for the most part.

[2] Marbut, *Soil Reconnaissance*, p. 99.

On the northern and eastern borders of the Ozarks the *Union soil* is widely distributed. The soil is formed in large part from the Jefferson City cotton rock and is therefore not very cherty. Most of it is found in a region of little relief, largely rolling prairie. In considerable part "the thickness of the soil layer goes beyond the point where it is a limiting factor in crop production."[1] Because of its compact texture the soil washes rather badly under improper cultivation. It is not a first-class

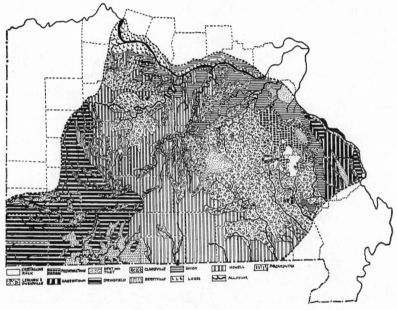

FIG. 11.—Soil map (after Marbut, *Bureau of Soils, Field Report*, 1911, and *Forty-sixth Ann. Rept. Missouri State Board of Agric.*).

soil anywhere, but in very few places is poor. In some sections, as between the Meramec River and Boeuf Creek, it is fairly good. The major part of it is cultivated and supports its industrious owners in moderate comfort.

An excellent soil of small areal distribution[2] is that of the *Iberia* "benches." It is limited for the most part to the valleys of the Gasconade, its tributaries, and Tavern Creek, and is supposed to be derived from

[1] *Ibid.*, p. 55.

[2] The areal extent is less than is shown on the map of report (*loc. cit.*).

soft limestones, which, by weathering, form benches.[1]   The benches on which it lies are usually not more than a mile wide, although Marbut reports maximum widths of eight to ten miles.   The soil is mostly clay containing more or less chert, and is highly esteemed.   The name is derived from the prosperous village of Iberia, which flourished upon such land, although miles removed from a railroad.   Its fertility has given the name Richwoods to a township in Miller County, which was described before the Civil War as having land "of excellent quality, and the growth of timber much larger than in much of the surrounding country."[2]

The *Howell soil*, derived largely from the Jefferson City formation, is the most extensive single soil type of the Ozarks.   Marbut characterizes it as having less chert than the Springfield soil and a rougher topography.[3]   Plate IX shows some of the stonier phases.   The cherts are largely on the surface and in the upper part of the soil.   In some sections, as in Howell County, they disintegrate into small fragments, making the soil gravelly rather than stony.[4]   On the whole the soil is more cherty than average and less productive.   It is thin in general and not suited to heavy cropping.   The southern counties contain some fairly good farmland.   Areas of Howell soil have been advertised heavily as fruit soil, and a number of large commercial orchards have been located on it in Howell and Oregon counties.   Probably the major part of it has never been put under cultivation.

Second in area and least in value is the *Clarksville soil*, which constitutes the climax of poverty in the Missouri Ozarks.   On the whole it contains probably as much chert as any other type of soil, is of lesser depth, and lies on steeper slopes.   This soil is derived from the Gasconade and Potosi limestones for the most part, and its deficiencies are due principally to the topography of its parent formations.   In no part of the area occupied by it is any large fraction of the surface suited to cultivation.   That its poverty is a matter of topography is indicated clearly by the fact that some of the choicest bottom lands of the Ozarks are formed by material washed down from hills covered with Clarksville soil.   The aggregate value of its area is less than that of the adjoining Fredericktown soils, one-tenth as extensive.

Non-cherty limestone soils: Three types of Ozark limestone soils are nearly chert-free.   These are the *Fredericktown, Hagerstown,* and

---

[1] Marbut, *Soil Reconnaissance*, pp. 62–64.   [3] Marbut, *op. cit.*, p. 68.

[2] *Reports Geol. Surv. of Missouri* (1855–71), p. 128.   [4] *Ibid.*, p. 71.

Berryville. The first of these is derived from the Bonne Terre limestone and other formations lying in proximity to the igneous rocks. The basins, which it forms among the knobs of igneous rocks and the hills covered by the Clarksville soil, are garden spots, cultivated from the earliest days of settlement in the Ozarks and liberally productive to this day. The deep red clays of this series are classed among the most fertile limestone soils of the United States (Plates I *b* and II *c*).[1]

The Hagerstown soil occupies a compact area in the Mississippi border region, including the major part of the uplands of Perry, Cape Girardeau, and Bollinger counties. This region has little relief, and consequently the soils have a satisfactory depth. The fertility is considerably above the average, and for the most part the land has been long in cultivation, chiefly for the production of small grains. Its farmers enjoy a very fair degree of prosperity. With a readjustment of farm practice they might be highly prosperous.

In sharp contrast to the two foregoing types is the Berryville soil, forming the "glade lands" of the White River basin. It is derived largely from the cotton rock of the Jefferson City limestone. It is for the most part a thin veneer upon rock. Where the slope has allowed the accumulation of soil to a sufficient depth it is reasonably productive. Because of the mature dissection of the area, however, such localities are few. Where cultivated on slopes it washes badly, as it lacks the chert fragments to hold it and to give good underdrainage. Chiefly because of its ease of erosion abandoned farms are most common where this soil is found (Plate VI *b*).

Sandstone soils: There are three principal areas of sandy soils: (1) the *Tilsit*, derived from the St. Peter sandstone, along the eastern border, (2) the *Dent*, derived from the La Motte sandstone, adjacent to the igneous core, and (3) the large area of Dent soils, from the Roubidoux sandstone, in Dent County and on the headwaters of the Gasconade. All are very sandy and for the most part very poor. They provide little sustenance to plants and retain water poorly. The sand is so loose that it washes badly, and hence even many moderate slopes cannot be cultivated. Marginal to these areas there is considerable land in a good state of cultivation, since here the sand has been mixed with the residuum of other formations. In spite of a relatively smooth surface only a small part of the Dent soils is farmed. Because of its more accessible location a larger proportion of the Tilsit area is improved.

[1] Marbut, *op. cit.*, p. 44.

Igneous rock soils:[1] Agriculturally the soils derived from the igneous rocks are almost negligible. They lie on steep slopes and are thin, mixed with fragments of talus, and of such an impervious nature that almost any disturbance of the surface leads quickly to serious soil erosion. At the base of most knobs igneous rock talus has slumped down upon the soils of adjacent formations, and thus extended the area of undesirable stony land well beyond the outcrops of granite and "porphyry."

Transported soils.—

Loess: Loess is known locally as "bluff soil," because it caps the bluffs of the Mississippi and Missouri rivers. At the riverward margin of the upland it is 10 to 25 feet thick. Away from the river it thins rapidly, and at a distance exceeding three or four miles it is not recognizable ordinarily, except on the northwestern margin of the area. The soil is prized because of its lasting fertility and its resistance to drought and because it can be cultivated on steeper slopes than is possible with any other soil of the region (Plate X a). Because most of this soil lies on an uneven surface it requires care and much labor in cultivation, but where these are bestowed it yields almost as large returns as do the alluvial lands. The passage from the loess to other upland soils is marked by the appearance of chert on the roadsides, of gullies in fields and pastures, of timber on the slopes, and, generally, by less prosperous farm conditions. On the lower Osage and Gasconade rivers and on some of the smaller tributaries of the Missouri, beyond the limits of the Missouri River loess belt, the valley slopes show evidence of an obscure loess cover, which enables their use for pastures and to some extent for cultivation.

Alluvial soils: Considering the relief of the region and the stage of dissection, the amount of alluvial land is great. Bottom lands are well distributed throughout the Ozarks, even the most rugged hill districts of the Gasconade limestone containing numerous spacious valleys. Some of the most valued alluvial land is on the lower courses of creeks flowing into the larger rivers. This land is in less danger of destruction by the lateral erosion of streams than are the river-bottom farms. It is, as a rule, very rich, heavy alluvium. When the larger rivers are in flood these tributaries are ponded, often for a distance of several miles. The streams are shortened, the zone of deposition is shifted upstream, and

[1] These are the soils called by Marbut "rough, stony land." As the term is equally applicable to thousands of square miles of surface in the Ozarks not underlain by igneous rocks, and as it is dissimilar in concept to the other soil names, it is not employed in this treatise.

the backwater forms a muddy lake in which most of the fine material carried down by the creek is deposited. The result is the accumulation of deeper deposits than the creeks would form unaided. The numerous terraces (see p. 22) also constitute an important part of the valley farmlands.

The valleys on the southeastern flank, as the Whitewater, Castor, St. Francois, and Black, are most subject to inundation, and here, well within the Ozarks, are swampy tracts. After leaving the Ozarks the streams from this section flow with sluggish currents for many miles through the lowlands of the Mississippi Embayment, their channels obstructed in numerous places, actually obliterated here and there, by rafts of driftwood. As a result flood waters are discharged more slowly than in the remainder of the region, and the valley lands are hence somewhat less desirable. Drainage operations now in progress in the lowlands may have some effect on these Ozark valleys.

The character of the country rock affects the nature of the alluvial deposits only to a small degree. In the area of sandstone outcrops the bottoms are somewhat sandy, but in all the limestone areas the alluvial soils are approximately of the same quality under similar conditions of deposition. On the headwaters rather thin, gravelly deposits, which rest upon cherty subsoils, are the rule, and here crops are likely to "burn out" in seasons of deficient rainfall. The great majority of the bottom land, however, is deep, rich in humus, well drained, and produces excellent crops (Plate X).

Ridge-top and prairie soils of uncertain origin.—The undissected uplands are surfaced by the Lebanon and Owensville loams, the latter being confined to the northern border. The Lebanon soils are heavy clays, commonly deficient in organic matter.[1] They are most productive in the western part of the region. The Owensville silt loam is of much better quality and forms a desirable small-grain soil. It is similar to the prairie soils of north Missouri and is possibly, like the prairie soils, in part of glacial or loessial origin.[2]

Influence of slope and exposure.—In general the most desirable soil types are those which are associated with gentle slopes, the undesirable ones those found for the most part in regions of greatest relief. The physical and chemical characteristics of soils are much less significant than the slope of the surface on which they lie. The dissected margins of areas of Springfield soils, in general the most desirable residual type of the region, are in places as unproductive as is the poorest Clarksville land,

[1] Marbut, *op. cit.*, pp. 66–67.   [2] *Ibid.*, pp. 67–68.

the least used soil of the region.   The two types are in general strongly contrasted, because most of the Springfield soil is on level prairies, the

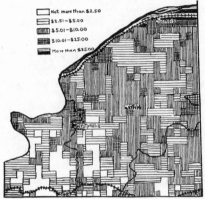

FIG. 12a.—Assessed value of land per acre in Osage County (taken from assessor's land book, 1914).

Clarksville almost entirely on rough hillsides. Low-lying solution basins in tracts of Howell soil, generally second class, furnish farming areas as choice as can be found in the Ozarks. The most important thing about the residual soils, therefore, is their depth, which in turn is dependent on the topographic expression of the rock formation from which they are derived and the position of the area with reference to drainage lines.'

The direction of slope also has an influence on the accumulation of soil.   North-facing slopes are conspicuously less stony than south-facing ones (Plate XI a).   The soil also has greater depth, contains more humus, and the angle of slope is in some instances less steep.   More shade and less heat make the soil less dry. The water table is also nearer the surface. For these reasons there is more vegetation on northern than on southern slopes and soil accumulates more rapidly and to greater depth. These conditions are not peculiar to this region but are made more evident by the presence of chert. The cherts, however, may have aided in establishing this contrast. The southern slopes are more subject to alternate thawing and freezing than the northern ones. The conductivity and low specific heat of the cherts aid temperature changes in the soil, and so facilitate soil creep on southern slopes when the changes cross the 32° point. The cherts, being less mobile than the soil, remain behind in large part.

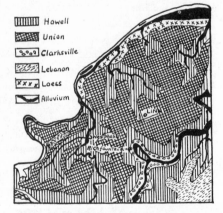

FIG. 12b.—Soil map of Osage County (after Marbut, Bureau of Soils, 1911).

The type of soil, the utilization of which is least dependent upon slope, is loess; those most dependent are derived from sandstones, igneous rocks, and non-cherty limestones. Except in small areas of these last groups, erosion has not been a serious problem in the Ozarks. The region is not densely populated, and land likely to wash is allowed as a rule to remain in timber or wild pasture.

Land values.—Land values in the Ozarks are an expression chiefly of slope, kind of soil, and transportation conditions; secondarily of mineral, water, and timber resources. The sketch maps (Figs. 12a,

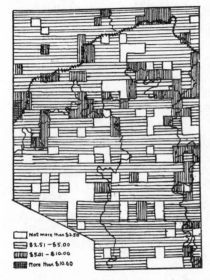

Not more than $2.50
$2.51 - $5.00
$5.01 - $10.00
More than $10.00

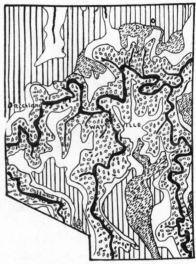

FIG. 13a.—Assessed value of land per acre in Pulaski County (taken from assessor's land book, 1914).

FIG. 13b.—Soil map of Pulaski County (after Marbut, Bureau of Soils, 1911). Legend same as for Fig. 12b. Iberia soils shown in white.

13a, 14a) show for selected parts of the Ozarks the average assessed acre values by square-mile units. For comparison, soil maps (Figs. 12b, 13b, 14b) are added.

Assessed values in the three counties selected are fairly comparable. The poorer lands are assessed at nearly their actual values (in part because they are timbered), while the more fertile lands usually sell at three to five times their assessed values. The rate of assessment is somewhat higher in Iron than in the other counties. Average values are highest in Osage County, on the northern border. This county is better located with regard to lines of transportation, and has less relief and more fertile land than the other two. Its highest priced lands are along the Missouri, the Gasconade, and the Maries rivers. Here broad bottoms, loess-covered uplands, and rail and water transportation combine to make the price of land high. Excepting the loess lands, the type of soil is not so significant in determining the value of land on the upland as is the slope of the surface. Parts of the Union soil are worth as much as fifty dollars an acre, as on the level uplands near Linn. Near the

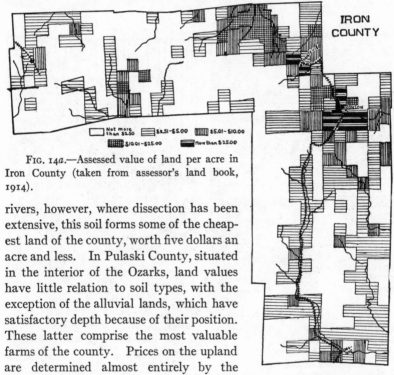

IRON COUNTY

Not more than $2.50 $2.51-$5.00 $5.01-$10.00
$10.01-$25.00   More than $25.00

FIG. 14a.—Assessed value of land per acre in Iron County (taken from assessor's land book, 1914).

rivers, however, where dissection has been extensive, this soil forms some of the cheapest land of the county, worth five dollars an acre and less. In Pulaski County, situated in the interior of the Ozarks, land values have little relation to soil types, with the exception of the alluvial lands, which have satisfactory depth because of their position. These latter comprise the most valuable farms of the county. Prices on the upland are determined almost entirely by the extent of dissection, and here the distinction of soil types for practical purposes is almost a matter of indifference. Where there is smooth prairie, as along the Frisco Railroad, land may bring fifty dollars for farming purposes. The streams are bordered by wide hill belts containing very little land that is suited to farming. Here values range from two to ten dollars per acre. Iron County, in the St. Francois Region, shows the closest accordance between soil type and land values. Here there is, however, as well a very close accordance between soil type and slope. Most of the crystalline rocks and Clarksville soils are worth about two dollars per acre. In sharp contrast to them are the alluvial and the Fredericktown soils, which sell ordinarily for fifty to one hundred and fifty dollars per acre. The Belleview basin of the Fredericktown soils forms the largest compact area of valuable farmland in the country.

A general conclusion that may be made concerning land values is that there is a preponderance of cheap, poor land in all parts of the region, except on the western border. Much of this inferior land is in the

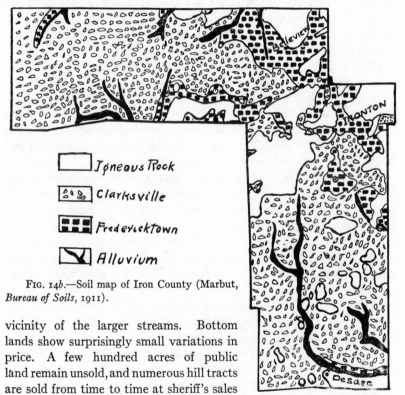

☐ *Jgneous Rock*

▨ *Clarksville*

▦ *Fredericktown*

◩ *Alluvium*

FIG. 14*b*.—Soil map of Iron County (Marbut, *Bureau of Soils*, 1911).

vicinity of the larger streams. Bottom lands show surprisingly small variations in price. A few hundred acres of public land remain unsold, and numerous hill tracts are sold from time to time at sheriff's sales for a few cents per acre. There are, on the other hand, also thousands of acres in the bottoms and on the western border that bring prices on a par with those of the best lands of the glacial prairies of north Missouri.

MINERALS

Lead and zinc ores; baryte; copper.—Galena, zinc blende, and baryte are commonly associated, but rarely all three in one locality. Galena is

most widespread in its distribution.   It has been found in all parts of
the Ozarks, and has been worked to some extent in almost every county.
The richest deposits center about St. Francois County in southeast
Missouri and about Jasper County in the southwestern part.   In the
former lead is and has been by far the most important mineral product;
this district also produces most of the baryte of the state.   In the latter
region zinc is first in importance, but large quantities of lead have been
mined as well.   The zinc ore becomes relatively more important as one
goes away from the central crystalline area.   This geographic distribution of the zinc about the margins of the Ozark Highland has been placed
in genetic relation to the movement of artesian waters outward to the
margins of the domed area.[1]

The ores are found either as residual material or "float" ore, in the
mantle rock, or in various sedimentary formations, usually in limestone.
Most of the early "mines" did not penetrate into bedrock, but were shallow pits in which the galena was picked out from the other materials
of the mantle rock.   Baryte has been produced almost solely from
residual material.[2]   Mining in the bedrock has been principally from ore
bodies of the following description: (1) sheet deposits of blende and
galena, formed along bedding, joint, and fault planes,[3] (2) great masses
of limestone, impregnated with disseminated ore,[4] (3) deposits of small
areal extent but of great thickness found chiefly in the northern part of
the Ozarks.   They are there called "circles" and are thought to be
filled sink holes.   These are similar in heaviness of yield to some of the
"breccia deposits" of the southwest, which consist of ore mixed with
residual chert, filling solution channels.[5]   The first class is one of the
common types of the Joplin district.   The second type of deposit, characteristic of the St. Francois area, enables mining operations on the
largest scale.   The third class are bonanzas while they last, but most of
them are exhausted after a short period.

Copper deposits are known principally in Shannon County.   Others
are in Franklin, Madison, and Ste. Genevieve counties.   All of them
are near crystalline rock areas.   The deposits are not large, but
the character of the ores and the low cost of flux, fuel, and labor
have made it possible to work them with profit at various times.[6]   The

---

[1] Siebenthal, *U.S. Geol. Surv., Bull. 606.*
[2] Buckley, *Missouri Bur. Geol. and Mines*, Ser. 2, IX, Plate CXX.
[3] *Ibid.*, Plate LXVI.
[4] Winslow, *Missouri Geol. Surv.*, VII, 442.   [5] *Ibid.*, pp. 461–65.
[6] Bain and Ulrich, *U.S. Geol. Surv., Bull. 267*, pp. 9–11, 50.

galena of the vicinity of the crystalline rock areas yields also copper, silver, and, more rarely, cobalt, on refining.

Iron ore.—Iron ore has been reported in almost every county in the Ozarks, most abundantly in the eastern half of the region. The ore bodies form three principal groups: (1) the specular ores in "porphyry" in the St. Francois region, (2) the hematites of the filled sinks in the central Ozarks, and (3) the brown ores of southeastern Missouri.[1] Of these the first have been most important. Iron Mountain, Pilot Knob, Shepard Mountain, Cedar Hill, and other porphyry knobs contain large bodies of hard ore in three forms: (1) ore bodies in the igneous mass, (2) conglomerate, and (3) weathered-out bowlders. The ore yields from 55 to 67 per cent of iron.[2] The hematites of the filled sinks are mostly in Phelps, Crawford, and Dent counties. They are in cone- or bowl-shaped pockets, which can often be worked by stripping. The Cherry Valley mines in Crawford County are among the largest known bodies of this type and give promise of yielding 1,000,000 tons of ore.[3] Brown ores are scattered widely through the southern part of the state. Because of their low grade they have attracted attention only recently.[4] The deposits are numerous but small, few of them exceeding 100,000 tons.[5]

Stone.—Stone of satisfactory quality and suited for many purposes can be had in most sections. Its exploitation, however, has been limited to a very few places, principally because of lack of transportation facilities and markets. A number of limestone formations yield superior quarry products, especially the Burlington, Jefferson City (cotton rock), and some of the Silurian. Because these rocks outcrop principally on the borders of the region, where there are also the best means of transportation, commercial quarries are chiefly in the Ozark margin.

The granite of the St. Francois knobs forms the most beautiful as well as the most durable stone of the state. It has a pleasing red or gray color, a medium coarse texture, takes and retains a high polish, and is jointed so as to facilitate working. It can be produced in blocks of almost any size, the Thomas Allen monument at Pittsfield, Massachusetts, containing a single block of 42 tons.[6] The porphyry on the other hand is fractured into small pieces, is difficult to work, and in pavings wears to a smooth and treacherous surface.[7]

[1] Crane, *Missouri Bur. Geol. and Mines*, Ser. 2, X, xv.

[2] *Ibid.*, p. 114.   [3] *Ibid.*, p. 92.   [4] *Ibid.*, p. xv.   [5] *Ibid.*, p. 57.

[6] Buckley and Buehler, *Missouri Bur. Geol. and Mines.*, Ser. 2, II, 74.

[7] *Ibid.*, p. 64.

The St. Peter sandstone furnishes glass sand of high grade. Production has been concentrated upon the Jefferson County outcrops, situated on the Mississippi River near St. Louis.

Clay.[1]—The commercial clays are classed mostly as fire clays and kaolins. They are on the whole highly refractory, lean, nearly free from grit, and a majority of them are white or cream-colored. Mixed with plastic clays the kaolin is excellent pottery material, which sells normally at the potteries at five to twelve dollars per ton. It will therefore bear the cost of mining by crude methods at some distance from a railroad. The so-called fire clays are less pure, more widely distributed than the kaolins, and bring a lower price. Most of the deposits have accumulated in ancient sink holes. They are in pockets rarely more than several hundred feet in diameter, but in many places sixty or more feet thick. Exceptionally large pits produce five thousand tons. In many sections their small size is balanced to some extent by the great number of clay "banks."

Because of the chert content of most of the surface clays brick clays are of rather limited distribution.

Tripoli.—Tripoli, a porous, decomposed siliceous rock, is found in Newton County, especially at Seneca and Racine.[2] There is increasing demand for this substance in the manufacture of filters, abrasive, and polish. The local deposits probably will be able to take care of the future demands of the United States for an indefinite period.

Salt.—Brine springs have been utilized in the past on a number of streams in Cooper and Howard counties, in Jefferson County, and on Saline Creek, Ste. Genevieve County.[3] They were a valuable resource in the early history of the region, but are no longer of significance.

Coal.—Although the Coal Measures do not extend into the Ozarks, coal has been found in thirty-five Ozark counties. It was formed mostly from vegetation which accumulated in sink holes and was buried. Few of these pockets are more than an acre in extent. Like the other sink deposits, it is remarkably thick, beds of ninety feet being known. They are small in yield, however, 500,000 tons being an exceptional aggregate for one pocket.[4] Because of their small size the deposits are of local value only. The coal pockets have been the instrument of numerous frauds, having been used in promotion schemes which exploited their vertical extent but concealed their horizontal limitations.

[1] Wheeler, *Missouri Geol. Surv.*, XI.   [2] *U.S. Geol. Surv., Bull. 349*, p. 429.
[3] Shumard, *Reports Geol. Surv. of Missouri* (1855–71), pp. 302, 313.
[4] Hinds, *Missouri Bur. Geol. and Mines*, Ser. 2, XI, 10.

Variety of mineral resources.—The Ozark Highland has no lack of minerals, except of mineral fuels. In only two counties, however, St. Francois and Jasper, is the mineral wealth so great as to have attracted much nonresident capital, resulting in mining development on a large scale. With these exceptions the mineral resources, though well distributed, are not large, and are important chiefly as (1) aids to the early development of the region, and (2) as accessory means of livelihood. The salt springs, iron ore, and "float" lead ore supplied pioneer needs, and thus were powerful factors in aiding settlement. At present a considerable quantity of minerals is being produced by small operators, especially by farmers, during the winter season.

WATERS

Streams.—On the northern and eastern margins of the Ozarks are the two largest rivers of the United States. They are also two of the most important interior waterways of the country and have been extremely significant in the development of the Ozarks. Although there are within the region at least a score of other streams sufficiently large to be called rivers, their utility for navigation is small. This is the result of their inaccessibility from producing areas, deficient volume, swift current, sinuous courses, and the character of their channels. Mostly they are bordered by poor and rugged hills, which act as barriers between river and the adjacent undissected uplands. The meanders of many of these streams, as of the Osage and Gasconade, impose very devious courses upon water-borne traffic. The stream channels are fairly stable for the most part, but they are shoaled in many places by bars of gravel or sand. These bars are serious obstructions, even to boats of shallow draft, except in high water.

Water power constitutes one of the great resources of the Ozarks. Rainfall, relief, character of rock formations, and extensive forest cover create excellent hydrographic conditions. There are many streams of moderate size, vigorous current, and steady flow. The large proportion of their water which is supplied by springs is a stabilizing factor of importance. "The minimum flow of these rivers is greatly increased by the springs, and is much greater than the flow of the streams of equal drainage areas in north Missouri."[1] The ordinary low-water flow of Black River, for instance, is principally from springs.[2] Because of the large

---

[1] Rodhouse, "Preliminary Study Relating to the Water Resources of Missouri," *Missouri State Univ. Eng. Exp. Sta. Bull. 15,* p. 12.

[2] *Ibid.,* p. 20.

amount of underground drainage and because the surface run-off flows largely down forested slopes, little sediment is washed into the streams, and the filling in of reservoirs is therefore not so serious a matter as in many hill sections. Gradients are for the most part steep. In the interior section they rarely fall below 3 to 5 feet per mile, and in many streams, sufficiently large for hydroelectric-power development, they reach 25 feet.[1] Rock-floored stream beds and narrow, precipitous valley slopes facilitate the construction of secure dams. Few measurements have been published on the regimen of Ozark streams or on their power possibilities. Current River at Van Buren had a mean discharge of 1,151 second feet in 1913, and on the basis of sixteen-hour service and a 50 per cent load factor is considered capable of developing at this place 7,500 h.p., with a mean head of 25 feet.[2] Power possibilities equally as good, and better, can be found on other Ozark rivers. Some of the best smaller sites are at the "shut-ins" of the St. Francois region, where streams form long rapids, inclosed by nearly sheer walls. The incised meanders of Ozark streams have resulted in projects at various places for the development of hydroelectric power. In Pulaski County the Gasconade River makes the 8-mile Moccasin Bend, which brings the river back to within a thousand feet of the beginning of the loop. A tunnel through this neck would give a fall of 20 feet, capable of developing 5,000 h.p.[3] Above and below are other similar bends.

Stages of low water are not very troublesome on most large Ozark streams. Underground drainage contributes to every river to a considerable extent, and the thousands of square miles of forest cover act as reservoirs. Current River at Van Buren, with a mean discharge of 1,151 second feet in 1913, had a minimum discharge nearly half as great, 540 feet.[4]

Floods are by far the most serious problem in the use of the Ozark valleys and their streams. During the spring and winter following the drought of 1901 the Osage was in places 40 feet deep.[5] At Van Buren, on the Current River, a discharge of 36,000 second feet has been recorded.[6] The Big Piney River in May, 1892, rose 30 feet from 4:00 P.M. to 12:00 midnight. The Current River during this same month

[1] Marbut, Missouri Geol. Surv., X, 89.

[2] Rodhouse, op. cit., pp. 23-31.

[3] Stevens, Missouri, the Center State, I, 116.

[4] Rodhouse, op. cit., p. 27.

[5] Ball and Smith, Missouri Bur. Geol. and Mines, Ser. 2, I, 14.

[6] Rodhouse, op. cit.

rose 27 feet in about the same time.[1] In October and November, 1914, rises of 20 to more than 30 feet took place overnight on the Meramec and Gasconade rivers and their tributaries. Small valleys, which had been without the semblance of a stream in the evening, held torrents the next morning which a man on horseback could not ford. In the summer of 1915 almost every large river and creek in the Ozarks was out of its banks from two to five times, and communication between many places was suspended for days at a time. It is said that Maries Creek rose 20 feet in three hours, tore loose a raft of 900 ties, and carried it 8 miles in 43 minutes. The streams usually subside nearly as rapidly as they rise, but while they are in flood they may do great damage. Banks are undercut, trees uprooted and swept away, fences demolished, haystacks and shocks of grain carried off, and fields overspread with gravel and driftwood. In the lower valleys the deposits of alluvium which are left often increase next year's crop sufficiently to make good the losses of the previous season. Floods are the result of heavy rains, of rains on frozen ground, or of sudden thaws, to all of which the region is subject. The thin soil may be saturated in a brief period, and as the water does not enter readily into the compact underlying rock much of it flows off. In very heavy rains brooks form in the smallest ravines and rapidly become torrents, which, emptying into a larger stream, may swell its volume so rapidly that its rise will be in a series of well-defined waves.

Springs and underground waters.—Excepting the crystalline core, parts of the sandstone areas, and a few border regions, almost no Ozark valley is without abundant spring water. Webster County claims "by actual count more than 2,400 living springs of clear water."[2] In Shannon, Oregon, and adjoining counties are springs "which are probably the largest in the world."[3] The largest of these is Greer Spring, 8 miles from Alton, which flows at the rate of 430,000,000 gallons per day[4] and forms a stream, at its minimum 25 feet wide and 3 feet deep.[5] Big Spring near Van Buren forms a stream 100 feet wide and discharges 223,000,000 gallons per day.[6] Bryce's Spring in Dallas County has an estimated flow of 161,568,000 gallons per day, and Hahatonka Spring in Camden County, of 158,982,000 gallons.[7] Other huge springs are

[1] Nason, *Missouri Geol. Surv.*, II, 90.   [2] *State of Missouri*, 1904, p. 539.

[3] Shepard, *U.S. Geol. Surv., Water Supply and Irrigation Paper 195*, p. 214.

[4] Bureau of Labor Statistics, *Missouri, 1912, 1913, 1914*, pp. 132–33.

[5] Shepard, *U.S. Geol. Surv., Water Supply and Irrigation Paper 114*, p. 217; also No. 110, pp. 117–20.

[6] Rodhouse, *op. cit.*, p. 17.   [7] Shepard, *op. cit.*

Alley's, near Eminence, Meramec, in Phelps County, Fullbright, in Greene, and Waynesville, in Pulaski County (Plate III *b*). Plate XI *b* illustrates springs of intermediate size, which exist in large numbers. Ozark springs attracted the attention of the earliest travelers and frontiersmen because of their number, size, and excellence; some of them were known early as the sources of rivers.[1] They are of value not only for water supply but as well for power purposes.

On the undissected uplands the underground water can be tapped by boring, but because of its depth and because of the stage of development of the region very few wells have been sunk. In mining operations generally large quantities of water are encountered and pumps are in operation constantly. In the southeastern lead region the mines furnish enough water ordinarily for concentrating the ore and for the water supply of the mining towns. In the Federal Lead Company's shafts Nos. 2 and 3, 900 to 1,600 gallons enter per minute; in shafts Nos. 6 and 7, about 2,000.[2]

Ponds.—The upland farmer is in many cases too far from springs to benefit by them. His water supply is from cisterns and ponds, both easily constructed in the heavy clay soils characteristic of the Ozark prairies. Many sink holes furnish a satisfactory water supply. If they have not become clogged accidentally, the farmer converts them readily into deep ponds by dumping in rocks or brush to catch the slope wash, or, if they have a floor of clay, by feeding stock in them and thus puddling the floor (Plate XII *a*).

NATIVE LIFE

Distribution of woodland and prairie.—When the first white men came to the Ozark Highland, they found that "both the bottoms and the high ground are alternately divided into woodlands and prairies."[3]   Old settlers unanimously state that the forest area is at present greater than when the region was first settled. "The greater part . . . . was up to the middle of the nineteenth century a region of open woods, large areas being almost treeless."[4]   It appears that the general distribution of prairie and woodland was much the same as at present, namely, that grasses grew on the undissected plateau remnants and forests occupied

---

[1] Brackenridge, *Views of Louisiana* (1st ed.), p. 100; Bradbury, in *Early Western Travels*, V.

[2] Buckley, *Missouri Bur. Geol. and Mines*, Ser. 2, IX, 97, 113.

[3] Stoddard, *Sketches of Louisiana* (1812), p. 213.

[4] Marbut, *Soil Reconnaissance*, p. 17.

the hilly regions. Prairie patches were, however, somewhat larger than at present and the forest areas correspondingly more restricted. Also many forested tracts had a parklike character, young trees and brush being largely wanting. The country north of the Meramec was observed in 1811 as rather thinly timbered.[1] It is related that a Spanish commandant in 1790 asserted his ability to drive a coach-and-four through the open woods from New Madrid to St. Louis.[2]

The relatively smooth western part was mostly prairie, whereas the hilly eastern region consisted largely of open woodland and small prairies. The boundary between the region predominantly of prairie characteristics and the region with open woods dominant lay west of the Gasconade and White River basins. At the north Jefferson City was approximately at the line of contact of the two areas.[3] East of this line were the famous pine forests of the Gasconade, as well as the forested country of the White River.[4] This eastern and northern region consisted in the main of woodland, the stand being less dense than at present. In it, however, the small areas of level upland, that is, the remnants of the original plateau surface, were in large part prairie. Stoddard, writing of the eastern part in 1812, characterized the interstream uplands as follows: "Prairies are very numerous; but few of them within our settlements, or in the neighborhood of them, are of any considerable extent. Some of them, indeed, are many miles long; but they are narrow."[5] Figs. 15 and 16 show the early distribution of prairie and woodland in Cooper County, on the northern border, and in Miller County, in the interior hill country. In these two counties prairies were coextensive with the level uplands, the densest stand of timber being in the most dissected regions.

(1) Of the various influences that caused prairies on the uplands, man was chief. Indians and other hunters were wont to set fire to the grass in fall or spring in order to improve the grazing for the buffalo, elk, and other big game. Fires were also set to drive the game toward the hunters.[6] Through this practice sprouts and tree seedlings were killed, and thus the grasslands were extended at the expense of the forests. Prairie fires are mentioned by almost every early writer as

[1] Brackenridge, *Views of Louisiana*, p. 108.

[2] Houck, *History of Missouri*, I, 26.

[3] State Board of Immigration, *Handbook of Missouri* (1881), p. 11; Bromme, *Missouri* (1835), p. 12.

[4] Schoolcraft, *View of the Lead Mines*, pp. 248–50; Brackenridge, *op. cit.*, p. 101.

[5] Stoddard, *loc. cit.*   [6] *Ibid.*

the cause of the prairies.[1] An incident illustrating this early opinion was a refusal in 1830 by the United States of a grant of land to raise timber in south Missouri, on the ground that "it is only necessary to keep out the fires to cover the prairies with timber by the operations of nature."[2] The practice of burning was continued by settlers for many years, principally to provide grazing for their stock. With

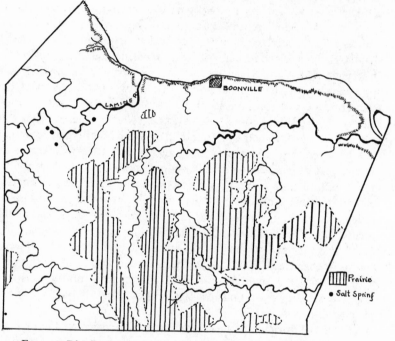

FIG. 15.—Distribution of prairie and woodland in Cooper County about 1855 (after *Missouri Geol. Surv.*, I, 202).

settlement the forest began to reclaim the burned-over tracts. The incipiency of such a change is recorded in an account of Howell County, on the Arkansas border, in 1844. "The table lands . . . . had very little timber growing on them, but were not prairie. There were what were known as post oak runners and other brush growing on the table

[1] Stoddard, *loc. cit.;* Brackenridge, *op. cit.*, p. 108; Featherstonhaugh, *Excursion through the Slave States*, I, 354–55; Swallow, *Lands and Minerals of Southwest Missouri*, p. 4; Duden, *Der Ansiedler im Staat Missouri*, p. 92.

[2] *American State Papers, Public Lands*, VI, 174.

lands, but the grass turf was very heavy and in the spring of the year the grass would soon cover the sprouts and the stranger would have taken all of the table lands, except where it was interspersed with groves, to have been prairie."[1] In the foregoing quotation the scattered groves

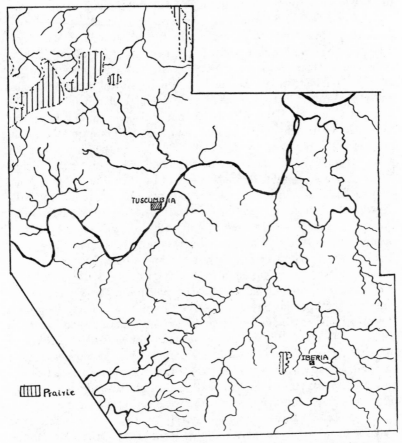

FIG. 16.—Distribution of prairie and woodland in Miller County before 1859. This county is unusually hilly (after *Geol. Surv. Missouri Repts.*, 1855–71, p. 110).

of old trees record the first cycle of vegetation; the turf, the next succession, consists of grasses resulting from fires, and the sprouts and seedlings are the third stage and the first step in the re-establishment of forest conditions. (2) In the western plateau region there are small,

[1] Monks, *History of Southern Missouri and Northern Arkansas*, pp. 7–8.

flat, and poorly drained areas which are unfavorable to tree growth. (3) The western border is continuous with the prairies of Kansas and Oklahoma, and like them is a response in part to high evaporation and occasional drought. (4) Small grassy areas, which are not known as prairies locally, are due to deficiency of soil and ground water. These are the so-called "balds" and "glades" (see p. 15).

The prairies enjoyed an excellent reputation among the stock-raisers. They were said to afford "an easy grass for cattle" and an "abundance of hay of no very inferior quality."[1] The most abundant grass and the most prized was the bluestem, because of its nutritiousness and rapid growth. It was said to grow "as high as a man's head and he upon an ordinary horse."[2] It has not withstood the severe grazing to which the region has been subjected, and is now rare. With the passing of the bluestem the Kentucky blue grass came into the region and now grows wild wherever the soil is of sufficient depth. Before 1850 it had not been found in pastures, but by 1870 it had become common in pastures and on roadsides,[3] and now is distributed generally through the limestone region of the Ozarks. More recently the sweet clover has made its appearance, establishing itself along roadsides, on stony slopes, and on gravel bars in creek beds. Although little used, it will prove probably a valuable forage plant. Japan clover (lespedeza striata) has begun its invasion of the Ozarks, from the south. Observed in the White River hills in 1896,[4] it has overspread the western border almost to the Missouri River. In Cape Girardeau and Perry counties it is growing wild in abundance, in forests, along roadsides, and in unused fields. A little of it has been observed north of the Missouri River, in Warren County. It was probably not introduced in the southeast before 1900, but it is spreading rapidly northward, thriving like the sweet clover, even on thin and stony soils. It is altogether the most significant forage plant that has naturalized itself in the state since the blue grass.

Forest associations.—Extensive forests of yellow and white pine were found in early years on the Piney forks of the Gasconade,[5] and in Ozark, Douglas,[6] Reynolds, Carter,[7] and Washington counties.[8] In

[1] Stoddard, Sketches of Louisiana (1812), p. 213.   [2] Monks, op. cit., p. 7.
[3] Broadhead, in Missouri Hist. Rev., VI, 154.
[4] Hoover, Missouri State Board Agric. Bull. III, No. 8, pp. 4–5.
[5] Flint, Hist. and Geog. of the Mississippi Valley, p. 304; Bromme, Missouri, p. 16.
[6] Shumard, Reports Geol. Surv. Missouri (1855–71), pp. 201–2.
[7] Eighth Ann. Rept. State Board of Agric., p. 54.
[8] Third Ann. Agric. Rept. of Missouri, p. 345.

Ozark County there were pine forests in the sixties, which, it was claimed with generous exaggeration, would compare favorably in size and quality with the forests of Wisconsin and Minnesota. One of these "pineries" embraced not less than 130 square miles, another about 90.[1] A portion of the interior hill section was said, in the forties, to yield logs 80 to 90 feet in length, and with a maximum diameter of 4 feet.[2] Fig. 17 shows

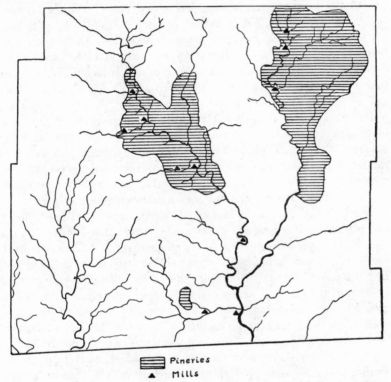

Pineries
▲ Mills

FIG. 17.—"Pineries" in Ozark County, 1855 (after *Geol. Surv. Missouri Repts.*, 1855–71).

the distribution of the larger areas of pine forest in Ozark County. Pine forests occupied most of the sandy land, part of the flint ridges (especially the southern part of the Clarksville soil),[3] and in the southern counties also grew on the flat clay uplands. The only other common

[1] Shumard, *op. cit.*
[2] Grund, *Handbuch und Wegweiser für Auswanderer* (1846), p. 213.
[3] Brackenridge, *Views of Louisiana*, p. 106.

evergreen tree is the red cedar. It grows chiefly on xerophytic lime-stone ledges, which are thinly covered with soil. Here it flourishes and forms the so-called cedar glades, parklike groves, composed of trees of highly symmetrical forms.

Upland and lowland hardwood types are sharply contrasted. The upland forests are composed almost exclusively of oaks, constituting one of the largest areas of oak forest and one of the least mixed stands of oak to be found in the country. White oak, post oak, black oak, and black jack are the main varieties. Of its total tim-bered area, Barry County reports 60 per cent in black oak, 20 per cent in post oak, and the remainder mixed. In some of the other counties the percentages have been given as follows: Douglas, white oak 20, black oak 24, black jack 10, post oak 5; Iron, black oak 40, white oak 40, pine 5; Miller, black oak 20, commercial white oak 5, black jack 35, post oak 30; Texas, black jack 35, black oak 25, white oak 20; Washington, white oak 35, black oak 25, black jack 15.[1] On the ridges black oak and white oak are most common; on the hillsides, post oak, white oak, and black jack, the last principally on very dry, stony hillsides. Besides the varieties mentioned, the chinquapin oak is found on the margins of bluffs. Hickories, especially the shellbark and pignut, grow among the oaks on the better upland soils. On the west the margin between true forest and true prairie is marked by a scrub oak, black jack association, denoting increasing xerophytism.[2] In most upland forests the timber other than oak forms a very small fraction of the stand, in many cases less than 1 per cent. The rate of growth of upland forests is slow. Giant trees are unknown on the ridges, even where there has been no cutting. The second growth, which is in very large amount, usually forms a dense stand of tall, slim trunks.

In the valleys, because of the deeper and richer soil and the greater shading and moisture supply, there is a greater variety of forest species, and individual trees grow to much larger size than on the uplands. Sycamore, cottonwood, sugar maple, water maple, walnut, butternut, hackberry, tulip tree, and bur oak were most abundant originally.[3] In addition the red oak, willow oak, sour gum, ash, pawpaw,[4] pecan, and

[1] State of Missouri (1904), county reports.   [2] Ibid., p. 234.

[3] Muench, Der Staat Missouri, pp. 35–37.

[4] Joutel (Hist. Coll. of Louisiana, I, 181–82), without naming it, gave an unmis-takable description of its fruit in 1687, based on an observation in Ste. Genevieve County. This marks probably the first appearance of the pawpaw in literature. He described the fruit as being "shaped like a middling pear, with stones in it as big as large beans. When ripe it peels like a peach; the taste is indifferent good, but rather of the sweetest."

many others are found abundantly. Oaks are represented by an extraordinary number of species. Richest of all is the forest flora of the lowlands and better limestone soils of Cape Girardeau, Perry, and Wayne counties, where such southern forms as the cypress, gums, pecans, and Spanish red oak mingle with representatives from the east, such as the beech, and with the forest associations characteristic of central Missouri. Wherever loess occurs the characteristic vegetation of the bottoms extends to the uplands, and grows as luxuriantly there as on the lower slopes.

Here, as in other sections, land has been judged largely by kind and size of trees growing upon it, and is still described commonly in terms of its prevailing tree growth. Any of the characteristic mesophytic species, such as tulip, hackberry, bur oak, or walnut, are the farmer's guaranty of first-class soil. Hickory lands are preferred to oak; black oak (*quercus velutina*) land is preferred to that on which post oak grows; and black jack or pine are considered proof of the agricultural unfitness of the soil.

Since the settlement of the region the following changes have taken place in the character of the forest: (1) greater density of stand and more undergrowth, as the result of the cutting of the large timber and the cessation of fires; (2) a great decrease in the lowland forest area; (3) a relative increase of those species that have the most efficient means of propagation. Here are, in the first place, the oaks and elms, with their coppicing habits, and in the bottoms the sycamore and cottonwood, with wind-blown seeds.

Game and fish.—The native fauna constituted one of the principal attractions of the region to early settlers. The open woodland, rich grasses, many fine springs, and numerous salt licks provided conditions under which deer, bison, and elk throve. In the homes of pioneers even now splendid elks' antlers and buffalo robes recall the days of big-game hunting. These animals attracted carnivorous beasts, wolves, bears, panthers, and wild cats. In the streams lived beaver,[1] otter, and muskrat. Other lesser fur-bearing animals, mostly found in the forests, were the mink, raccoon, opossum, skunk, fox, gray squirrel, and cottontail rabbit. Bison, elk, and beaver have disappeared from the region. The others still are found, though for the most part in rapidly declining numbers. It is asserted that deer and wolves are on the increase recently, because the slash left by lumbermen in certain sections affords means of concealment.[2]

[1] Schoolcraft, *View of the Lead Mines*, p. 249.
[2] *State of Missouri* (1904), p. 227.

Game birds were similarly abundant in early years. In 1819 was said that passenger pigeons "are so numerous that the woods seem alive with them."[1] The region still affords some of the best turkey and quail hunting in the country, but turkeys are found only in remote sections, and quail are probably not so plentiful as formerly.

Ozark streams are stocked abundantly with fish of many kinds. Typically such a stream consists of a series of shoals or "riffles" and of pools which are lined with rock ledges or with driftwood. The water is cool and clear and flows in the main over a firm gravel bottom. These are ideal conditions for game fish, and consequently every stream of this character abounds in bass as well as in jack salmon (wall-eyed pike), stone cat, and, in quiet pools, sunfish, locally called "perch" or "peerch," and suckers. On rocks, colonies of hog suckers may be seen lying. The shoals are frequented by schools of minnows, largely of the dace, darter, silversides, and chub varieties. Trout have been introduced with success into the Meramec and other cold, spring-fed streams. On the lower stretches, where the current is sluggish and the bottom muddy, channel cat, bullheads, buffalo, crappie, short-nosed gar, and eels are numerous.

[1] Schoolcraft, *op. cit.*, pp. 36–37.

CHAPTER VI

GEOGRAPHIC REGIONS

BASES OF SUBDIVISION

In 1896 Marbut[1] proposed a division of the Ozarks into physiographic provinces on the basis of escarpments. This scheme was adopted with some simplification by Adams,[2] who also added the St. Francois Mountains as a separate division. For purposes of geographic discussion the subdivision by escarpments is unsatisfactory, because it does not imply geographic contrasts and because it is based on a single physiographic element which is applicable only to the border region, and even there only in small part, since the escarpments are discontinuous over considerable distances.

In the following pages an attempt is made to subdivide the Ozark Highland of Missouri in such a way as to distinguish each area which has internal unity of geographic environment and is in contrast with the surrounding areas. To this end the location of the area, topography, drainage, soils, minerals, water supply, and vegetation are taken into account. Evidently in each region the relative significance of these elements varies greatly. In the final analysis the test of the appropriateness of these divisions is determined by the contrasts exhibited in the conditions and occupations of the inhabitants of the different areas so set apart.

There are three border regions (Fig. 18): on the north the Missouri River Border, on the east the Mississippi River Border, and on the west the Springfield Plain. The St. Francois region occupies an intermediate position, in some respects belonging to the border groups, in others to the central group. The Ozark Center is composed of the Central Plateau, together with a broad belt of hills partially surrounding it. These hill sections are designated the Courtois, Osage-Gasconade, and White River hill regions. Topographically the Central Plateau and the hill regions are in sharp contrast, but the isolation which is common to both types has expressed itself in a similar development and has differentiated them from the border areas.

[1] *Missouri Geol. Surv.*, X, 29–67, and Plate II.

[2] *U.S. Geol. Surv.*, *Twenty-second Ann. Rept.*, Part 2, pp. 69–75; also *Folio 119*.

MISSOURI RIVER BORDER

The Missouri River Border occupies nearly 5,500 square miles, of which one-sixth lies north of the river, along the southern edge of the glacial plains. As it is a transition area to the plains of north Missouri, it is not always included in the Ozarks in common usage.

In its most generalized form the region is a shallow trough, through which the Missouri River flows. The trough is elongate east and west

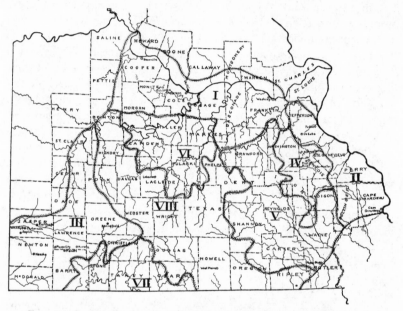

FIG. 18.—Geographic provinces of the Ozark Highland of Missouri: I, Missouri River Border; II, Mississippi River Border; III, Springfield Plain; IV, St. Francois Knob and Basin Region; V, Courtois Hills; VI, Osage-Gasconade River Hills; VII, White River Hills; VIII, Central Plateau.

and is tilted up at the west. To this form the southern tributaries of the Missouri have adapted themselves so as to flow in general in a north-easterly or even in an easterly direction. Perennial streams are more numerous and on the average larger than in any other part of the Ozarks. The southern tributaries of the Missouri are characterized by incised meanders of a large pattern, whereas the northern ones have relatively direct courses. The number and size of the streams give this region accessibility but also make it subject to floods.

The greater part of the region is rolling upland, some of it of no greater relief than pronounced morainic topography (Plate V *b*). It contains few large tracts too rough for agriculture. Fig. 19, a profile across Franklin County, shows only one narrow strip along the Meramec River in which steep slopes prevail. Near the Missouri the slopes are lowest on the average. Plate XII *b* illustrates the rolling upland of northern Gasconade County. The steepest slopes are along the middle courses of the tributaries, that is, usually at a distance of 5 to 15 miles from the Missouri. North of the river the stage of dissection is more youthful; the valleys are deep and steep-sided and the interstream areas, even near the Missouri, are flat. The topography north of the river is distinguished also by two interrupted escarpments. In the proportion of arable area this subdivision ranks second to the Springfield Plain. About half the land is in improved farms and is divided between uplands and valleys.

In its course through this region the Missouri River is confined between rock walls, the width of the immediate valley exceeding two miles only in a few places, and averaging about a mile and a half. The current is deflected from one side of the valley to the other and the meanders shift rapidly. Missouri River bottom farms therefore are notoriously precarious, many having been destroyed entirely. Its changing course keeps the valley slopes undercut to a large degree, so that bluffs are a feature of every Missouri Valley landscape.

Solution features are not conspicuous because of the maturity of stream erosion. Springs and caves are in general small. Sink holes are most numerous in the Burlington limestone of the extreme western part of the area.[1]

Soils are much above the average of the Ozark region. The proportion of alluvial lands to total area is greater than in any other section. The upland soils in the order of their desirability are loess, Owensville loam, Union, Lebanon, and Howell. Loess areas are more extensive than in any other section. The Owensville loam is confined to this region.

Mineral resources are varied, but not of great value. Lead, iron, copper, salt, and saltpeter have been produced

[1] Van Horn, *Missouri Bur. Geol. and Mines*, Ser. 2, III, 14.

FIG. 19.—Profile across Missouri River Border from Warrenton through Bourbon to the Meramec River. Distance, 28 miles.

in times past.   Coal pockets are most numerous in this region, and fire clay is found in many places.

The boundary of this subdivision on the east is placed so as to exclude the dissected Big River region and the sandy Tilsit soils.   The southern boundary is for the most part along a definite break in topography, at which soil conditions also change, namely along the northern margins

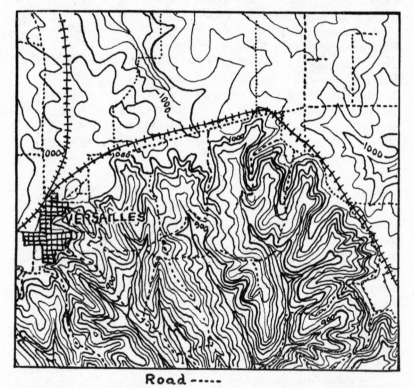

Road ----

Fig. 20.—Contact between Missouri River Border and Osage-Gasconade River Hills at Versailles.   Contour interval, 20 feet (Gravois Mills Topographic Sheet)

of the Gasconade limestone.   This boundary line parallels the Meramec River to the vicinity of Rolla.   From Rolla north to Summerfield it follows the edge of the dissected Gasconade Valley.   The boundary from Summerfield to the Osage River is a more indefinite zone.   To the south the crowding of drainage lines has resulted in intricate dissection, which is further emphasized by erosion of the Gasconade limestone.   This line also excludes the Iberia bench lands from the Missouri River Border. Beyond the Osage River the margin of the Clarksville soils and flint hills again provides a clear-cut boundary (Fig. 20).

The region, well supplied with means of transportation and possessed of fairly desirable farmlands, is in a rather advanced degree of agricultural development and was chosen for settlement at an early date. The Missouri River, as the one great natural highway leading west from the Mississippi, was the first line of settlement beyond the Mississippi. Later the lower Missouri country became the starting and outfitting station for most expeditions to the Far West. Lewis and Clark, the Sante Fe traders, the fur hunters, and the Californian gold hunters all left the frontiers of civilization on the lower Missouri. The peculiar significance of this river highway has made the Missouri River Border, together with St. Louis, the most historic ground in the state.

MISSISSIPPI RIVER BORDER

On the east the Ozark Border comprises about 2,500 square miles, forming a narrow strip along the Mississippi River. From this river the entire area is readily accessible.

The only large stream crossing the region is Big River. The surface in general slopes rather sharply from the igneous knobs and Gasconade limestone hills on the west down to the Mississippi, and is crossed by many small streams. These have relatively straight courses, and for the most part flow radially from the St. Francois region.

Especially on the north, elevation, slope, nearness of the Mississippi, and the nature of the rock formations have aided dissection, resulting in a region of sharply contrasted hills and valleys.[1] Here the sides of the Mississippi Valley consist of wooded hills and sheer bluffs (Plate XIII). On the south, especially in Cape Girardeau County, the greater width and lesser elevation of the area have expressed themselves in a gently rolling limestone upland, similar to north central Kentucky. The belted structure of the rocks is reproduced in the topography by a parallel series of scarps and platforms, best developed in Ste. Genevieve County, and nearly wanting in the southern part. In the central and southern sections sink holes are more numerous than in any other part of the Ozarks, and over many square miles determine the character of the topography. Springs are mostly of small size, uncertain flow, and in the sink-hole region subject to surface contamination.

[1] See the Crystal City or Renault topographic sheets.

Due to the structure of the rocks the residual soils form belts extending from north to south, as shown in Fig. 11. The excellent Hagerstown soils belong exclusively to this region, as do the Pocahontas and the Tilsit soils, the last of inferior value. The proportion of alluvial land is considerably less than on the Missouri River Border, and at least in the southern part it is less desirable because of poor drainage. The loess belt along the river is also much less important than along the northern border. As in the latter, the resources of this province are mainly agricultural, Cape Girardeau County especially constituting one of the most productive counties of Missouri.

The forest is more varied in composition and more luxuriant in growth than in any other part of the Ozarks, although its area is not so extensive as in the interior districts.

Mineral resources are small and limited mostly to quarry products and kaolin. In the past, salt and lead have been produced from this region.

The boundary on the west is defined by a belt of rugged flint hills, forming in part the Avon escarpment of Marbut[1] and represented on the soil map as the easternmost extension of the Clarksville type. The area could readily be further subdivided into a southern and northern portion, the economic resources of the former being far superior to those of the latter.

SPRINGFIELD PLAIN

This region corresponds in the main to the Springfield Structural Plain of Marbut,[2] and has an area of more than 5,500 square miles. It forms the western border of the Ozarks and is bounded on the east by the Burlington escarpment and the dissected country of the Pomme de Terre and Osage valleys. For the most part it is a gently sloping plain, covered by the fertile Springfield soils, and is less diversified in surface and soil than any other district of the Ozarks. The relief is less and the soil conditions are better than in the rest of the Ozarks. Streams flow in rather steep-sided valleys, which, however, are not deep, except along the eastern margin. The Neosho topographic sheet shows the characteristically youthful stage of dissection, especially in the near approach of Diamond Grove Prairie to Shoal Creek, the largest stream of the county. The distribution of timber along the valley sides is characteristic. The Springfield area, in fact, resembles, in appearance and conditions of life, the plains region of eastern Kansas more than the

[1] *Missouri. Geol. Surv.*, X, 34-35.   [2] *Ibid.*, pp. 60-67.

Central Plateau of the Ozarks. It is, however, the western border of the Ozarks, historically as well as physiographically. Springfield insists upon the title of "Queen City of the Ozarks."

The upland was covered originally by prairie grasses, trees being confined then as now to the valleys.

In contrast to the two other border regions, the Springfield Plain is well supplied with large springs of constant flow.

In mineral resources this subdivision is first in importance. It has long been the world's leading producer of zinc ore and tripoli, has yielded large quantities of lead, and has the most important quarrying industry of the state. Carthage "marble" is the most widely used building stone in Missouri.

In pioneer days the Springfield Plain was peculiarly isolated because of its distance from large streams and of the difficult country situated to the east of it. Its history is therefore much more meager than that of the other border sections.

ST. FRANCOIS KNOB AND BASIN REGION

Geologically and physiographically the St. Francois region is the center of the Ozarks. In a geographic sense, however, it has been largely a border region, (1) because of its nearness to the Mississippi and accessibility from that stream, and (2) because the agricultural conditions of its basins are on a par with those of the border regions and superior to most interior sections.

Its topography has no counterpart in the Ozarks and perhaps not in this country. The knobs of igneous rocks rise like irregularly distributed mountain islands above the basins formed by the weak limestones and shales (Plates I and II). The conical symmetry of the knobs and their detached character are not duplicated elsewhere in the Ozarks, nor are the "shut-ins." The relief of this area is the greatest of the state and the topography in part is mountainous.

Only two soil types are represented to any extent, the crystalline rock soils and the Fredericktown group. The latter is one of the two best residual soils of the Ozarks; the other has almost no agricultural value. The one type is almost uninhabited; on the other nearly every available acre of land is farmed.

In known mineral wealth this region is second only to the Springfield Plain. In variety it is first. For many years it has been the most important producer of lead in America and yields at present (under normal conditions) half the output of the country. It embraces the once famous iron mines of Iron Mountain and Pilot Knob, yields much of the baryte and all of the granite of the state, and from time to time has produced silver, copper, and cobalt.

As a result of the relief and the superimposed drainage this region contains many fine power sites. Most of the streams are small, but they make up for lack of volume by amount of fall.

The region is inclosed completely by ridges of Gasconade and Potosi limestone. It includes four major basins, Fredericktown, Farmington, Mineral Point–Potosi, and Richwoods. Some of the minor basins are Caledonia and Belgrade in Washington County, Belleview and Arcadia valleys in Iron, and Patterson and Lodi in Wayne County, all of them prosperous farming communities surrounded by a wilderness of igneous knobs and flint ridges.

COURTOIS HILLS

This is roughly the major area of outcrop of the Gasconade-Potosi limestones and therefore the most hilly as well as the poorest part of the Missouri Ozarks. The hills are steep-sided, chert-covered ridges, monotonous in their similarity. The narrow ridges are almost invariably forested, mostly with oak. Timber is the principal resource of the region, both agricultural and mineral wealth being small. The population is for the most part confined to the valleys. The best farming conditions are at the south where the Castor, St. Francois, Black, and Current rivers have developed wide bottoms, and have worn the flint hills to fairly gentle slopes. In the valleys springs of excellent quality are extraordinarily numerous.

Because it is the largest and most compact body of intricately and deeply dissected country, this region is the most isolated of the Ozark Highland. Roads follow the ridges and are both devious and difficult. In most cases the distance by road at least doubles the airline distance between two points.

Wanting a popular name, this region is here called the Courtois Hills, because Courtois Creek, in Crawford County, was one of its earliest valleys to be settled and because along its course the features of this region are developed typically.

OSAGE-GASCONADE HILLS

This region embraces the dissected country of the Gasconade and Osage valleys, and the intervening basins of the upper Maries, Tavern, the Auglaize, and the lower Niangua rivers. Because of the crowded drainage lines and the extensive outcrops of the Gasconade limestone, the

Ozark Highland in this section forms a hill country nearly as rugged and intricate as in the Courtois region and very similar to it (Plate XIV *a*). The contrast in topography between it and the Missouri River Border is shown by Fig. 20. The main watersheds, especially the one between the Gasconade and Osage, form a narrow but fairly level upland, on which there are some important farm areas, as at Vienna, Dixon, and Richland. The other types of land which are desirable for agriculture are: (1) the Iberia bench lands, mostly confined to this region, (2) the "slip-off" slopes of the incised meanders, developed perhaps most extensively in this area, and (3) bottom lands, numerous and large because of the number and size of the streams.

Springs and solution features, such as caves, sinks, and natural bridges, are exceedingly numerous, and have received some notoriety through the park at Hahatonka.

Mineral resources are small. Lead and iron have been produced in a small way.

WHITE RIVER HILLS

The upper White River country lies at and beyond the margin of the Burlington limestone, here forming the highest escarpment of the state. This escarpment has been dissected by the White River and its tributaries into a series of long, lobate ridges. In a number of cases outliers from one to a dozen miles across have become detached from the main body of the limestone and form high buttes, which are a conspicuous feature in almost every long vista. In fact, on these buttes panoramic views are disclosed that are unrivaled in extent in the state. The next highest level is formed by non-cherty limestone, which has formed innumerable glades. The bench lands which line the White and its larger tributaries represent a third level. From 50 to 75 feet below the bench lands are the present valley floors. The amount of incision of drainage lines is not equaled even in the Osage-Gasconade region, nor does any other section present such a steplike topography. The relief of the area is nearly as great as in the St. Francois region, and portions of it are as rugged as the Courtois and Osage-Gasconade hills. The topography combines, however, more varied elements than in the latter hill belts, and the scenery accordingly is more attractive. Here are forested slopes, gleaming limestone cliffs, and parklike cedar glades, overtopped by level-crested buttes and interrupted at lower levels by the horizontal lines of well-farmed benches and bottom lands (Plates VII and VIII). The result is a scene which combines magnificence and charm to a rare degree.

Because of the slopes and the great extent of the non-cherty Berryville soils, soil erosion is a most serious problem in this section. Where it can be checked farm conditions are fair. Where it has not been, one finds abandoned farms (Plate VI *b*). The bench lands are the best soils of the region. Neither Berryville soils nor bench lands are found to any notable extent outside of this area.

The region has probably the largest caves of the state. Water-power opportunities are excellent.

CENTRAL PLATEAU

The Central Plateau is surrounded on all sides except on parts of its western boundary by hill regions. Plate XIV *b* is a view of its most elevated portion, at Cedar Gap. Excepting the Springfield Plain, it is the only part of the Ozark Plateau which has not been dissected extensively. Streams flowing across the region have divided it into a large number of small plateaus or prairies (Plate VI *a*). The farms are mostly on the upland and provide a livelihood for by far the greater part of the population. The cherty Howell soil predominates (Plate IX), but there are also large areas of Lebanon clay and Dent sandy soil. Most of the soil is of moderate productiveness. With the exception of the southern part the region was not timbered at the time of settlement.

Although travel across the region is easy, communication with the outside world is difficult because of the hill belts which lie between it and the Missouri, Mississippi, and Arkansas valleys. This isolation has retarded development and still operates to the disadvantage of the region.

PART II

SETTLEMENT AND DEVELOPMENT

CHAPTER VII

FRENCH COLONIZATION

BEGINNINGS OF SETTLEMENT

For more than a century the French were sole masters of this region. At the beginning of the seventeenth century French settlements had been founded on the lower St. Lawrence. From this base, aided by the water routes of the St. Lawrence Basin and stimulated by the large profits of the fur trade, they advanced to the western Great Lakes in less than half a century. From the lakes it was a short and easy step by portages to the Mississippi Basin, hardly interrupting the continuity of water transportation for their canoes. Once the Mississippi was reached it was inevitable that boats soon would penetrate to its mouth. Thus the Ozarks, located on this great pioneer highway between eastern Canada and the Gulf of Mexico, became the scene of French enterprise before France had been established in the New World a century. On the east English colonists at this time had barely passed the Fall line of the Atlantic rivers, hardly a hundred miles from the open sea. Their way to the interior was not pointed out by waterways, as on the north. Shortly they confronted the Appalachian barrier, which was not passed by any large number of colonists until nearly a century after French settlement in the Mississippi Valley.

Since the French came into the Mississippi Valley first from the north, the earliest settlements were of Canadian stock, and in the middle valley this stock remained dominant throughout the French period.[1] In Canada the increase of French population was rather rapid. Climate and soil limited the agricultural opportunities of the St. Lawrence settlements. Part of the surplus population drifted west from time to time in quest of furs, milder climate, and better land, and thus found its way to the Wabash and Illinois countries.[2] After the French secured a foothold near the mouth of the Mississippi the region came into contact with Lower Louisiana, and therefore Creole blood also was introduced into the settlements of the middle Mississippi. Commercial relations were most largely by the Mississippi River with New Orleans, and found their

---

[1] Du Pratz, *History of Louisiana* (London, 1763), I, 105–6. Alvord, in *Illinois Historical Collections*, II, xvii; Memoirs of Dumont in *Hist. Colls. of Louisiana*, V, 37.

[2] Monette, *History of the Valley of the Mississippi*, I, 292.

73

expression in the political union of the Mississippi Basin, the middle Mississippi and Illinois country forming the District of Upper Louisiana.

Following the voyage of Marquette and Joliet in 1673, numerous exploring expeditions descended the Mississippi from the Great Lakes in quick succession and accumulated favorable information concerning its valley. This knowledge was disseminated rapidly and soon resulted in exploitation and settlement.

The first permanent settlements between the mouths of the Missouri and Ohio rivers were in the Mississippi Valley. These settlements were convenient to all the important routes between the Great Lakes and the Mississippi River. They lay at the convergence of the routes using the Illinois, Wisconsin, and Ohio rivers. As in Canada and Lower Louisiana they were riparian settlements or *côtes*. They lay opposite the mouth of the Missouri, the great highway for the furs of the western mountains and plains. They possessed an abundance of fertile river bottoms and were convenient to the lead mines of the St. Francois region. They were also in close proximity to Indian villages. All things considered the French could not have selected a better interior site than the valley of the Mississippi between St. Louis and Cairo. It is possible that the first French establishment in this section was a mission post on the river "des Pères," now St. Louis.[1] This place was soon abandoned because of its unhealthiness. The first settlement of which there is certain knowledge was Kaskaskia on the Illinois side of the Mississippi, across from the site of Ste. Genevieve, founded probably in 1699 as a mission to the village of the Kaskaskia Indians.[2] Cahokia and Fort Chartres were founded soon after, also on the Illinois side. The settlement was in the usual order, missionary first, then fur trader, soldier, and farmer. "Habitants" who became established gradually engaged in a combination of fur trade, boating, and desultory agriculture.[3] By 1740 they were supplying New Orleans with furs and skins, as well as with wheat and hams.[4]

Apparently by reason of their roaming habits and association with the Indians the French of the Illinois side became acquainted at an early date with the country west of the river and with its mineral wealth. In 1700 Father Gravier mentioned a rich lead mine on the river "Miaria-

[1] Journal of M. Austin, *Amer. Hist. Rev.*, V, 538.

[2] Thwaites, *Early Western Travels*, XXVII, note on p. 29.

[3] A good account of these settlements is to be found in Alvord's introduction to *Illinois Hist. Colls.*, II.

[4] Memoirs of Dumont in *Hist. Colls. of Louisiana*, V, 37.

migoua" (Meramec). His statement that the "ore from this mine yields 3 fourths metal" indicates mining previous to this time.[1] In 1702 d'Iberville asked for the exclusive privilege of working the mines on the Meramec.[2] The wording of this petition implies that lead had been mined there before that date. The salt springs on Saline Creek, below Ste. Genevieve, attracted attention as early as 1687, when they were pointed out to Joutel by Indians.[3] In 1700 Penicaut described the "river of the Saline" in Ste. Genevieve County.[4] It is stated that even then its salt licks were resorted to by the French and Indians.[5] The use of the salt springs and the presence of lead mines is confirmed by Father Marest, of Kaskaskia, in 1712.[6] Lead ore and salt springs and to some extent furs were the first resources of the Missouri region of which the French made use. From temporary visits in quest of these commodities to permanent habitation was an easy transition, the date of which, however, is as uncertain as that of the discovery of these resources. In 1704 Governor Bienville reported that French were settled west of the river.[7] Penicaut, in his journal of 1700, says that "presently" there was a settlement on the Missouri side.[8] From these obscure notes the conclusion may be drawn that Frenchmen were established on the Missouri side, probably only intermittently, at the beginning of the eighteenth century, the incentive being primarily mineral wealth.

The great stores of silver and gold found by the Spanish in Peru and Mexico, and the legends of far greater treasure which were current and credited at the time, inflamed the French with the hope that their colony in the New World might produce mineral riches comparable to those of the Spanish possessions. The sections previously opened by France in America had disclosed nothing to encourage such a hope. Accordingly tales of mineral wealth, emanating from Upper Louisiana, were seized upon with avidity, were carried to the Gulf settlements and thence to France, and aroused the imagination and cupidity of speculators and adventurers. Their desires heightened their credulity so that when finds of silver were reported the reports were accepted without question

[1] *Jesuit Relations*, LXV, 101.   [3] *Hist. Colls. of Louisiana*, I, 181.

[2] Houck, *Hist. of Missouri*, I, 274.   [4] Houck, *Hist. of Missouri*, I, 247.

[5] Carr, *Missouri*, p. 21.

[6] *Jesuit Relations* (Thwaites), LXVI, 227, 291, 293. The note by Thwaites, referring these to a number of Illinois counties, is in error. Marest says "in the neighborhood." The Ste. Genevieve salines are nearly across from Kaskaskia, and but a few miles removed.

[7] Houck, *op. cit.*, I, 243.   [8] Carr, *loc. cit.*

and created great enthusiasm.[1] As a result of such tales the Company of the West, which had come into control of Louisiana in 1717, dispatched several expeditions to explore the region of the Ozarks and to work its ores, especially of silver. "In 1719 the Sieur de Lochon, sent by the Company of the West in the capacity of a smelter, having dug in a spot which had been pointed out to him [on the Meramec River], raised quite a large quantity of ore." From this ore he attempted to produce silver and finally departed with a few ounces, which it is suspected were introduced fraudulently, and with forty pounds of lead, as the result of mining two or three thousand pounds of ore. His successor disregarded the lead and attempted to smelt silver only.[2] This nonexistent silver mine became a tradition which would not down. It appears in Dumont's Memoirs,[3] and in the account of Du Pratz,[4] both belonging to the middle of the eighteenth century. Stoddard revived it in 1812,[5] and residents to this day insist that the region contains lost silver mines. This persistent fiction perpetuated the hope of finding precious metals and stimulated exploration and development.

The next step in the opening of the region was the beginning of organized mining by the Sieur Renault, who "left France in the year 1719, with two hundred artificers and miners, provided with tools, and whatever else was necessary. . . . . In his passage he touched at the island of St. Domingo, and purchased five hundred slaves for working the mines. . . . ."[6] This imposing expedition was organized expressly to try out the mineral wealth of southeastern Missouri. The first place at which operations were undertaken was at the old workings on the Meramec, where he found, in 1720, rich deposits of lead.[7] The site, at the junction of the Big and Meramec rivers, was granted to Renault in 1723 and constitutes the earliest land grant in Upper Louisiana of which there is any record.[8] The next discovery of note was made in 1723 by Renault's agent, La Motte, at the place which still bears the latter's name. This mine was worked rather extensively for a period, and from 1738 to 1740 furnished almost all the lead exported from the region.[9] The mines at Fourche à Renault were opened in 1724–25 by his company of miners, and the so-called "Old Mines" are said to date

[1] Carr, op. cit., p. 23; Monette, History of the Valley of the Mississippi, I, 207.

[2] Charlevoix, Journal (1744), VI, 137–38.   [5] Sketches of Louisiana, p. 216.

[3] Hist. Colls. of Louisiana, V, 37.   [6] Schoolcraft, View of Lead Mines, p. 15.

[4] Houck, op. cit., I, 275.   [7] Charlevoix, op. cit., p. 139.

[8] Casselberry, in Western Journal and Civilian, I, 190; Houck, op. cit., p. 281.

[9] Austin, Amer. State Papers, Public Lands, I, 208.

from the following year.[1] A traveler of a century ago wrote: "Other mines of lead were also found, but their distinctive appellations have not survived; and a proof to the diligence with which Renault prosecuted [his] object, is furnished by the number and extent of the old diggings which are now found in various parts. These diggings are scattered over the whole mine country, and hardly a season passes, in which some antique works, overgrown with brush and trees, are not found."[2] In the years spent in exploration and mining the party headed by Renault achieved a number of important results: (1) The great extent of the shallow deposits of lead in this section was determined, and at least one mining camp, Mine La Motte, which is still an active producer, was located. (2) The systematic production of lead was begun, of which "there is reason to conclude, that very great quantities were made."[3] (3) Lead was conveyed from the interior to the river on pack horses and thence by boat to New Orleans. From the latter point most of it was exported to France.[4] Commercial relations with the Gulf and with France were thus established through the lead trade. (4) The expedition resulted in the first notable immigration into the region since the founding of Kaskaskia. A number of families, following Renault's party, came to the neighborhood of Kaskaskia from the Gulf and there occupied lands.[5] Although most of the miners left Missouri with Renault, it is almost certain that a number remained in the Missouri region. In 1803 the "Old Mine" claim of Washington County was granted under that name to 31 concessionaires, who were established on it.[6] Even at that time this tract was considered ancient. It is likely that some of its concessionaires were descendants of Renault's miners, who first worked that property in 1725–26. A suggestion to this effect is contained in an entry of the year 1748 in the parish records of Fort Chartres, which refers to the "habitans du village des mines."[7] (5) The mining of lead by this party probably introduced slavery into Upper Louisiana.

SETTLEMENT OF STE. GENEVIEVE AND ADJACENT REGION

As a result of the gradual development of mining interests, a settlement was formed on the right bank of the Mississippi, to serve as a

[1] *Ibid.*, p. 207.   [3] *Ibid.*
[2] Schoolcraft, *op. cit.*, p. 16.   [4] *Ibid.*
[5] Carr, *Missouri*, p. 24.
[6] Record Books, Secretary of State, *Survey No. 3039.*
[7] Houck, *op. cit.*, p. 378.

shipping-point for the mines. The site chosen was on the Mississippi
flood plain, in the so-called Big Field, below the present site of Ste.
Genevieve and across the river from Kaskaskia.[1] Here the original
village of Ste. Genevieve was located. The date of earliest settlement
is uncertain but probably is before 1732, as a well stone with that date
carved upon it has been found in the Big Field.[2] Stirling, writing in
1765, stated that the settlement was about thirty years old.[3] Pittman,
writing about 1770, places the date at about 1742.[4] This author sums
up the advantages of the site in these words: "The situation of the village
is very convenient, being within one league of the salt spring. . . . .
A lead mine, which supplies the whole country with shot, is about fifteen
leagues' distance. The communication of this village with Cascasquias
is very short and easy, it being only to cross the Mississippi, which is
about three quarters of a mile broad at this place, and then there is a
portage, two miles distance, to Cascasquias." At the outset Ste.
Genevieve was merely a dependency of Kaskaskia, placed on the right
bank of the river because of the salt and lead on the Missouri side.
To these advantages are to be added fertile alluvial lands, abundant
timber and stone, position on the river bank, and easy access to the
interior because of the absence of river bluffs.

Before 1763 the settlement increased very little. Few grants of
land were made on the western bank, and these were "mostly designed
to embrace mineral riches."[5] The farming population remained for the
most part on the older, Illinois side, where the bottom lands were sufficiently extensive for the small needs of the settlement.[6] Only one grant
on the west side of the river is known certainly to have been made for
purposes of cultivation in this period.[7]

After 1763 a number of causes aided the growth of the settlement.
In that year occurred the cession of the lands east of the Mississippi
River to Protestant England. Many of the French families left the
English district in the succeeding years to settle under a Catholic govern-
ment, administered by their countrymen. These families notably
increased the settlements of Ste. Genevieve and later of St. Louis.
In October, 1765, Stirling estimated the population of Ste. Genevieve

---

[1] Watrin, in *Illinois Hist. Colls.*, X, 77.   [2] Houck, *op. cit.*, p. 338.

[3] *Illinois Hist. Colls.*, X, 210.

[4] Pittman, *European Settlements on the Mississippi*, p. 50.

[5] Stoddard, *Sketches of Louisiana*, p. 224.

[6] *Ibid*.   [7] Houck, *op. cit.*, p. 337.

at twenty-five families, and in December at fifty.[1] In 1766 the inhabitants of Kaskaskia and Fort Chartres were reported as having gone largely to the west bank of the river.[2] Among those who came to Ste. Genevieve was Francois Vállé, long the wealthiest man in Upper Louisiana, owner in 1770 of one hundred slaves.[3] At about the same time Mine à Breton (Potosi) and Mine à Robina (two miles southeast of Potosi) were discovered and increased mining activities resulted.[4] Mine à Gerbore (Flat River district)[5] had been discovered at a somewhat earlier date.[6] By 1769 the population of Ste. Genevieve and surroundings was estimated at more than 600.[7] In 1772 the district possessed 691 inhabitants, of whom 287 were slaves. Its population was about one-seventh greater than that of the St. Louis district at the time.[8]

The American Revolution caused numerous French to emigrate from the Illinois country. They were pressed into unwilling service against the "Bostoneses" by the British.[9] Clark's capture of Kaskaskia brought the Revolution to their midst.[10] At the same time the Spanish government was offering food, stock, and implements to those who would come to Upper Louisiana,[11] and thus a second transfer to the right bank took place.

In 1780 the river bank on which Ste. Genevieve was built began to cave rapidly, and in 1784 a few families moved to the present site of the city, on the upland adjoining the river bottoms.[12] In 1785 the official account states: "The waters have risen so greatly from their source that they have entirely submerged the village. All its inhabitants having been obliged to retire with great haste to the mountains which are one league away from the said village. They abandoned their houses which were inundated, and their furniture and other possessions which they had in them."[13] This year is remembered as the "year of the great

---

[1] Illinois Hist. Colls., XI, 108, 125.

[2] Gordon, Illinois Hist. Colls., XI, 298.

[3] Don Piedro Piernas, in Houck, Spanish Régime, I, 70; Pittman, op. cit., p. 50.

[4] Austin, op. cit., p. 208.   [5] Missouri Geol. Surv., VII, 667.

[6] Austin, ibid.   [7] Piernas, loc. cit.

[8] Piernas, op. cit., p. 53.

[9] Cruzat, in Houck, Spanish Régime, I, 154.

[10] Houck, Hist. of Missouri, I, 356.

[11] Galvez, in Houck, Spanish Régime, I, 156.

[12] Houck, Hist. of Missouri, I, 350–51.

[13] Miro, in Houck, Spanish Régime, I, 235.

waters." The destruction of the old village proceeded rapidly; many of the houses being "washed into the River by the falling of the Bank, it was thought advisable to remove the Town to the hights."[1] By 1791 the old village was deserted.[2] The new site possessed not only security from flood and erosion, but it also had a good water supply and was healthful, the old site having been deficient in all these respects.[3] Kaskaskia, Cahokia, and Fort Chartres, all situated on the flood plain, also were flooded and in part destroyed in 1785, "l'année des grandes eaux," and again in later years. The opportunities for relocating these villages were not so favorable as in the case of Ste. Genevieve. As a result many of the inhabitants of the Illinois side sought safety in New Ste. Genevieve.[4]

In 1787 the ordinance was passed which prohibited slavery and invol-untary servitude in the Northwest Territory. Slave-owners were made welcome by the authorities at Ste. Genevieve and St. Louis.[5] A number of prominent families effected their removal at this period.[6] ·

For these various reasons, which are connected in the main with the formation of an international boundary along the Mississippi River, a large part of the French population of the American Bottoms of Illinois gradually was transferred to the right bank of the Mississippi. In the old graveyard at Ste. Genevieve the most ancient inscriptions usually record the birth of the deceased at Kaskaskia, or at one of the other Illinois settlements.

New Bourbon was founded in 1794, a little more than a mile down the river from Ste. Genevieve. The chief element in the selection of the site seems to have been the desire of the colonists to be near an established French village. New Bourbon was a small settlement of French Royal-ists, refugees from the French Revolution, who came to the United States, fell into the hands of promoters of the Scioto Company, were settled at Gallipolis, Ohio, and there in the midst of the wilderness left to a miserable existence. Their lands belonged to another company.[7] Their location caused them to be subject to fevers.[8] By their training

[1] Journal of Moses Austin, Amer. Hist. Rev., V, 541.
[2] Houck, Hist. of Missouri, I, 351.
[3] Fragments of Colonel Aug. Chouteau's Narrative of the Settlement of St. Louis, p. 1.
[4] Souvenir of Ste. Genevieve.
[5] Stoddard, Sketches of Louisiana, p. 225.
[6] See, for instance, the Beauvais and Janis families in Illinois Hist. Colls., III.
[7] Mississippi Valley Hist. Rev., II, 123.
[8] Ellicott, Journal (1796), p. 13.

these people were unfitted for pioneer life. Finally the Spanish government aided them to remove to Upper Louisiana, where they could be in contact with their more experienced French-Canadian countrymen of Ste. Genevieve. It was in large measure an attempt to ameliorate the hardships of frontier life.[1] The specific purpose for which the Spanish government secured these settlers was that they might raise grain for the plantations on the lower Mississippi, the food exported from the upper region at the time being insufficient to supply the needs of the sugar and cotton planters on the lower river and the Gulf.[2] The census of 1794 reports 153 people settled at New Bourbon; at the same time Ste. Genevieve had 849 inhabitants.[3] In 1797 New Bourbon, including plantations on Saline Creek, numbered 461 people.[4] Because of its dependent location the settlement was gradually absorbed into Ste. Genevieve.

At the close of the eighteenth century, near the end of the French period, the French population of the Ste. Genevieve district lived in these two villages and in scattered and more or less temporary groups as far west as Crawford County and as far south as Madison County. These outlying settlements were composed largely of miners, as at Mine à Breton, Old Mines, Mine La Motte, and St. Michaels (Fredericktown (Fig. 25, p. 104).[5] In spite of its extent the district usually was considered one settlement. It was relatively isolated from the settlements north and south; its inhabitants had intermarried extensively;[6] and there was a high degree of economic interdependence.

OCCUPATIONS IN THE STE. GENEVIEVE DISTRICT

Salt making.—The making of salt, the earliest authenticated occupation of the region, was important for more than a century. It served not only for the needs of this district, but was a highly profitable article of commerce. Salt was made by the evaporation of weak brine from springs on Saline Creek below Ste. Genevieve, extending for a distance of about two miles from its mouth.[7] In 1750 they were said to supply "all the salt consumed in the surrounding country, and in many posts which are dependencies of Canada."[8] As early as 1769 there were four

[1] Houck, *Spanish Régime*, I, 373–409.   [3] Houck, *Spanish Régime*, I, 326.
[2] Houck, *Hist. of Missouri*, I, 331.   [4] *Ibid.*, II, 248.
[5] Austin, in *Amer. State Papers, Public Lands*, I, 209.
[6] Trudeau, in Houck, *Spanish Régime*, II, 248.
[7] Shumard, *Repts. Geol. Surv. of Missouri* (1855–71), pp. 302–3.
[8] Vivier, in *Jesuit Relations*, LXIX, 221.

or five houses on this creek, and the amount of salt made was sufficient for the settlements on both sides of the river.[1] At this time Pittman wrote: "The salt spring . . . . is for the general use of the French subjects, and several persons belonging to this village have works here, and make great quantities of salt for the supply of the Indians, hunters, and the other settlements."[2] In 1778 Hutchins found a hamlet here, where "all the salt is made, which is used in the *Illinois* country."[3] In 1797 Moses Austin reported: "Much Salt is now made and when the Works are Extended may furnish all the Upper Settlements on the Missisipi."[4] The census of 1799 lists 965 bushels, worth $1.50 per bushel.[5] In 1807 the works were in a flourishing condition. Their product commanded a high price and was shipped extensively, as few salt springs were then known in the upper settlements and the cost of shipping from New York was prohibitive. They were said to "supply the whole upper country with salt at the rate of two dollars a bushel. Considerable quantities are also sent up the Cumberland river into Kentucky and Tennessee, where it frequently commands four and five dollars a bushel. These works . . . . at present have forty-six kettles, containing about twenty-five gallons each, which produce about fifteen thousand bushels annually."[6] In 1812 the salines still supplied a large portion of the population on both sides of the Mississippi, and a considerable proportion of the salt was carried in boats up the Ohio.[7] By this time the salines of southern Illinois had become important competitors.[8] In 1820 the works were abandoned,[9] as the operation of better salines in other sections, especially on the Kanawha and in western Pennsylvania, and the introduction of steamboats, enabled the cheap importation of salt from the upper Ohio Valley as well as from New Orleans.[10] This is the first of numerous instances in which a resource of the Ozark Border, highly important in early days both to settlement and commerce, after a time ceased to be utilized, not because of exhaustion, but because of improved means of transportation.

[1] Piernas, in Houck, *op. cit.*, I, 71–72.
[2] *European Settlements on the Mississippi*, p. 50.
[3] *Topographical Description* (Burrows ed.), p. 110.
[4] *Amer. Hist. Rev.*, V, 536.
[5] Dept. of State, *Account of Louisiana* (1803), App. II.
[6] Schultz, *Travels*, II, 73.
[7] Stoddard, *Sketches of Louisiana*, p. 401.
[8] Bogess, *Chicago Historical Society Collections*, V, 170–71.
[9] Shumard, *op. cit.*, p. 303.   [10] Wetmore, *Gazetteer* (1837), p. 171.

Lead mining.—Ste. Genevieve is characterized in early accounts as the place of deposit for the lead from the "mine country," which is the district now embraced in Washington and St. Francois counties, and as the storehouse which supplied the workers at the mines.[1] Most of the inhabitants of Ste. Genevieve and New Bourbon were interested in mining.[2] "The greater part are more or less employed in the lead mines. This is a career of industry open to all, and the young, in setting out to do something for themselves, usually make their first essay in this business."[3] The almost universal participation in mining was due chiefly to the following factors: (1) Lead occurred as residual or "float" ore at or near the surface. Capital was therefore not necessary to operate. (2) Most of the lead was worked without paying rent or taxes.[4] (3) It was the export product of the region that was most in demand, and most readily commanded a cash price. As a result, it was said, "every farmer may be a miner, and, when unoccupied on his farm, may, by a few weeks' labor, almost at his own door, dig as much mineral as will furnish his family with all imported articles."[5] "The poor class depend upon the mines to furnish them with lead to purchase all imported articles."[6]

Mining for the most part was a seasonal occupation. Stephen Austin goes so far as to say that not a single family had spent a winter at the well-known Mine à Breton previous to the advent of the Americans in 1798.[7] Especially after the harvest the inhabitants of Ste. Genevieve and New Bourbon resorted to the mines; the rich sent their negroes, the others did their own mining. This period of activity continued from August to December.[8] Mining was restricted to autumn in part because farm work at that season was light, and in part because least rain fell then, so that seepage into the pits was least troublesome.[9]

The presence of great quantities of residual ore enabled mining by the simplest methods. In fact the most important limiting factor was the amount of labor available. The account, published by the United States at the acquisition of Louisiana, states: "Lead is to be had with ease, and in such quantities as to supply all Europe, if the population were sufficient to work the numerous mines to be found within two or

[1] Schultz, *Travels*, II, 56; Brackenridge, *Views of Louisiana* (1811–13, 1st ed.), p. 124.

[2] Austin, *op. cit.*, p. 207.

[3] Brackenridge, *op. cit.*, p. 126.

[4] Austin, *op. cit.*, p. 208.

[5] *Ibid.*

[6] Austin, *op. cit.*, p. 207.

[7] *Amer. Hist. Rev.*, V, 519.

[8] Austin, *loc. cit.*

[9] Stoddard, *op. cit.*, p. 395.

three feet from the surface."[1]   Prospecting was limited mostly to the areas of the red Fredericktown soil (Bonne Terre limestone),[2] in which surface concentration was greatest.   During the French period, it was stated, "the ore has not been sought for in the rock, but has been found in the earth in detached lumps. . . . . The workmen employed have no other implements than a pick-axe and a wooden shovel, and when at work, appear as if employed in making *tan pits*, rather than in mining. When they come to the rock, or to such a depth that it is no longer convenient to throw the dirt out of the hole, they quit, and perhaps commence a new *digging*, as they term it, within a few feet of that which they have previously abandoned."[3]   Bradbury states that at Richwoods, in northern Washington County, there had been "made forty trials, by simply digging holes, not more than four feet deep."   In thirty-eight of these ore was found.[4]   Single pits at a maximum produced one to two thousand pounds; usually, however, the yield was about fifty pounds.   Where yields were good the entire surface was dug over, so that the pits and dumps of a single "mine" not rarely covered fifty acres or more.[5]   Because of the uncertainty of the returns each digger worked on his own account.   Once in a while one man would produce two thousand pounds in a day.   The miners were said, however, not to "grow rich faster than their neighbors," because of the uncertain returns and the extravagant habits which this life engendered.[6]

Smelting was done in as primitive a manner, and but for the rich ores and the low cost of labor the industry could not have survived its careless methods.   The way in which the French smelted was by throwing the ore on heaps of burning logs, "by which means about $\frac{2}{3}$ of the Lead is lost.   Notwithstanding the Imperfect manner in which they Melt the Ore, Yet at the Mines of Briton [Breton] last summer [1796] was made 400 000 lb Lead."[7]

The smelted lead was at first taken to the river by pack horses on a bridle path.   "When carried by pack-horses, the lead, instead of being moulded into 'pigs,' was moulded into the shape of a collar and hung across the neck of the horse."   Later, two-wheeled carts came into use and their traces across the hills to Ste. Genevieve formed the first wagon roads in Missouri.[8]

[1] Dept. of State, *Account of Louisiana* (1803), p. 10.

[2] Bradbury, in *Early Western Travels*, V, 248; Brackenridge, *op. cit.*, p. 147.

[3] Bradbury, *op. cit.*, p. 249.   [6] Bradbury, *loc. cit.*; Brackenridge, *loc. cit.*

[4] *Ibid.*, p. 250.   [7] Austin, *Amer. Hist. Rev.*, V, 540.

[5] Brackenridge, *op. cit.*, p. 149.   [8] Houck, *Hist. of Missouri*, I, 284.

Agriculture.—The Big Field, on the margin of which both Ste. Genevieve and New Bourbon were located, is one of the largest compact areas of alluvial land on the borders of the Ozarks. This tract was famed at an early date for its fertility and constituted the principal farming land of the villages throughout the French period.[1] The chief handicap to its cultivation was frequent inundation. Trudeau claimed that the inhabitants "are accustomed to lose two out of five harvests regularly, but such is the power of custom and of preoccupation that they always persist in cultivating there."[2] A second large tract was the Grand Park Common Field, on the upland southwest of Ste. Genevieve, used chiefly for grazing land. The French seem to have occupied almost no farmland outside of these two tracts before the end of the eighteenth century, excepting a few grants in creek bottoms. On these detached farms stock was kept, and they were known as "vacheries."[3] The ease of cultivation on the bottoms, the large yields secured, the ample size of the Big Field, and the small wants of the population resulted in the almost complete neglect of the uplands until after 1796, when American immigration was first attracted to the loess lands. At this time also inundation and erosion by the Mississippi were troublesome, and to make good their losses in the Big Field and escape further damage a number of French secured upland grants.[4]

The common fields were divided into lots, distributed among the heads of households according to station, size of family, and other considerations. In the Big Field each lot fronts on the river and extends to the bluffs. Most of the lots are 60 arpents long. None are wider than $3\frac{1}{2}$ arpents. The lots in the Grand Park Common Field had the same form. In both cases the entire field was surrounded by a fence, perhaps in part a protection against marauding Indians, as Brackenridge suggests,[5] but probably chiefly to exclude stock. The common field, inclosed by a fence or palisade, is a familiar feature of pioneer settlement. The curious form of the individual holdings, however, a form which persists to this day, is not accounted for readily. In the Big Field the river frontage may have been of some value to owners of an allotment,

[1] Stoddard, *op. cit.*, p. 216.

[2] Houck, *Spanish Régime*, II, 248; Stoddard (*loc. cit.*) placed the loss at one crop in ten or twelve years.

[3] Brackenridge, *op. cit.*, p. 128; Record Books, Secretary of State, *Survey Nos. 2085, 3062, 3063.*

[4] Record Books, Secretary of State, *Survey Nos. 1889, 2046, 2091, 3336.*

[5] *Views of Louisiana*, p. 127.

but on the upland Grand Park accessibility certainly did not determine this form.   In neither field were different kinds of land to be distributed equally by this plan.   It is probable that these attenuated strips were a heritage from the lower St. Lawrence or, less likely, from the Mississippi, on which they were introduced by the early French because of geographic advantages.   The French followed the same custom, without apparent geographic justification in other localities, as at Vincennes and in Michigan.

Isolation necessitated the production of a greater variety of crops than is now grown in the region.   "They cultivate maize, wheat, oats, barley, beans (phaseolus), pumpkins, water and musk melons, and tobacco and cotton for their own use.   Apples and peaches are very fine. . . . . They pay great attention to gardening, and have a good assortment of roots and vegetables."[1]   The principal crops were corn, pumpkins, and spring wheat.[2]   Corn was the leading crop, and of this Ste. Genevieve and New Bourbon produced, in 1794, 30,980 minots as against 20,150 in the other French settlements of Upper Louisiana. In 1796 the amount was 46,190 minots against 29,228.   This superiority of the Ste. Genevieve district was due in part to the large area of fertile bottoms, in part to the fact that trading interests were of smaller relative importance than on the Missouri River, in the St. Louis and St. Charles districts.   In the same year the two villages produced 13,585 minots of wheat against 21,480 for St. Charles, Florissant, St. Louis, Carondelet, and Marais des Liards.[3]

Stock ranged at will, securing its own sustenance.   "They have abundance of horses, cows, and hogs, all of which run at large. . . . . They mow a little grass on the prairie, which they make into hay, and give it to their horses and cattle when the ground is covered with snow: at other times they leave them to provide for themselves.   The hogs live on strawberries[?], hazle and hickory nuts, acorns and roots, and must be occasionally sought for in the woods, to prevent them from becoming entirely wild."[4]   As in most pioneer communities stock raising was based largely on an abundance of free range.

All observers were agreed that even for pioneer conditions agricultural methods were poor and that they compared unfavorably with those of the American settlers who succeeded the French.   It was said that after planting the crop was "left entirely to nature, no further attention

---

[1] Bradbury, Early Western Travels, V, 260.

[2] Views of Louisiana, p. 127.

[3] Houck, Spanish Régime, I, 324–25; II, 142–43.   [4] Bradbury, loc. cit.

[being] paid to it until harvest. There is a great contrast between the lots cultivated by the Americans, and those of the creoles," the former producing a crop at least one-third greater.[1] One of the foremost botanists of Europe made the observation that the French were "so much attached to the manners of their ancestors, and even to their practices in husbandry, that although they see their American neighbors, by the application of improved implements and methods, able to cultivate double the quantity of ground in the same time, nothing can induce them to abandon their old practices."[2] The official American account of 1803 states that, "though the inhabitants are numerous, they raise little for exportation."[3]

The production of grain early led to the building of water mills. We have the first record of milling in 1770, at which time the village was supplying the traders of St. Louis with flour.[4] Because of the agricultural advantages of Ste. Genevieve the authorities encouraged the production and milling of wheat to supply the demands of the plantations on the lower Mississippi. In 1793 Baron Carondelet advanced money to build mills at Ste. Genevieve and New Madrid for the purpose of making the whole of Louisiana "independent of the supply of American flour shipped down the Ohio."[5] There is record of a mill in 1793 on Dodge's Creek,[6] and of another about 1797 in the Establishment region.[7] The French district, however, due chiefly to its people, never produced sufficient flour to compete seriously with the American trade on the Mississippi, which had assumed large proportions. Flour was even imported at times.[8] At the time of cession to the United States only $60 worth of flour was exported in a year.[9]

There is no record of other productive activities, excepting the chase and the record of a number of grants of creek bottom land for the somewhat dubious purpose of making maple sugar.[10]

Trade.—The village of Ste. Genevieve, founded for commercial purposes, developed a trade in Upper Louisiana second only to that of St. Louis. The greatest volume of trade was with Lower Louisiana;

[1] *Views of Louisiana*, p. 127.   [2] Bradbury, *loc. cit.*

[3] Dept. of State, *Account of Louisiana*, p. 10.

[4] Pittman, *European Settlements*, p. 50.

[5] Houck, *Hist. of Missouri*, I, 331.   [6] *Ibid.*, p. 365.

[7] Record Books, Secretary of State, *Survey No. 888*.

[8] Ashe, *Travels in America*, pp. 289-90.

[9] Dept. of State, *Account of Louisiana* (1803), App. IV.

[10] Record Books, Secretary of State, *Survey Nos. 443, 2093, 2572*.

then came that with the American settlements on the Ohio, Cumberland, and Kentucky rivers.[1] With the growth of St. Louis the latter also became an important customer. The export trade of Ste. Genevieve was largely in lead and salt.[2] Grain and flour were much less important shipments. The goods imported came up the river for the most part, and consisted of "British goods, French and West-India produce."[3] In earlier years the stations at Michilimackinac and Detroit are said to have supplied the French merchants to a large extent.[4] In contrast with the situation at St. Louis and St. Charles, the fur trade never occupied more than a subordinate position in the commercial relations of Ste. Genevieve. The village did not possess the river routes by which to penetrate to the far interior, and the furs that came to this place were collected from a few neighboring Indian tribes.[5] The cheaper furs of Upper Louisiana took the easier route, down the Mississippi, whereas the more costly furs found their way largely as contraband trade by canoe to the great fur markets of Canada.[6] As a result of its commerce a number of the inhabitants of Ste. Genevieve were engaged as boatmen.[7]

CAPE GIRARDEAU AND SETTLEMENTS ON THE MERAMEC

Besides the Ste. Genevieve settlements there were two semidetached groups of French in the Mississippi River Border, one at Cape Girardeau and one on the Meramec. Cape Girardeau was founded for military reasons in 1793. Several hundred Indian families were induced to settle on Apple Creek, above Cape Girardeau, under the supervision of a French agent. They were considered "at the devotion of the Spanish authorities" and were to be a safeguard against attack from the east bank.[8] The location of Cape Girardeau was suited excellently to guard the Ohio Valley, as it lies on the first large tract of high ground on the right bank of the Mississippi north of the Ohio. Because of the swampy land to the south any invasion of Upper Louisiana from the east could not take place below Cape Girardeau. In 1796 General Collot expressed the opinion that it was the most eligible location for a military establish-

---

[1] Austin, *Amer. Hist. Rev.*, V, 541; Schultz, *Travels*, II, 56.

[2] *Ibid.*   [3] Ashe, *loc. cit.*

[4] Parker (1787), in *Illinois Hist. Colls.*, IV, 411.

[5] Brackenridge, *Views of Louisiana*, p. 127; Austin, *loc. cit.*

[6] Dept. of State, *Account of Louisiana* (1803), App. IV.

[7] Brackenridge, *loc. cit.*

[8] Stoddard, *Sketches of Louisiana*, p. 215.

ment above the Ohio.[1] The Indian settlement attracted a few Frenchmen, but at the time of its cession to the United States Cape Girardeau
contained only five French families out of a total population of about
twelve hundred.[2] In 1812 there were only three or four Frenchmen in
the Cape Girardeau district.[3]

A few families lived on the lower Meramec, in closer touch with St.
Louis than with Ste. Genevieve. The year 1774 has been cited as the
date of earliest settlement in this section. Cattle raising and the manufacture of salt seem to have been the chief occupations.[4] As late as
1812 salt works on the Meramec supplied in large part the district of
St. Louis.[5]

After 1776 the eastern settlements were united more closely by the
laying out of the King's Trace from St. Louis to New Madrid. This
road crossed the Meramec a mile above its mouth and Joachim Creek
near Horine, passing through Sulphur Springs, Ste. Genevieve, and
Cape Girardeau.[6]

FRENCH IN THE MISSOURI VALLEY

French adventurers, facile voyagers in the canoe, made their appearance on the Missouri River almost as soon as they did on the Mississippi.
In 1703 a party of twenty-three made a trip up the Missouri in search of
mines.[7] Two years later a Frenchman reported, probably with considerable exaggeration, that he had been to the frontier of Mexico by
way of the Missouri. His statement nevertheless displays a correct
conception of the geography of the Missouri River system at a very
early date. In the same year fifty Canadians arrived at Mobile, among
them some who had traded in many Indian villages on the Missouri.[8]

The fur trade on the Missouri River is therefore nearly as old as are
the lead mines and salt works of the Mississippi Valley. The meager
records of the time indicate that the Indian trade was prosecuted more
or less steadily from the outset. In 1722 Fort Orleans was built in the
Missouri, near Brunswick,[9] for the purpose of controlling the nearby
Indians.[10] In 1724 a convoy of furs from the Missouri was received at

[1] Houck, *Hist. of Missouri*, II, 174. [3] Stoddard, *op. cit.*, p. 214.

[2] Houck, *Spanish Régime*, II, 403–7. [4] *Missouri Hist. Rev.*, I, 141.

[5] Stoddard, *op. cit.*, pp. 218, 221.

[6] *Missouri Hist. Rev.*, I, 141–42; Houck, *Hist. of Missouri*, II, 150–53.

[7] Houck, *op. cit.*, I, 243.

[8] *Ibid.*, p. 244. [9] *Amer. Nation*, VII, 83.

[10] Houck, *op. cit.*, p. 258; Du Pratz, *Hist. of Louisiana* (London, 1763), I, 296–97.

Fort Chartres.[1]   By 1744 it appears that a number of French traders had established themselves along this stream, as the census of that year records 200 white males then resident on the Missouri.[2]   By 1758 the French had penetrated 300 leagues up the river and had become fairly well acquainted with the Osage River.[3]   Previously, in 1719, Du Tisne had traveled across southern Missouri, probably reaching a point near the headwaters of the Osage River in Kansas.[4]

The founding of St. Louis in 1764 provided an adequate base for the fur trade, which increased rapidly from that time on.   Thereafter the Missouri was freighted with an increasing number of traders' bateaux going to their various posts laden with implements, powder, lead, clothes, trinkets, and often with whiskey, and returning with precious cargoes of furs.

For many years the only settlements on the Missouri were St. Charles and La Charrette, or St. John's.[5]   The latter was the last group of houses passed by Lewis and Clark on the outward journey in 1804.[6] It was a frontier post and village at the mouth of Charrette Creek in Warren County, and probably was founded as early as 1766.[7]   In 1811 it consisted of ten or twelve families, half hunter, half agriculturist.[8] The site possessed small merit, and the village was after a time destroyed by the river.   About 1808 Côte sans Dessein was founded, on the left bank of the Missouri, near the mouth of the Osage River.[9]   Its inhabit- ants supported themselves chiefly by hunting.[10]   This village also was located poorly on the bottom land, and was destroyed after a time by the encroachments of the river.   The people then crossed to the other bank, where they established themselves on the upland.[11]   Descendants of this group still live in the vicinity of Bonnot's Mill, Osage County.

The Missouri River settlements were concerned primarily with the fur trade.   It was quite natural that a few half-wild French traders should locate on the great route to one of the most important fur districts of the New World.   Their dependence was on the Missouri River rather than on the adjacent country, and so they selected sites at creek mouths,

[1] Houck, loc. cit.

[2] Houck, op. cit., p. 286.

[3] Du Pratz, op. cit., p. 295.

[4] Houck, loc. cit.

[5] Houck, op. cit., II, 91.

[6] Gass's Journal Lewis and Clark Expedition (McClurg ed.), p. 3.

[7] Bradbury, in Early Western Travels, V, note on p. 42.

[8] Brackenridge, Views of Louisiana (Journal), p. 205.

[9] Ibid., pp. 115, 209.

[10] Ibid., p. 209.

[11] Maximilian, Prince of Wied, in Early Western Travels, XXII, 242.

whence they could easily launch their boats into the river. In part they traded independently, in part they attached themselves to parties from St. Louis. Their villages were a collection of poor huts and their habits of life very primitive. As a result of their association with the Indians, intermarriages were frequent, and the Missouri River settlements contained a considerable admixture of Indian blood in contrast to the French of Ste. Genevieve.

MODE OF HABITATION

The French gravitated invariably toward villages except when engaged in hunting, trapping, or in some instances in mining.[1] Before the period of American immigration almost the entire population was included in villages. It has been suggested that this condition was due to danger from Indians.[2] The French seem to have been, however, on the best terms with the savages, and early American residents of this section lived in isolated establishments with impunity. The most likely explanation rests on the social instincts of the French and on the character of their cultivation. They cared a great deal for the social amenities, and could supply these only by living together in villages.[3] Those who were, for a time, removed from their neighbors in the pursuit of furs or the collection of lead returned to the settlements with increased desire for the convivial diversions they afforded. Moreover, the French produced the food needed to supply their small wants from garden patches, which did not necessitate the detached farms on which the Americans, producers of extensive crops, lived.

"The villages were regularly laid out in squares . . . . , the houses standing towards the streets, and the interior of the area composed of gardens and orchards."[4] Houses built out to the street are still characteristic of Ste. Genevieve. In contrast to the American dwellings the houses of the French were constructed from hewn logs placed in the ground perpendicularly and plastered with mud on the outside.[5] The type is still extant in Ste. Genevieve. The most inviting feature of these old houses is the large porch space which they have. Most of them were long and had only one story. The porch commonly extended the length of the house, and its roof was continuous with that of the

[1] Brackenridge, op. cit., p. 113; Viles, Missouri Hist. Rev., V, 214.

[2] Austin, Amer. Hist. Rev., V, 519.

[3] Every traveler who wrote about this region has described the social life of the French; one of the best accounts is by Thomas Ashe, Travels in Amer., p. 289.

[4] Bradbury, in Early Western Travels, V, 259.   [5] Flint, Recollections, p. 100.

house.[1] This semitropical style of architecture is said to have been introduced from the West Indies.[2] It has given to the streets of Ste. Genevieve, where it is best preserved, a peculiar charm.

CONDITION OF THE FRENCH SETTLEMENTS AND ITS CAUSES

The French, as earliest inhabitants of the region, established in a section possessing mineral wealth and more than average agricultural possibilities, might be expected to have developed prosperous conditions and to have maintained precedence in wealth and social position over later comers.   Most of the French families had been in the region for several generations, some of them for a full century, before the Americans came.   The people were not oppressed by their government; indeed, they were ruled benevolently and on various occasions had been subsidized liberally.   It was said that anyone could obtain as much land as he chose to cultivate.[3]   Conditions therefore should have been favorable to progress.   According to the accounts of the time, however, the average habitant was little better off at the beginning of the nineteenth century than was his ancestor at the time of immigration.   The American settler speedily dominated almost every field of activity and improved on French methods.   The French proved inferior to the Americans in the following respects: (1) Efficient lead smelting was unknown to them. (2) They had sunk no shafts into rock to mine lead, but were content to hunt it out from the surface débris.   (3) The salt as well as the lead industry soon passed into the hands of Americans.   (4) French methods of farming were distinctly inferior, both as to yields secured and area cultivated.   (5) In spite of recurrent losses by flood their cultivation was limited to bottom lands.   (6) With liberal encouragement by the government they failed to produce an appreciable surplus of agricultural products, especially of flour.   (7) Although land grants of generous size were to be had with little trouble, in most cases titles were not secured until the Americans came.   (8) Their settlements, as Old Ste. Genevieve, Kaskaskia, Cahokia, Côte sans Dessein, and Charrette, were located with little regard to the safety of life and property, the sole consideration being accessibility to waterways and nearness of rich land. They were, in large part, truly *côtes sans dessein*.   (9) The Americans built better houses at the outset than the French did after long residence.[4]

[1] Baird, *View of the Valley of the Mississippi*, p. 243.

[2] Brackenridge, *Views of Louisiana*, p. 119.

[3] *Ibid.*, p. 141.   [4] Trudeau, in Houck, *Spanish Régime*, II, 256.

The contrast between the two races was commented upon at length by early travelers, most of whom ascribed it to an inherent inferiority of the French, manifesting itself in indolence. The official American account of 1803 described them as characterized by "aversion to labor, and love of a wandering life."[1] Their environment, however, contributed in several ways to this condition. (1) The settlements because of their dependence on rivers were in or adjacent to bottoms, which were malarial. "The inhabitants seem indolent, yawning as if under the constant influence of fever and ague; which, in fact, they often have."[2] (2) The isolation of the settlements resulted in consanguinity,[3] which possibly had deleterious results. (3) The somewhat Arcadian conditions in which the population lived did not stimulate endeavor. "Finding themselves in a fruitful country, abounding in game, where the necessaries of life could be procured with little labour, where no restraints were imposed by government, and neither tribute nor personal service was exacted, they were content to live in unambitious peace, and comfortable poverty."[4] "In this remote country, there were few objects to urge to enterprise, and few occasions to call forth and exercise their energies."[5]

These environmental handicaps were all temporary, however, and when removed the development of the French stock should have been parallel to that of the American and later of the German immigrants. This has not been the case. A few have been markedly successful in trade and professions; few indeed have succeeded in agriculture. The majority have remained poor.[6] In a number of cases the successful French families are not of Canadian stock. The descendants of the latter have, on the whole, fared poorly indeed. For the complete answer to their lack of success it is therefore necessary to go back of their present environment, probably to the conditions under which the emigration from France to Canada took place.

PRESENT DISTRIBUTION OF THE FRENCH STOCK

Fig. 21 shows roughly the area in which French influence was felt, as recorded by place-names of French origin. French traders have given names to the more important features along the Mississippi and

[1] Dept. of State, *Account of Louisiana*, p. 10.

[2] Flint, *Recollections*, p. 97.

[3] Brackenridge, *op. cit.*, p. 135.

[4] Hall, *History, Life, and Manners in the West*, I, 180.

[5] Brackenridge, *op. cit.*, p. 134.

[6] Oelshausen described their condition as such (1854) in *Staat Missouri*, p. 66.

Missouri rivers, most abundantly so in the vicinity of St. Louis and Ste. Genevieve. The majority of the places bearing French names, however, have never been occupied by Frenchmen, but are river features, named by passing traders.

A large part of the early French stock, distributed as outlined in the previous section, has been absorbed. A great many have drifted to St. Louis, where they have found congenial occupation in commercial

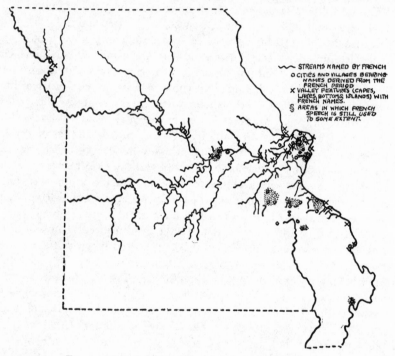

FIG. 21.—Distribution of French influence in Missouri

pursuits. The remnant areas in which traces of the French language still persist are shown in Fig. 21. Ste. Genevieve retains in part its French characteristics, and the French still dominate in the old mining settlements of Mine La Motte, Old Mines, Fertile, and Valle Mines, and on the Missouri at Bonnot's Mill. In Ste. Genevieve, which until recently has been a secluded place, they have retained race consciousness and pride and a fine Old World courtesy. Here centuries-old customs may be observed, such as the festival procession and the chanting of "la gaie année" at the turn of the year. In the outlying settlements, as in Washington County, long-continued isolation and poverty, due to their establishment in the least desirable districts, have told to their disadvantage. The people are dimly conscious of their past. Their language has been corrupted to a very poor patois, and for the most part they have retrograded with time. The largest district in which the French language is spoken today is in the remote hills of Washington County, by scattered groups of very backward settlers, half farmers, half laborers at opportune employments.

CHAPTER VIII

AMERICAN SETTLEMENTS IN THE MISSOURI AND MISSISSIPPI BORDERS AND IN THE ST. FRANCOIS REGION

BASES OF IMMIGRATION

The first American immigration into the trans-Mississippi country was from the Ohio Valley, in response to encouragement by the Spanish authorities. Morgan's colony at New Madrid, begun in 1788, is perhaps the earliest American settlement in undoubtedly Spanish territory. Spain for a time favored American immigration to demonstrate to the trans-Appalachian settlements the benefits of Spanish suzerainty and so to seduce them from their adherence to the United States. Spain also suspected England of designs against Louisiana, and welcomed the American frontiersmen as defenders against such an aggression. In 1796–97 Spain feared an attack from Canada on Upper Louisiana. "The distance of this province from the capital, added to a wilderness of nearly a thousand miles in extent between them, seemed to point out the necessity of strengthening it."[1] For this purpose inducements were held out to immigrants. Lands were given gratuitously, except for the cost of survey and confirmation, and were exempt from taxes. Americans were preferred, "as their prejudices against the English were a sure guarantee of their attachment to the Spanish interest."[2]

The inhabitants of the New West as yet possessed but poorly defined ideas of the body politic to which they belonged. Their isolation from the seaboard states excluded them at first from an active part in the government of the country and denied them most of the benefits to be anticipated from their adherence to the Union. Neither actual benefits nor the sentiments that arise with time had provided the strong bond of patriotism to hold them fast to the United States. Granted some material inducement, many a frontiersman was quite ready to transfer his allegiance from the United States to the king of Spain. In fact, the transfer meant little change in his political condition, for the governmental control exerted by either power over the inhabitants of the interior regions was slight and little was demanded in taxes or service. The American resident of the west bank of the Mississippi, having complied with the formalities of his transfer, lived, as he had lived previously,

[1] Stoddard, *Sketches of Louisiana*, p. 225.　　[2] *Ibid.*, p. 249.

by self-constituted order which he established and enforced in his pioneer community. His law was not determined by federal statute nor royal promulgation, but was the code of frontier society.

A number of conditions made the Spanish offer of free lands attractive to many. (1) The Ohio River led directly from the older American settlements to Upper Louisiana. By it especially were emigrants directed westward. Thus a tongue of settlement extended down the Ohio in advance of the settlement of districts remote from that river. By the end of the eighteenth century American settlements had extended to the mouth of the Ohio and into western Kentucky and Tennessee, and the vanguard of emigrants was ready to cross the Mississippi. (2) The prairie region, beginning a short distance north of the Ohio, was considered unsuited to agriculture. The opinion of one of the best-versed men of the day was: "A small part only of that extensive tract between the Mississippi and Vincennes . . . . will ever be settled. The scarcity of wood and water furnish insuperable objections to it."[1] (3) The resources of the trans-Mississippi country had been made known, although little developed, by the French, whom the Americans were encountering continually on the Mississippi and Ohio rivers. (4)

Fig. 22.—Areas having a population of more than two to the square mile in 1800 (after Spanish census of 1800, in Houck, *Spanish Régime*, and contemporary sources).

The lead mines were favorably known throughout the country. (5) Bradbury sums up the agricultural attractions of the region as being "inferior to no part in soil or climate," while the sparse stand of timber gave excellent grazing and made the clearing of land for cultivation an easy matter. (6) The same author stated the following commercial advantages of its location: (*a*) the transit to New Orleans could be made at

[1] *Ibid.*, p. 262.

any season, whereas because of low water the upper Ohio was not navigable in the months following the harvest; (b) the region in general was
600 to 1,000 miles nearer that city, the only market then available, than
was the upper Ohio Valley.[1]   Another early visitor to the region gave the

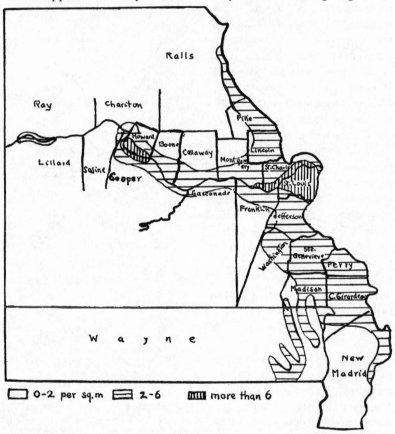

FIG. 23.—Population of Missouri, 1820–21 (after census of 1820, Campbell's
Gazetteer, and other contemporary sources).

following account of prices in the Mississippi Valley as determined by
the stage of water in the Ohio. "In December and January the price
of beef would rise to 27 cents a pound, flour to $8\frac{1}{2}$ dollars, and everything
else in proportion.   The inhabitants of Missouri at this time would have
no compunction and could sell as they chose, and did sell at a fourfold

[1] *Early Western Travels*, V, 262.

advance. No sooner did the Ohio rise than the states contiguous to it flooded the markets with produce and a barrel of flour dropped from $8\frac{1}{8}$ to $2\frac{1}{2}$ and 2 dollars."[1] (7) Men of means were attracted because the

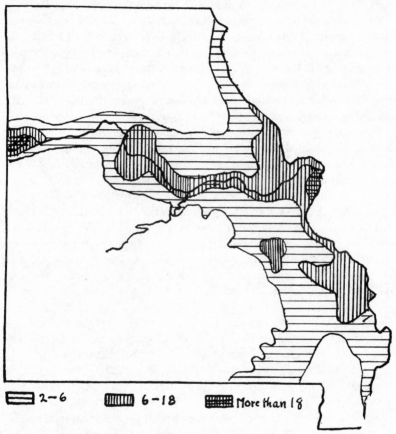

FIG. 24.—Population of Missouri, 1830 (after census of 1830 and other contemporary sources).

keeping of slaves was permitted.[2] (8) Land titles in Kentucky were in considerable part defective and were often contested.[3] (9) Some left

[1] Sealsfield (Sidon), *Nordamerika*, II, 126.

[2] Stoddard, *op. cit.*, p. 225; Bogess, *Chicago Historical Society Collections*, V, 55; Record Books, Secretary of State, Petitions of E. Cohan, *Survey No. 1015*, and of N. Cook, *Survey No. 342.*

[3] Volney, *The Soil and Climate of the U.S.* (1804), p. 339.

the American territory south of the Ohio because of increasing taxes and land values.[1] In the minds of many westerners the sale of lands by Congress, even at a very normal sum, contrasted unfavorably with the attitude of Spain.[2] (10) Until 1799 public lands in the Northwest Territory could be bought only in tracts of 4,000 acres[3] and no land was sold west of the mouth of the Kentucky River before 1804.[4] (11) Almost the entire area of Illinois was held by Indian tribes, the first important extinction of Indian titles being in 1803.[5] Similar conditions prevailed in other parts of the Northwest Territory. (12) Settlers on the west bank of the Mississippi had at all times free access to New Orleans, the only available seaport west of the Appalachians.

As soon as the way was opened immigration began with a rush. In 1796 it was claimed that more than eight hundred Americans were fixed in the Missouri country and that they were driving out the French, who were returning to Canada and Lower Louisiana.[6] In this year Austin said, "Land have already been granted to 1000 Famelies Near four Hundred of which have arrivd from different parts of the United States."[7] In 1804, 1,721,493 arpents of land were claimed in Upper Louisiana, largely by Americans.[8] From 1796 to 1803 the Spanish officials were overwhelmed with petitions for land grants. In the Missouri and Mississippi borders and in the St. Francois region a large part of the most desirable agricultural and mineral lands was granted to American immigrants before the cession of Louisiana. These Spanish claims, as they are still called, form a mosaic of irregular tracts, large and small. They include most of the Fredericktown soils, a large part of the Hagerstown, loess, and alluvial lands of the eastern and northeastern borders, and extensive areas of surficial lead deposits. These grants outline in some sections the most desirable tracts of land with great nicety.

After the transfer of Louisiana to the United States the land policy of the new government affected the settlement of the region unfavorably to some extent. It was made the subject of memorials and of much criticism on the part of citizens of the territory, by whom speedy occupation of the public domain and security of possession were the objects most desired. (1) At the end of the Spanish period fraudulent practices were

[1] Volney, *loc. cit.;* also Record Books, Secretary of State, Petition of Wm. Murphy, *Survey No. 2053.*

[2] Parker, in *Illinois Hist. Colls.,* IV, 410.   [4] *Ibid.,* p. 80.

[3] Bogess, *Chicago Hist. Soc. Coll.,* V, 76.   [5] *Ibid.,* p. 79.

[6] Volney, *The Soil and Climate of the U.S.* (1804), p. 339.

[7] *Amer. Hist. Rev.,* V, 535.   [8] Stoddard, *op. cit.,* p. 245.

employed to secure claims of land.[1] Congress accordingly refused to confirm many of these Spanish grants. They were subjected to numerous investigations and the titles of many of them were not decided for several decades. As a result, the Mississippi River Border especially, in which most of these grants were located, suffered. (2) In 1815 an act was passed providing for the relocation of lands lost or damaged in the New Madrid earthquake. The act was said at the time to have led to "more downright villainy than any law passed by Congress."[2] These relocations were largely made in the Missouri Valley and introduced many questionable titles into that section. (3) As an early attempt at conservation the government reserved the public lands supposed to contain lead, iron, or salt,[3] of which 150,000 acres were classed as lead-bearing lands.[4] In 1828 the state of Missouri made application for the sale of these lands, representing that large fertile tracts were thus kept from entry and that under existing conditions they were of benefit to no one.[5] In 1830 the reserved lands were offered for sale.[6] (4) Sales of public land were not held until 1817,[7] and for some time thereafter were infrequent. The minimum price of $1.25 an acre was considered prohibitive for nine-tenths of the land of the state.[8] As a result of these conditions it was claimed in 1828 that "hundreds of our citizens have left to seek lands in the Mexican states; and not one-third are possessed of lands."[9] The principal result of the government restrictions, however, was probably not so much to retard growth as to increase the proportion of squatters.

CHARACTER OF THE IMMIGRANT STOCK

The early immigrants were mostly of southern stock,[10] a majority coming from Tennessee and Kentucky. In fact the settlement of this portion of Missouri was by the extension of the settlements of these states. Of the thirty-two framers of the state constitution in 1820 whose birthplaces are known, nine came from Kentucky, eight from Virginia, three from Tennessee, two each from Maryland, Pennsylvania, and Missouri, whereas North Carolina, South Carolina, the District of

[1] *Ibid.*, pp. 253–57.
[2] *Amer. State Papers, Public Lands*, IV, 47.
[3] *Ibid.*, V, 622.   [7] *Ibid.*, XV, 125.
[4] *Ibid.*, IV, 559.   [8] *Amer. State Papers, Public Lands*, V, 622.
[5] *Ibid.*, V, 604.   [9] *Ibid.*
[6] *Niles' Register*, XXXVIII, 123.   [10] *Niles' Register*, XVII, 288.

Columbia, New York, Ireland, and Wales each contributed one.[1] Perhaps the five best-known names of early years in Cape Girardeau County
are those of Ramsay, Byrd, Russell, Rodney, and Randol. The first
of these families came directly from Virginia. The Byrds moved from
North Carolina to Washington, and later to Knox County, Tennessee;
thence the whole kindred set out for Missouri. The Russells were
originally from North Carolina, but had been long resident in Tennessee.
The Randols were from Pennsylvania.[2] A record of the old settlers
of American descent, taken in 1888, for Cape Girardeau, Perry,
Franklin, St. Francois, Bollinger, and Wayne counties shows that the
following states contributed most numerously, in order: Tennessee,
North Carolina, Virginia, Pennsylvania, and Kentucky.[3] Virginia,
Pennsylvania, and North Carolina were situated at the eastern termini
of the only routes across the Appalachians then available. Tennessee
and Kentucky received the overflow from the seaboard states, and in
their turn became the distributing centers for newer regions farther
west and south. Those who went west from Kentucky or Tennessee
were at most one generation removed from the Atlantic seaboard states.
For example, Senator Lewis Linn was a native of the Bluegrass of
Kentucky, his parents having removed to that region from Pennsylvania.[4] Emigration from southern states was due in the first place to
the economic pressure caused by extensive, wasteful farming, largely
with slave labor, which demanded large farms, depleted the soil rapidly,
and tended to drive out the farmers who were not slave-owners. The
lack of manufactures and the primitive condition of commerce in the
southern states prevented absorption of the surplus farm population into
other pursuits. The result was the first great wave of emigration from
the seaboard to the West, which was not spent until it had overspread
the Mississippi Basin as far west as Texas and Kansas. Southern Missouri was so situated as to intercept a large part of this westward-moving
stream of population, especially that which descended the Ohio, Cumberland, and Tennessee rivers. Some of the Missouri and Mississippi River
portions of the state of Missouri still retain in large part dominant
southern traits, and are referred to occasionally by their political antago-
nists as Bourbon districts.

Many of the emigrants from the southeastern states were of the
restless frontier type, leading a seminomadic life at hunting and farm-

[1] *Missouri Hist. Rev.*, VI, 62–63.

[2] *History of Southeastern Missouri*, pp. 272–79.

[3] Summarized from *Hist. of Southeastern Missouri*.   [4] *Life of Dr. Linn*, chap. i.

ing and removing to newer lands whenever the older region became fairly well settled. In the main these people formed the advance guard of civilization on the outer margin of the frontier. From Missouri many later moved to the newer West. A few remained because of the excellent hunting which the state afforded. The last home of Daniel Boone was in this state; near by Kit Carson spent his early years. A more stable group, which came from the South at an early date, was composed of slave-owners, who found a climate and soil suited to the successful employment of slave labor and a government which permitted their ownership.[1] A third group included small farmers, notably Scotch-Irish and Germans, chiefly from the Appalachian Valley and from the Piedmont.

NUCLEI OF SETTLEMENT IN THE MISSISSIPPI BORDER AND THE ST. FRANCOIS REGION

The Mississippi River Border of the Ozarks, being nearest the Ohio, was the first part of Missouri to receive settlers (Fig. 25). Because its various parts were almost equally accessible settlements were formed throughout the length of the region at about the same time. The more favored parts of the adjacent St. Francois region were occupied within a few years of the first locations in the Mississippi Border. The principal attractions to settlement were accessibility, bodies of Hagerstown, Fredericktown, loess, and creek bottom soils, lead mines, and salt springs.

Because the resources of this eastern region are distributed very unequally settlement was not effected by gradual, even expansion, but consisted in the early formation of nuclei of population at the most desirable locations, and the filling in of the intermediate areas slowly, and in some instances at much later dates.

Cape Girardeau was one of the earliest American settlements in the Mississippi Border and soon became the most flourishing. In 1795 Ramsay located on a creek southwest of Cape Girardeau and subsequently a settlement formed around his plantation, most of the older farms being in the creek bottoms. A settlement was made on Hubble Creek in 1797,[2] and on the Whitewater, with the most extensive bottoms in the county, in 1796.[3] In 1798 the American settlers numbered thirty

---

[1] Brackenridge, *Views of Louisiana*, p. 116.

[2] Houck, *Hist. of Missouri*, II, 185.

[3] *Encyclopaedia of the History of Missouri.*

families,[1] mostly located in these first years on Hubble, Whitewater, and Cape La Croix creeks.[2] Shortly the desirability of the Hagerstown upland soils was recognized. In 1799 the Byrd settlement was formed on the upland, its location being described as resembling a park.[3] This soil attracted rapidly great numbers of settlers,[4] most of its area in this

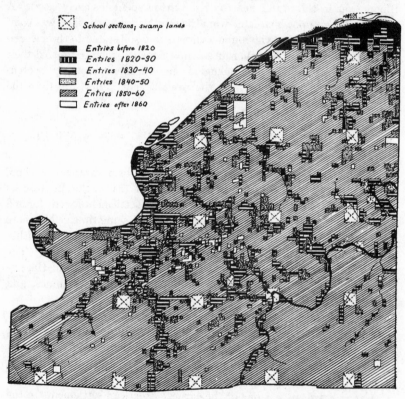

FIG. 25.—Order of land entries in Osage County (prepared from *Land Entry Book*, County Clerk's Office, Linn).

county being included in Spanish surveys. In 1812 the Hagerstown upland was described as possessing a luxuriant soil, well covered with timber and inferior to none in Upper Louisiana; "the richest and most

[1] Trudeau, in Houck, *Spanish Régime*, II, 247.

[2] *Amer. State Papers, Public Lands*, II, 477–82.

[3] Houck, *Hist. of Missouri*, II, 184.

[4] Viles, *Missouri Hist. Rev.*, V, 198–99.

industrious farmers in this part of the world are the proprietors."[1] Most of the loess soils of the southern part of the county also were entered before 1803. With its large areas of desirable soils and good streams for mill purposes[2] the population of the district grew rapidly. In 1799 there were 521 settlers.[3] In 1800 it contained 740 people; in 1803, 1,206; and in 1810, 3,883.[4] In 1818 Cape Girardeau had the reputation of being "one of the most flourishing settlements on the western waters."[5] In 1821 the county had a population of 7,852[6] (see Figs. 22, 23).

The town of Cape Girardeau was the river port for this section, being located on "the first bluff that offers a site for a town above the mouth of the Ohio."[7] It had 300 inhabitants in 1811.[8] Subsequent to 1815 its growth was checked by the founding of Jackson,[9] which was located more centrally with reference to the fertile Hagerstown and loess soils, and was made the county seat. Even in pioneer days Jackson derived an unusual affluence from its tributary territory.[10] It contained houses "built of brick and handsome,"[11] both unusual in a western town. In 1826 the Jackson community was said to be the most compact settlement in the state.[12] On the west there was an isolated settlement in the St. Francois Valley, which developed a small trading center in 1819 at Greenville,[13] on a ford of the St. Francois River, and later became expanded into Wayne County.

In Perry County the first American settlements were made about 1787 by a group of Pennsylvanians in the Bois Brule bottoms of the Mississippi. The fertile bottoms of Brazeau and Apple creeks were occupied next, in 1797.[14] Custom directed the first settlers to the bottoms, but experience soon demonstrated the advantages of the upland limestone soils. The first large settlement in this district was made by Kentuckians, at the Barrens, in 1801–3.[15] The Barrens were an almost

[1] Stoddard, *Sketches of Louisiana*, pp. 214–15.

[2] Flint, *Recollections*, p. 232.

[3] Dept. of State, *Account of Louisiana* (1803), App. II.

[4] Darby, *Emigrants' Guide*, p. 142.   [6] Beck, *Gazetteer of Missouri*, p. 228.

[5] *Ibid.*   [7] Flint, *loc. cit.*

[8] Brackenridge, *op. cit.*, p. 131.

[9] *Hist. of Southeastern Missouri* (1888), p. 425.

[10] James, in *Early Western Travels*, XVII, 39.

[11] A. A. Parker, *Trip to the West and Texas* (1835), p. 266.

[12] Flint, *loc. cit.*

[13] *Hist. of Southeastern Missouri*, p. 458.

[14] Houck, *op. cit.*, I, 381–87.   [15] *Ibid.*

treeless upland tract[1] of Hagerstown soil, described as "a body of good second rate soil, well adapted to the growth of all the small grains, lies high, is well watered, has excellent timber, and is settled by a considerable number of industrious and independent farmers."[2] In the Barrens, Perryville was laid out in 1822.[3] Later St. Mary's was founded and became the river port for this important interior farming district, as well as for Mine La Motte.[4]

The town of Ste. Genevieve remained French in its dominant characteristics long after it became a possession of the United States.[5] In the region adjacent to Ste. Genevieve only a small number of American farmers settled, selecting principally the loess uplands.[6] The country in general was too rough, its soils were not sufficiently rich to attract much immigration,[7] and there was a rather large indigenous population. The development of the region to the west, however, by American settlers enlarged the trade and population of Ste. Genevieve. In 1811 the town, together with New Bourbon, had about 1,400 inhabitants,[8] among whom were a number of Americans, engaged in commerce.

As with the French, the lead mines were again the first attraction which brought American immigrants to the district now included in Washington and St. Francois counties. In 1798 Moses Austin was granted a square league of land at Mine à Breton,[9] and in 1799 the first family settled there.[10] Austin's settlement formed a nucleus for the Americans who came into that section, and soon a considerable village was formed.[11] By 1804 there were twenty-six families at this place,[12] and as the operation of the mines increased in the following years many more were attracted.[13] Thus Mine à Breton became the town of Potosi, which shortly was made the county seat, as the miners were an unruly class and their control from distant Ste. Genevieve was a difficult matter.[14]

---

[1] *Handbook of Missouri* (1881), p. 214.

[2] Van Zandt, *Full Description of the Military Lands*, p. 104.

[3] *Hist. of Southeastern Missouri*, p. 449.

[4] *Ibid.*, p. 410.

[5] Baird, *View of the Mississippi* (1832), p. 243.

[6] Trudeau, in Houck, *Spanish Régime*, II, 248.

[7] Stoddard, *Sketches of Louisiana*, p. 216.

[8] Brackenridge, *Views of Louisiana*, p. 125; Stoddard, *op. cit.*, p. 215.

[9] *Amer. State Papers, Public Lands*, I, 209.

[10] *Amer. Hist. Rev.*, V, 519.

[11] *Ibid.*

[12] *Amer. State Papers, Public Lands*, I, 209.

[13] Schoolcraft, *Travels*, pp. 243–44.

[14] *Ibid.*

Near the close of the eighteenth century the increased prospecting due to American immigration led to the discovéry of a number of mines. The Mines à Joe (Desloge), à Lanye, à Maneto, and à la Plate (all on Big River) were opened between 1795 and 1801[1] and formed the beginnings of St. Francois County. In 1804 ten mines were worked in the neighborhood of Ste. Genevieve.[2] Mine au Shibboleth (three miles east of Old Mines) was discovered in 1805 or 1806[3] and Bryan's (Hazel Run) in 1809.[4] Schoolcraft in 1819 listed forty-five mines, of which twenty-five were in the vicinity of Potosi.[5] From 1798–1816, it is said, 9,360,000 pounds of lead were smelted in the Potosi region.[6] Some of the discoveries were highly remunerative. Mine au Shibboleth is said to have produced 4,000,000 pounds in one summer,[7] and Bryan's Mine yielded between 600,000[8] and 1,000,000 pounds in a year.[9] As long as such finds were made immigration to the Potosi region continued.

Agricultural settlements in the St. Francois region kept pace with the mining development. Before the end of the first decade of the nineteenth-century settlements of some size had been formed on all the larger basins of the Fredericktown limestone soil. Early descriptions of areas of this soil are, without exception, in highly appreciative terms. According to an account of the time they "embrace a large body of very rich land, having every necessary advantage of timber and fine water, and are in a high state of cultivation, and improvement by a large number of excellent farmers."[10] Belleview Valley and Murphy's were both settled in 1798.[11] Belleview Settlement was mentioned frequently in early accounts for its fertility and prosperity.[12] In 1804 it contained twenty families.[13] It is now a quiet little community, little larger than a century ago. Murphy's Settlement is in the largest tract of good land

[1] Austin, in Amer. State Papers, Public Lands, I, 207–8; locations from Missouri Geol. Surv., VII.

[2] Stoddard, Sketches of Louisiana, p. 394.

[3] Bradbury, in Early Western Travels, V, 251.

[4] Brackenridge, Views of Louisiana, p. 154.

[5] View of the Lead Mines, pp. 65–66. [8] Brackenridge, loc. cit.

[6] Schoolcraft, Tour into the Interior, p. 4. [9] View of the Lead Mines, p. 75.

[7] Bradbury, loc. cit. [10] Van Zandt, op. cit., p. 104.

[11] Houck, Hist. of Missouri, I, 372, 375.

[12] Schoolcraft, View of Lead Mines, p. 51; Van Zandt, op. cit., p. 105. Oelshausen, Staat Missouri, pp. 13–14; Beck, Gazetteer (1823); Dana, Geog. Sketch on the Western Country (1819); Brown, Gazetteer, p. 19.

[13] Amer. State Papers, Public Lands, I, 209.

in the St. Francois region. In 1818 it was said that Murphy's is "a large and flourishing neighborhood of industrious farmers, and presents many well cultivated fields, fenced in a neat and substantial manner."[1] Here Farmington was founded in 1822[2] and soon became a substantial town. Other early settlements were at Caledonia in southeastern Washington County,[3] Cook's in southeastern St. Francois County,[4] Stout's in Arcadia Valley, and St. Michael's near Fredericktown.[5] The last named is in a large basin, isolated from other agricultural areas by igneous knobs and ridges of Gasconade limestone. It has developed individually therefore and has become the administrative seat of Madison County.

In the northern part of the Mississippi River Border the places available for settlement were fewer and smaller. On the Meramec the river bottoms are of small extent, and farms were opened slowly.[6] Here Schoolcraft observed in 1825 "still a dearth of settlements. . . . . In the distance of twelve miles, there are but six farm-houses passed."[7] The early population of this district centered about Joachim and Plattin creeks,[8] where the principal farming districts lie.[9] These valleys are also readily accessible from the Mississippi. The isolated bottoms of Big River were settled after 1799 through a grant which stipulated that the settlements should be fifteen miles from any previous ones.[10] The steepness of slopes and absence of desirable residual soils prevented the spread of early settlements beyond the valleys and kept this section from becoming as well populated as were other parts of the eastern border (Figs. 23, 24).

Topography, soils, and mineral resources determined the location of these well-defined nuclei, in each of which, with the exception of the Big River settlements, a community center developed shortly. Eight of these nuclei grew into counties. They are Cape Girardeau–Jackson (Cape Girardeau County), the Barrens (Perry County), Ste. Genevieve (Ste. Genevieve County), Murphy's (St. Francois County), Mine à Breton or Potosi (Washington County), St. Michael's (Madison County),

[1] Schoolcraft, Tour into the Interior, p. 90.

[2] Hist. of Southeastern Missouri (1888), p. 440.

[3] Schoolcraft, View of the Lead Mines, p. 51.

[4] Van Zandt, op. cit., p. 104.

[5] Houck, Hist. of Missouri, I, 377–78; Beck, Gazetteer, p. 239.

[6] Brackenridge, Views of Louisiana, p. 114.   [8] Houck, Hist. of Missouri, I, 379.

[7] Schoolcraft, Travels, p. 237.   [9] Beck, Gazetteer, p. 236.

[10] Hist. of Franklin and Jefferson Counties (1888), p. 372.

Greenville (Wayne County), and Joachim and Plattin valleys (Jefferson County). In each instance but the last the approximate site of the pioneer community has become the county seat.

SETTLEMENT OF THE MISSOURI RIVER BORDER

Whereas the Mississippi lay across the path of westward migration and settlements were made in its various parts almost simultaneously, the Missouri Valley was a continuation of this course of movement and was occupied from east to west.

The first important American settlements were in St. Charles County and southern Warren County and formed a tongue extending upstream from the mouth of the Missouri. Here Daniel Boone and his colony located on the rich bottoms of Femme Osage Creek in 1797. On Tuque (1799), Charette, and Lost creeks (1801) numerous locations were made under the Spanish authorities, in part by the expansion of Boone's colony. The settlement of the Femme Osage–Charette vicinity constituted the district of St. Andrews and was sufficiently important by 1803 to be noticed in the account of the Department of State of that year. This account also mentions the Kentucky origin of the Missouri River settlements.[1] The river margins of Franklin County had settlers at least as early as 1803.[2] Loutre Island, Montgomery County, a large tract of Missouri River bottom land, insular only at high water, was occupied probably in 1798, and a few years later had a sufficiently strong settlement to withstand serious attacks by the Indians.[3] By 1799 the American settlements above St. Charles on the Missouri had taken second place among the districts of Upper Louisiana in the production of corn and tobacco.[4] Because of the hostile attitude of the Indians pioneers for a time did not pass the Loutre,[5] and some even withdrew from their exposed locations.[6]

The next area of extensive settlement was the Boonslick country, which included, according to a definition of the time, "the whole tract of country comprehended in Cooper and Howard counties, extending on both sides of the Missouri from the mouth of the Osage to the western Indian boundary,"[7] but which was limited more commonly to the present limits

---

[1] Dept. of State, *Account of Louisiana*, p. 10.

[2] *Hist. of Franklin County* (1888), p. 222.

[3] Thwaites, *Early Western Travels*, XIV, note on p. 134; Bradbury, *ibid.*, V, 47.

[4] Dept. of State, *Account of Louisiana*, App. II.

[5] Darby, *Emigrants' Guide*, p. 303.   [6] Houck, *op. cit.*, II, 94.

[7] Quoted from *Franklin* (Missouri) *Intelligencer* (1819), in *Missouri Hist. Rev.*, I, 311.

of Cooper and Howard counties.   Boone came here at least as early as
1807 to make salt.   A permanent settlement was begun in 1810.[1]   The
earliest locations were at Heath's Creek Salt Springs,[2] on the Lamine
River in Cooper County, where Brackenridge describes a thriving
settlement in 1811,[3] and in Howard County near New Franklin.   Of
these, one on the Lamine was the largest, and extended six or eight
miles.[4]   Fig. 15 shows the location of the principal brine springs in
Cooper County.

The Boonslick country contained numerous salt springs, good
water, fine grass, sufficient timber (Fig. 15), the largest area of loess
soils in the state, and many good bottoms.   It amply supplied, therefore, the necessities of pioneer life.   The fame of this new country spread
quickly, and one of the most notable rushes of immigrants in the annals
of the state resulted.   In 1811 there were sixty families in the district.
In 1815–16 the county of Howard was created.   In 1816 alone more than
one hundred families came.[5]   By 1817, 1,050 white males were enumerated.[6]   It was praised at the time as "no doubt the richest considerable
body of good land in the Missouri territory; and is equal, if not superior,
to the best part of Kentucky."[7]   Three years later there was a total
population of more than eight hundred families (Fig. 23).[8]   In 1835
it was still considered "the largest and most populous settlement in the
State."[9]   "The whole current of immigration set towards this country,
Boon's Lick, so called. . . . . Boon's Lick was the common center of
hopes, and the common point of union for the people.   Ask one of them,
whither he was moving, and the answer was, 'To Boon's Lick, to be
sure.' . . . . And thus wave propels wave."[10]   This section was sought
largely by southern slave-owners,[11] who were bent on establishing plantations of generous size, but also by families from New England and New
York, who made the tedious journey by way of New Orleans.[12]

Two towns were founded at an early date in the Boonslick country,
on opposite sides of the river, nearly across from each other.   In 1812
Cole's Fort was built, on the upland overlooking the Missouri River,

[1] Thwaites, op. cit., V, note on p. 52.

[2] Cooper County, in Encyclo. of Hist. of Missouri.

[3] Views of Louisiana, p. 115.   [4] Ibid.   [5] Darby, loc. cit.

[6] View of the U.S.A. (London, 1820), p. 666.   [7] Ibid.

[8] James, in Early Western Travels, XIV, 148–50.

[9] A. A. Parker, Trip to the West and Texas, p. 261.

[10] Flint, Recollections, p. 202.   [11] Darby, loc. cit.

[12] Schoolcraft, View of Lead Mines, pp. 231, 234.

for protection against the Indians.[1] It became the town of Boonville in 1817.[2] The site not only was well suited to defense but formed an excellent river harbor and a place for transshipment for the region to the west and south, as it lies near the southwestern extremity of a large rectangular bend of the Missouri. The town of Franklin was laid out on the flood plain of the Missouri in 1816,[3] near the present site of New Franklin. In 1818 one of the three land offices of the state was established here.[4] In less than two years the transformation of a cornfield had taken place into a city of two hundred houses with "a great number of genteel habitations, many merchants' storehouses, a court-house, all appendages of a seat of justice," and other improvements of civilization.[5] Both places became great distributing points for emigrants,[6] not merely for Boonslick but for points farther west, as they were for a time the westernmost towns of the Mississippi Basin.[7]

The settlement of Boonslick was followed by the filling up of the country between it and the older settlements to the east. In 1811 there were two families in the Gasconade region.[8] By 1818 settlements were strung all along the Missouri Valley. Deeds from that period in the Gasconade County courthouse record a lively transfer of real and personal property by a considerable number of people. In this intermediate region settlements for some time were confined to the Missouri Valley and the adjacent loess bluff lands,[9] as the quality of most of the uplands was not such as to attract early settlement, and the tributary valleys were somewhat isolated. Land values along the Missouri in 1835 were given at one to five dollars an acre.[10]

The rapid influx of immigration gave rise to many town projects. The town of Gasconade was laid out, at the mouth of the river of the same name, as the site of the state capital. Osage City had a similar location relative to the Osage Valley,[11] and lots to the amount of $20,000

[1] Hist. of Cole County (1888), p. 203.

[2] Thwaites, Early Western Travels, XIV, 89, 134.

[3] James, in Early Western Travels, XIV, 148–50.

[4] Houck, Hist. of Missouri, III, 183–84.

[5] View of the U.S.A. (London, 1820), pp. 54, 680.   [6] Niles' Register, XVI, 256.

[7] See C. A. Murray, Travels in North America (1834–36), p. 245, for an early correct estimate of the relative value of the two sites.

[8] Brackenridge, Views of Louisiana, p. 207.

[9] Hist. of Franklin and Jefferson Counties (1888), p. 220.

[10] Murray, ibid., I, 241.

[11] James, in Early Western Travels, XIV, 144; Niles' Register, LXVII, 304.

to $30,000 were sold, but no improvements were made.[1]   Newport, seat of justice of Franklin County, was located at the mouth of Boeuf Creek.[2]   Other towns along the Missouri River were Pinckney, Thorntonsburg, Missouriton, Roche au Pierce, and Columbia.[3]   Most of them had no geographic justification.   In 1819 it was said: "Numerous other towns, ... containing from one to half a dozen houses each, are to be met within a few miles. . . . . Almost every settler, who has established himself on the Missouri, is confidently expecting that his farm is in a few years to become the seat of wealth and business, and the mart for an extensive district."[4]   Almost without exception these places were located on the river flood plain at landings.   Consequently they were malarial,[5] subject to flooding, and in time most of them were destroyed by the river.   The fate of Franklin was foretold within seven years of its foundation.[6]   Of the entire number only two remain, Boonville and Jefferson City, both located on the river bluffs.

LOCATION AND IMPROVEMENT OF THE HOMESTEAD

Settlement proceeded by a rapid and rather even expansion wherever the surface presented only slight irregularities, the soil was uniformly good, and timber was generally available.   This was the case in the areas of loess, Hagerstown, and Fredericktown soils, and to some extent in the valley of the Missouri.   In the rest of the Missouri and Mississippi River Borders, however, the progress of settlement has been very unequal and in some sections vacant lands existed until recently.

Fig. 25 shows the order in which land entries were made in Osage County, and is typical of a large part of this region.   The entries before 1820 comprised all of the Missouri bottoms, about ten locations at short distances from the Missouri River on small creeks, several on the loess bluffs adjacent to the river, and one on the Gasconade River.   In the next decade a few small entries were made on the Gasconade, on the smaller creeks, and on the loess lands, and the first one on Maries Creek. The increase from 1820 to 1830 was slow because of the attraction of the Boonslick to immigrants of this period.   By 1840 all of the desirable loess land had been entered, a great number of entries had been made on the creeks, and a few in the Osage and Gasconade valleys.   By this time the entries outlined the drainage of the county in considerable

[1] Wetmore, *Gazetteer*, p. 63.
[2] Beck, *Gazetteer*, p. 264.
[3] Houck, *loc. cit.*

[4] James, *op. cit.*, p. 146.
[5] *Ibid.*, p. 158.
[6] *Ibid.*, p. 149.

detail. A majority of these entries were of small size, consisting of from forty to eighty acres, and were located in small valleys in which there is relatively little cultivable land. With the exception of the river bluffs, the uplands remained unoccupied. By the end of the forties the choice ridgelands within fifteen miles of the river had been taken up and by another decade all the uplands in the rest of the county which were sufficiently extensive to farm. The great number of entries in the decade 1850–60 was due largely to the passage of the Graduation Act, which reduced the cost of land in accordance with the length of time it had been subject to entry. The entries subsequent to 1860 have been mostly of rough hillsides. The factors determining the order in which the land was entered in this county are: (1) accessibility, primarily from the Missouri, to a lesser extent from the Osage and Gasconade, and later from the railroads; (2) open texture of soil and suitability for working with weak implements; (3) fertility of the soil, the higher-priced lands today being in large part the earlier entries; (4) presence of good water; (5) timber and stone; and (6) healthfulness.

One of the more notable things about the early locations is the large number of small entries which were made on small creeks before the much-superior bottom land on the larger streams was occupied, except in the Missouri Valley, and also before the smooth upland was taken. Except in the case of the very best lands, the pioneer used different standards than are employed today by which to judge the merits of a location. These small homesteads on the "branches" were almost invariably at a spring, and this was the first consideration in their selection. Timber and stone also were to be had near by for buildings and fences. In most cases there was enough arable land at hand to grow "truck" for the family. Many of the early settlers came from the hill country of Tennessee and Kentucky, were more hunters than farmers, and derived part of their support from the raising of stock, which ranged about at will. For them a clearing on the wooded hillside, close to the grassy uplands, was most desirable. Here game was secured most readily, and here the cattle and hogs could find ample sustenance. These settlers needed neither much land nor fertile land. Finally, in contrast to the bottom lands, the hillside clearings had good water and good drainage and were therefore healthful.

From the days of first settlement the larger bottoms were breeding places of malaria, differing, however, in the degrees of the unhealthfulness. The Mississippi River bottoms, which had perhaps the worst reputation, were low, subject to flood, and contained many sloughs.

Schoolcraft strikingly describes the contrasted conditions of health in the upland of the mine country and in the Mississippi lowlands.

Those diseases which prevail more or less every summer on the *American bottom*, and other rich and level tracts of Illinois, Ohio, and Indiana, have not found their way into the interior of Missouri, where there is no stagnant water, no repositories for mud and slime, brought down by the annual floods, as is the case on the immediate banks of the Mississippi, Ohio, and other great western rivers, and no pestilential airs from decaying vegetable, and drying ponds. The *fever and ague* is a very rare thing at the mines. . . . . During a residence of ten months at the mines, I have not witnessed a single death, or heard of any happening in the country. At the same time, the margin of the Mississippi, on both sides, has been the scene of frequent deaths, and, during the summer months, of almost continued disease.[1]

Featherstonhaugh described the settlers in the Mississippi bottoms as follows: "Their sallow, emaciated countenances, that looked distressed by the monstrous quantities of calomel they were accustomed to take, and the feeble and uncertain steps with which they went about their avocations, betrayed how dearly they paid by the loss of health for the privilege they enjoyed of occupying a fertile soil."[2]   As a result of the prevalence of fevers few Americans were willing at first to locate in the Mississippi lowlands, preferring generally the uplands.[3]   The lower valleys of the St. Francois, Castor, and Black rivers were also very unhealthful, as they were drained poorly.   In Greenville, on the St. Francois, the first settlers were said to be dying "by inches of chills and fevers."[4]

On the Missouri River conditions were somewhat better, as the land is on the whole higher, and the river, flowing in a relatively narrow valley, has not developed sloughs to any great extent.   On this stream most of the undrained depressions are near the base of the bluffs, and these places were most feared by the settlers.[5]   Fevers were sufficiently common in the Missouri bottoms so that immigrants were advised to avoid them.[6] Nearly all the farmers who cultivated land on the flood plain built their homes "on the eminences, rather than below on the bank of the river, where the air is said to be less salubrious."[7]   The lower Osage and

[1] *View of Lead Mines*, pp. 30–31.

[2] *Excursion through the Slave States*, I, 302.

[3] Stoddard, *Sketches of Louisiana*, p. 237; Brackenridge, *Views of Louisiana*, p. 111.

[4] Featherstonhaugh, *op. cit.*, I, 335.

[5] Muench, *Der Staat Missouri* (1859), pp. 26–27.

[6] Baudissin, *Der Ansiedler im Missouri Staate*, pp. 2–3.

[7] Maximilian, Prince of Wied, in *Early Western Travels*, XXII, 240.

Gasconade valleys also had evil reputations. The scanty settlements on the Gasconade prior to 1850 (Fig. 25) are to be explained primarily by the prevalence of malaria. The fertility of the river lands was well appreciated, but the fear of fever kept most of the early settlers in the more healthful creek valleys. As a result, the best farms of the northern border were along creeks which had ample land for cultivation and for pasturage, and were sufficiently drained to be reasonably free from fevers.[1]

The malarial nature of these lowland fevers is indicated clearly by the statement that the disease was generally of the intermittent kind, was limited largely to lowlands, and was induced "by the pestilential vapors, which arise from the rivers, and from the decayed vegetable substances."[2] Most settlers, especially those from the North, had to undergo a period of acclimatization; they were warned that "sooner or later comes the fever."[3] The control of malaria has been a slow and difficult matter. In 1811 it was observed that the disease was due partly to decaying vegetation.[4] It was discovered early that the clearing of the land reduced the fevers.[5] Chiefly by thus reducing the breeding places of the mosquito through clearing and drainage the larger bottoms have been made tolerable.

Extensive upland prairies were avoided during the first years of settlement for the usual reasons. The earliest settler on the prairie in Gasconade County is said to have abandoned his claim owing to the absence of water and the difficulty he experienced in breaking the sod.[6]

The location for a home having been chosen, the improvement of the homestead proceeded after the established fashion. The help of the neighbors was given freely to the newcomer in the erection of his home and in the clearing of land. The typical homestead consisted of a one- or two-room log cabin, surrounded by fields in which the deadened trees remained standing.[7] Many of the log houses were made in the Virginia style, consisting of a double cabin with an intermediate space which was roofed over. This place formed a "cool and airy retreat," in which most of the household labors were transacted during the hot season.[8] The furnishings of the house were few, simple, and homemade.

[1] Muench, op. cit., p. 28.

[2] Stoddard, Sketches of Louisiana, p. 237.   [3] Muench, op. cit., pp. 59-60.

[4] Brackenridge, Views of Louisiana, p. 111.   [5] Baudissin, loc. cit.

[6] Hist. of Franklin and Jefferson Counties (1888), p. 620.

[7] Tixier, Voyage aux Prairies Osages, p. 81.

[8] James, in Early Western Travels, XIV, 134-35.

"A four-posted sassafras bedstead was regarded with admiration. Earthenware cups, saucers and plates were unknown, and knives and forks did not exist until after the first quarter of the century had passed."[1] Most of the first settlers had mills of their own for grinding corn, ranging from hollowed-out stumps to band mills operated by horse power.[2] The dwelling-house was the only building erected at first. Granaries were not needed, tools were too few to require a shed, and stock remained out of doors throughout the year, finding shelter under trees or projecting ledges of rock.[3] In not a few instances the lack of a cellar was made good by a cave, in which "the farmer keeps his meat or butter fresh and sweet."[4] On many farms a small springhouse, built of logs or stone over a spring, provided a cool and sanitary place for the storing of perishable food. The timber supplied a great number of pioneer needs. Furniture was made from black walnut, cherry, or sassafras. The water maple and butternut furnished dye for homespuns. From the sugar maple "long and short sweetening," that is, sugar and syrup, were made, as well as vinegar. In the hollow trunks of the sycamore grain was stored. Hickory furnished wagon-tongues and handles. Oak was used for shingles, boards, cooperage, and wagons; red cedar for shingles, churns, and chests, and almost any long-grained wood for fence rails.[5]

PRODUCTIVE OCCUPATIONS

The activities of the pioneer were not directed toward the production of specialized commodities. Because of his isolation he was forced to produce whatever things were necessary to the sustenance of his family, or as many of them as possible. The intermediate climate of Missouri, the favorable association of forests and grassy tracts, the abundance of springs, the many mill sites, and the varied mineral resources enabled the pioneer in most localities of the border regions to live in almost complete independence of the older sections. This diversity of resources was more important then than now, and caused many sites to be more desirable for settlement to the pioneer than they are to the farmer of today.

Hunting and fishing.—Few of the American settlers were hunters or fishermen by avocation, but almost all of them supplemented their living by these means. Venison, bear meat, wild turkey, and wild honey were an important part of the food supply of the pioneer.[6] Deer

[1] Bryan, *Missouri Hist. Rev.*, IV, 89–90.

[2] James, *loc. cit.*

[3] *Ibid.*

[4] *St. Louis Republican*, November 3, 1863.

[5] Muench, *op. cit.*, pp. 35–41.

[6] Baudissin, *op. cit.*, pp. 12–21.

were common along the Missouri River until well after the Civil War. Fish were taken in quantity by nets and traps, especially on creeks, in the backwaters formed by rivers in flood. Along the Missouri River on such an occasion farmers not infrequently secured a year's supply by salting down their catch and packing it in barrels.[1]

Field agriculture.—The agricultural settlers formed at all times an overwhelming majority in the northern and eastern border regions. In 1819 it was stated that "the farming class is by far the largest; as the fertility of the soil, and the advantages of procuring lands on easy terms, and in a mild climate, afford the strongest and surest prospects of gain to the emigrant."[2]

Agricultural conditions of the time were well summarized by Duden, a German traveler, who compared them with the European conditions. He observed the following points of contrast: (1) Land was easily procured, whereas labor was scarce. (2) Buildings and fences were inexpensive. (3) The only land fenced was that from which stock was excluded. (4) Stock received almost no attention. (5) Fertilizers were not used. (6) Corn raising was the basis of all agriculture, cotton was produced in sufficient quantity for home needs, and tobacco was one of the most important cash crops. (7) Maple trees supplied the farm requirements of sugar and syrup. (8) The character and amount of production were affected by the fact that markets were for the most part hundreds of miles distant, and that it was often necessary to construct one's own boat in order to ship to market.[3]

In variety of products the pioneer farm surpassed the farm of today. In 1812 the characteristic products of the region were said to include corn, wheat, rye, oats, barley, buckwheat, tobacco, hemp, cotton, flax, melons, sweet and Irish potatoes, apples, pears, peaches, plums, and berries.[4] Of these, corn, wheat, cotton, tobacco, and flax were the more important.[5] The earliest record of production by Americans is a census of the Cape Girardeau district in 1803. According to this there were produced 58,990 bushels of corn, 39,000 pounds of cotton, 2,950 bushels of wheat, 9,200 pounds of flax and hemp, and 19,000 pounds of maple sugar.[6]

[1] Muench, *op. cit.*, p. 68.

[2] Schoolcraft, *View of Lead Mines*, pp. 171–72.

[3] *Reise nach den westlichen Staaten*, pp. 269–71.

[4] Stoddard, *Sketches of Louisiana*, pp. 227–28.

[5] *Hist. of Franklin and Jefferson Counties* (1888), p. 220.

[6] Houck, *Spanish Régime*, II, 403–7.

At first corn was produced much more extensively than all other crops, because (1) it is equally satisfactory as food for men and stock; (2) it keeps in the fields as long as desired; (3) it gives large returns for the seed used; (4) it grows on newly cleared land which is too rich in humus for small grains, and which is not in condition to have the seed bed prepared as carefully as is necessary in the case of small grains; (5) the climate of the region is well suited to the production of corn; and (6) it was readily marketable as whiskey. Between the rows of corn a secondary crop often was grown, usually pumpkins or beans.[1] Corn was produced on uplands and bottoms alike. All the rich upland soils were heavy producers. This is true especially of the loess lands of Cooper and Moniteau counties, but also of the Hagerstown and Fredericktown soils. On the uplands after a time other crops were introduced, but the bottom lands almost invariably were planted to corn year after year. Even under the careless tillage of the day they are said to have produced fifty to sixty bushels an acre.[2] In some bottom fields probably no other commercial crop ever has been produced down to the present day.

The leading corn-producing sections, such as Cooper County, also grew most of the oats. Because of the climate the culture of oats never assumed large proportions.

Wheat production increased rather slowly, and finally displaced corn only on certain uplands.[3] In 1840 the yield of wheat exceeded one-tenth the yield of corn only in Cole, Franklin, St. Francois, Ste. Genevieve, and Washington counties. It was at about this time that wheat first became a staple crop of the border regions.[4] There were three chief reasons for the increased interest in wheat-growing at this period. (1) The upland soils, which at first produced good corn, became depleted, especially in humus, through the continued cultivation of this one crop and no longer furnished favorable moisture conditions for corn. The older counties, with large areas of cultivated uplands, therefore first took up the extensive cultivation of wheat. (2) "Many lands, which formerly were little regarded and considered infertile, because of a scant growth of timber, and yielded only poor corn, now produce the most abundant crops of wheat."[5] At about this time the cultivation of the somewhat less desirable Union and Lebanon soils commenced, and these clay soils of rather low humus content proved well suited to wheat. These lands

---

[1] Muench, *Staat Missouri* (1859), p. 111; Beck, *Gazetteer*, p. 185.

[2] Stoddard, *op. cit.*, pp. 228–29.　　　[4] Muench, *op. cit.*, p. 112.

[3] *Ibid.*　　　　　　　　　　　　　　[5] *Ibid.*

are usually in good condition for the preparation of the seed bed in fall, but are cold in spring. They are therefore wheat but not corn soils. (3) Many Germans settled in the border regions about the middle of the century. These people were expert growers of small grains. By 1860 the wheat crop in every county exceeded 10 per cent of the corn crop, except in Cooper, Moniteau, and Morgan counties, which were located in the region of the most extensive loess soils. In Perry and Ste. Genevieve counties the value of the wheat crop equaled or exceeded that of corn. In Ste. Genevieve, Perry, and Cape Girardeau counties the Springfield soils, previously little desired, had been found peculiarly adapted to the raising of wheat.[1] Similarly, on the Hagerstown soil of the same section, wheat was found to grow unusually well. In these three counties, therefore, wheat growing became increasingly important. The city of Cape Girardeau became a milling center of note, which took highest honors on its flour at three international exhibitions in one decade.[2] At present much of the Hagerstown soil of Cape Girardeau County is "tired," as the farmer puts it, from several generations of dominant wheat farming.

Tobacco was a most valuable export crop[3] because it had least bulk and commanded a good and fairly steady price. Its cultivation was aided by the following facts: (1) It was most profitable on newly cleared ground, of which there was an abundance for many years. (2) The early settlers came mostly from tobacco-growing sections and were skilled in its production. (3) Slave labor was employed, especially on the river bottoms, in the laborious task of cultivation. The early interest taken in this crop is shown by an act passed in 1821–22, which provided for county inspection in order to control the quality of the leaf. In 1824 thirty-eight hogsheads of tobacco, grown in the Boonslick country, were sold in New York.[4] Other sections that were known at an early date for the quality and quantity of their product were Ste. Genevieve[5] and Perry counties.[6] Loutre Island was also one of the famous producing sections, and its tobacco planters were among the most aristocratic citizens of the state. Its plantations were said to resemble those of the southern states in point of luxury.[7] In 1840 Franklin, Cape Girardeau, Cole, and Cooper counties each produced in excess of 100,000 pounds. In 1850 Franklin and Cooper counties alone

---

[1] *Eighth Ann. Rept., State Board of Agriculture*, p. 410.

[2] *Handbook of Missouri* (1881), p. 105.

[3] Beck, *Gazetteer* (1823), pp. 186, 228. [5] Beck, *Gazetteer*, p. 251.

[4] *Niles' Register*, XXVI, 150. [6] Wetmore, *Gazetteer*, p. 144.

[7] Zimmermann, in *Missouri Hist. Rev.*, XX, 40.

remained in this class.   In 1860 Franklin, with 792,000 pounds, produced ten times as much as the next Ozark county.[1]   In 1866 tobacco still was considered the great money crop of Franklin County, and from one to three "barns" were raised on every average farm.[2]   The concentration of this industry in Franklin County appears to have been due principally to an early immigration of tobacco planters, largely from Virginia.   The tobacco grown in the Missouri and Mississippi River counties was the principal factor in making St. Louis a tobacco market and later a manufacturing center.   Although tobacco has almost disappeared from the farms of Missouri, St. Louis is still one of the first tobacco centers of the United States.

Tobacco, produced on the bottom lands, yielded a heavy or "shipping" lead, and on newly cleared uplands, especially on "dog-wood land," a lighter leaf of higher quality.[3]   On the upland both yield and quality decreased with each crop, and after two or three crops were grown the land usually was planted to corn and another tobacco patch was cleared. The decadence of the tobacco industry was due: (1) primarily to the lack, after a time, of newly cleared land; (2) as shipping facilities were provided, other lower-priced agricultural products became profitable; (3) most of the later immigrants, coming from Germany or the northern states, did not know how to raise tobacco, and many of the old tobacco planters moved away.

At the outset cotton was produced in every section, from the margins of the southeastern lowlands to the Boonslick.[4]   Some cotton was grown in the Missouri River Border even after the Civil War.[5]   In 1873 Cape Girardeau still shipped 2,500 bales.[6]   On the whole, however, cotton belonged to the pioneer period and was produced chiefly for household use.   The region in general is too far north for the commercial production of cotton, the crop being "sometimes destroyed by early frosts."[7] When railroad transportation supplied manufactured cloths cheaply, its production declined and after a time ceased, except in the extreme South.   Hemp and flax were introduced into Missouri by planters from Kentucky.   Both were grown by slave labor on the river-bottom

[1] Census of 1840, 1850, 1860.

[2] *Agric. Rept. of Missouri* (1866), p. 251.   [3] Muench, *op. cit.*, p. 118.

[4] Darby, *Emigrants' Guide* (1818), p. 304; Beck, *Gazetteer*, p. 186.

[5] *First Ann. Agric. Rept. of Missouri*, Appendix, p. 56.

[6] *Prospectus of Illinois, Missouri and Texas Railroad*, p. 9.

[7] Beck, *Gazetteer*, p. 186; see also Wetmore, *Gazetteer*, pp. 144–45.

lands, especially in Boone County and farther west, where they constituted large and profitable crops. The industry was ruined by the Civil War and by foreign competition.[1] These three textile fibers, once constituting some of the most important crops of the Ozark Border, are at present unknown in this region, except as garden curiosities.

Among the early "agricultural" products maple sugar often is mentioned. Sugar maples were very common in the bottoms. When the land was cleared for a farm, a grove or "camp" of these trees usually was allowed to remain. Not only were the household needs, said to average a hundred pounds a year per family,[2] thus supplied, but a considerable surplus was exported. "Some families would make as much as 1,000 pounds per year. . . . . This was exchanged at ten cents per pound for dry goods."[3] When southern sugar entered the local market, the industry declined[4] and the groves were largely cut out to make room for fields.

Stock raising.—As long as a large part of the region was unoccupied, stock raising probably gave the largest returns with least expense and effort. In 1812 it was said that the cattle "in summer subsist on the grass, with which the country is covered; and in the winter they retire to the bottoms, where they find plenty of cane and rushes."[5] The swine "subsist on the mast found in the woods; and hence both the cattle and swine keep fat most of the year. No hay is necessary, except for such cows and horses as are stabled, and plenty of this is always to be obtained in the proper season from the prairies. The high grounds are seldom so thickly covered with wood as to prevent the growth of grass. They exhibit more the appearance of extensive meadows than of rude and gloomy forests."[6] The ease of raising stock has been described by Schoolcraft as follows:

The farmer here encloses no meadows—cuts no hay. The luxuriant growth of grass in the woods affords ample range for his cattle and horses, and they are constantly kept fat. Hogs also are suffered to run at large, and in the fall are killed from the woods; I have seen no fatter pork than what has been killed in this way. There is, perhaps, no country in the world, where cattle and hogs can be raised with so little expense and trouble as here. . . . . Horses are raised in considerable numbers by the inhabitants generally, and with little

[1] De Bow, *Industrial Resources, etc., of the Southern and Western States*, II, 60.

[2] Duden, *Reise nach den westlichen Staaten*, p. 68.

[3] Broadhead, *Repts. Geol. Surv. of Missouri* (1855–71), pp. 59–60. [4] *Ibid.*

[5] Stoddard, *Sketches of Louisiana*, p. 229. [6] *Ibid.*

labor. They subsist themselves in the woods, both summer and winter, nothing more being required than to look after them, to see that no bells are lost, that they are duly *salted*, and that they do not go astray.[1]

In a new region, abounding in grass and water, the raising of stock was a matter of Arcadian simplicity at first and of considerable profit as well. The raising of cattle was most extensive in the northwestern counties of the Ozarks, where the most corn was grown,[2] and in the southwestern counties, which had the most free range, that is, the largest areas of unoccupied grasslands. Boonville as the principal river port for both sections became an important live-stock market and developed a meat-slaughtering industry. After 1860 there was a gradual decline in the number of cattle kept, which has continued until recently. This was primarily the result of the continued decrease of the grazing area with increasing settlement. The beginning of the decline coincides with the opening of the first railroads. With the building of railroads grain could be marketed profitably, and it was no longer necessary to drive the products of the farm to a distant market in the form of stock. In the second place, the German immigrants, whose influence became dominant in the northern and eastern borders after 1850, have paid little attention to cattle raising until recently.

Sheep were not kept in large numbers. The physical conditions of the country were suited to them, but they fell prey to wolves and dogs, and the wool of the unconfined sheep became so fouled as to be worth little.[3] In this, as in other regions, sheep-raising without herding has not proved suited to pioneer conditions.

Mule breeding in America has been developed most highly in central Missouri, especially in the river counties. The industry began early, the census reports from the first half of the nineteenth century showing the largest number of mules in these counties and in the vicinity of Springfield. By the middle of the century the exportation of mules to the South, especially to the sugar plantations, had become a well-established and flourishing business.[4] Mule breeding in Missouri appears to have originated through the Santa Fe trade, which had its eastern termini on the lower Missouri River. One of the earlier Santa Fe trading parties returned to Old Franklin in 1823 with 400 jacks, jennets, and mules, an extraordinary importation for the time.[5] This may have been the begin-

[1] *View of Lead Mines*, pp. 34–35.

[2] Oelshausen, pp. 163, 166; *Third Ann. Agric. Rept. of Missouri*, p. 321.

[3] Wetmore, *Gazetteer*, p. 71; Muench, *Staat Missouri*, p. 150.

[4] Muench, *op. cit.*, p. 149.   [5] *Niles' Register*, XXV, 230.

ning of mule breeding in Missouri. At any rate, for many years not only the Santa Fe traders but most travelers to the west and southwest secured their animals from Missouri River points. Parties also were fitted out at Springfield. These expeditions, whenever possible, used the hardier mules in preference to horses, and thus created a brisk local demand, which resulted in extensive breeding of mules. Later, as the demand from this source decreased, that from the southern plantations increased, and, since the region had established itself substantially in the industry, it continued to supply the new market. The Boonslick country is probably still the first mule-raising region of the world.

Lead mining.—The stimulus which lead mining derived from American immigration was the result of the increased number of workers who became available, of the greater energy which they displayed, and of the more advanced views which they held.[1] As a result there was a notable increase in the discovery of ore bodies, improvement in the methods employed, and enlarged production.[2]

The figures given by Winslow[3] as the total production of lead for the state to the year 1860 are shown below. The lead produced in Missouri between 1800 and 1859 was worth $16,318,000 and came

1720–1799	18,000 tons	$1,800,000
1800–1819	25,300 tons	2,280,000
1820–1829	19,100 tons	1,908,000
1830–1849	73,400 tons	6,604,000
1850–1859	51,100 tons	5,526,000

almost entirely from the eastern and northern borders. During this period Washington County yielded $6,193,000, St. Francois $3,204,000, Madison (Mine La Motte) $2,028,000, and Jefferson $929,000. In the Missouri River Border, Franklin County with $1,648,000 was the most important producer, Moniteau ranking second with $108,000.[4]

As long as mining was limited to the residual ore, secured by digging shallow pits, Washington County, with its large areas of red limestone basins, maintained its supremacy. The life of a given "mine" was short; but the decrease at one mine was made good by new discoveries. Mine à

[1] Schoolcraft, *View of Lead Mines*, p. 20.

[2] The principal changes in method were (1) the introduction of the reverbatory furnace, (2) the sinking of shafts into bedrock, and (3) the manufacture of sheet lead and of shot from shot towers (Schoolcraft, *op. cit.*, pp. 19, 138–39).

[3] Winslow, *Missouri Geol. Surv.*, VII, especially p. 540.   [4] *Ibid.*

Breton, opened in 1796, was reported nearly abandoned in 1811, but in that same year there were five other localities with operating mines in the county, each of which produced 100,000 to 600,000 pounds of lead.[1] After 1830 rich deposits were found in the northern border, in Franklin County, and later in Moniteau and Morgan counties.[2] The development of shallow deposits continued at widely scattered places to the Civil War. In 1863 the first shafts were sunk in the disseminated lead deposits of the Bonne Terre field[3] and inaugurated the modern period of lead mining in southeast Missouri.[4]

The number of workers fluctuated greatly.[5] In the twenties mining languished, as the flourishing condition of the Galena, Illinois, mines on the upper Mississippi caused a large part of the miners to withdraw from this region.[6] As the miners were paid according to their output, a diminution in production was attended by an exodus, which became speedy and unceremonious if a promising discovery at another place was announced.[7] The population therefore was extremely unstable, and the habits of the miners reflected their uncertain condition. "The digging itself is a species of gambling, and there are few miners who are not addicted to this practice."[8] The social consciousness of such a fluctuating population necessarily was slight, and lawlessness and violence in personal relations were common.[9] In their working relations, however, the need of security early made itself felt in "traditionary laws, which have so many years governed the community of miners, that like the Stannary laws of Cornwall, they are become prescriptive rights."[10]

The miners were recruited from four classes: (1) Many of the indigenous French engaged by preference in this pursuit, and in fact continue to do so to this day. (2) Agriculturists of the mine region devoted part of their time to digging for lead,[11] usually to the injury of their farms. It was said that increase of mining led invariably to a neglect of agriculture.[12]

[1] Brackenridge, *Views of Louisiana*, pp. 151–54.

[2] Meek, *Ann. Repts. Missouri Geol. Surv.*, II, 116; *Missouri Bur. Geol. and Mines*, Ser. 2, VII, 66.

[3] *Second Ann. Rept., Trustees St. Joseph Lead Co.*, p. 9.

[4] Stevens, *Missouri, the Center State*, I, 49–50.

[5] Schoolcraft, *op. cit.*, pp. 113–14.

[6] *Amer. State Papers, Public Lands*, V, 347; De Bow, *Industrial Resources*, II, 63.

[7] Flint, *History and Geography of the Mississippi Valley*, p. 302.

[8] *Ibid.*   [9] Schultz, *Travels*, II, 52–53.

[10] Schoolcraft, *Travels*, p. 287.   [11] *Ibid.*

[12] Schoolcraft, *View of Lead Mines*, p. 38.

Miners were known to have earned thirty dollars a day for several weeks.[1] Farming offered no such prizes, and the farmer was level-headed indeed who was not tempted from his plow by such alluring, if temporary, gain. (3) "A large proportion of those formerly engaged in mining were persons of the most abandoned character, refugees from justice in the old States."[2] (4) "A considerable proportion of these emigrants are indigent Europeans, who, having no capital to set up their trades . . . . have been directed to the mines."[3]

As long as mining was prosecuted in primitive fashion there was little permanent settlement. The two principal exceptions are Potosi and Mine La Motte. The latter has been a village of some note for a long period, solely because of the extraordinary productivity of the mine at this place, which has yielded rich returns, under various systems of mining, almost continuously for nearly two hundred years. Potosi, the center of the Washington County mines, added to its mining interests the manufacture of sheet lead and of shot,[4] and also became the trade center for the basin of the rich Fredericktown soils in which it lies.[5]

As Ste. Genevieve was not the nearest river port for most of the later mines, and as many steep hills intervened, another outlet on the river was opened at Herculaneum.[6] The road from Potosi to Herculaneum followed the easy grade of Joachim Valley, which was also a more direct line between the mines and the river. In 1819 Herculaneum was said to ship half the lead of the state,[7] and Ste. Genevieve suffered considerably through its competition. Herculaneum possessed another advantage over its rival in its river bluffs, which were utilized as shot towers, the melted lead falling nearly 300 feet.[8] For a time the village prospered and was one of the more important trading centers of the Mississippi River Border.[9] Later the small landing of Selma, just below Plattin Creek, also became an important shipping point.[10]

[1] Stoddard, *Sketches of Louisiana*, p. 395.

[2] Schoolcraft, *View of Lead Mines*, p. 39.　　[3] Schoolcraft, *Travels*, p. 287.

[4] Austin, in *Amer. State Papers, Public Lands*, I, 209.

[5] Schoolcraft, *View of Lead Mines*, p. 48.

[6] Schoolcraft, *Travels*, p. 245.

[7] Schoolcraft, *View of Lead Mines*, p. 120.

[8] Brackenridge, *Views of Louisiana*, p. 131; Tixier, *Voyage*, p. 76; Flint, *Recollections*, p. 101.

[9] Schoolcraft, *View of Lead Mines*, p. 48; De Bow, *Industrial Resources*, II, 63.

[10] *Amer. State Papers, Public Lands*, IV, 558; Shumard, *Ann. Repts. Missouri Geol. Surv.*, II, 147.

Iron mining.—Iron ore was known in the St. Francois region before the American period. Probably its first use was at the "shut-in" of Stout's Creek, near Ironton. Here a small furnace was built in 1815, which used ore from Shepard Mountain, wood from the adjacent hills, and made bar iron by water power.[1] Its product found ready local sale, but the difficulty of transportation prevented extensive production. There existed also an early prejudice that the ore was not suitable for smelting, and this had to be overcome before development on a large scale could be undertaken.[2]

Capital became interested in Iron Mountain in 1836, mining began in 1844 or 1845, and the first furnace was put in blast in 1846.[3] Superficial explorations had been made of this ore body, and it was thought to be a mountain of nearly pure ore.[4] Early skepticism gave place to wildest enthusiasm. In 1846 it was declared that Iron Mountain and Pilot Knob "have enough material in their bowels to supply the world for a century."[5] The original company of 1836 proposed to pay its investors $108.50 annually for every $100 invested.[6] Pilot Knob was bought originally for $18,000; six acres, used as a town site, sold a few years later for $50,000. An offer of $3,000,000 was made for the Iron Mountain property, which was said to be worth $5,000,000,000! According to the authority for this statement, it was a "national injustice, that three men should own a treasure nearly sufficient for a continent."[7]

Limestone for flux could be had near by. The forested knobs supplied fuel for the blast. At first the ore was smelted at the mines, and at Valle(y) Forge in St. Francois County, which made iron blooms. This forge was on the direct road to the river, had both limestone and fuel, and was able therefore to have the ore brought to it.[8] The pig iron was hauled to Ste. Genevieve, the nearest river port, at one-fourth of a

[1] *Missouri Geol. Surv.*, II, 304.

[2] Litton, *Ann. Repts. Missouri Geol. Surv.*, II, 75.

[3] *Missouri Geol. Surv.*, II, 305.

[4] See, for instance, Barker, *History of All the Western States*, p. 439.

[5] *Hunt's Merchants' Magazine*, XVI, 94.

[6] *Prospectus of Missouri Iron Company*, 1837.

[7] Muench, *Staat Missouri* (1859), pp. 50–51.

[8] "The forge was located near Farmington for the reason that wood was plenty in the vicinity. Fuel getting in the early days of iron making was a problem even more vexing than the transportation question. Vast quantities of charcoal were used in the furnaces. To keep up the supply the company bought tracts of land solely to acquire the timber on them" (Stevens, *Missouri, the Center State*, I, 196).

cent a pound.[1] Even at this cost the industry was profitable, as the demand for iron was great, and the only competition was from Ohio and Tennessee furnaces, which were said to yield iron of inferior quality.[2] The iron industry again restored to some extent the fortunes of Ste. Genevieve, which did a thriving business at shipping Missouri pig iron to points on the Mississippi and Ohio rivers.[3]

The remote location of the mines presently made improved transportation facilities a necessity. The first improvement was the construction of the Ste. Genevieve, Iron Mountain, and Pilot Knob Plank Road in 1853.[4] It was estimated that by the increased loads which could be hauled this road would reduce the cost of a ton of iron, delivered at Ste. Genevieve, from $18.72 to $16.00.[5] Before the completion of the plank road steps were taken to build a railroad from St. Louis to the iron and lead region. As early as 1837 "the importance of bringing, with cheap transportation to St. Louis, the iron from the neighborhood of Iron Mountain, as the true foundation for future and permanent growth of St. Louis," had been recognized.[6] A charter was granted to the St. Louis and Iron Mountain Railroad in 1851, "on condition that the road be located within five miles of Potosi, the center of the lead diggings."[7] St. Louis at that time is said to have sent out $1,500,000 annually to pay for iron products sold there, in addition to the cost of the pig metal used locally. By constructing this road it was hoped that the city would develop its own foundries, rolling mills, and nail factories, which would drive out articles manufactured elsewhere.[8] The greatest of St. Louis' expectations, in 1854, was the manufacture of iron.[9] Accordingly the support of St. Louis was assured to the railroad project from the outset. The road was completed as far as Pilot Knob in 1858.[10]

By 1865 there had been built as a result of the railroad, in addition to the six furnaces and bloomeries at the mines, one at Irondale, and one at Carondelet, adjoining St. Louis.[11] Before 1850 the total production

[1] *Hunt's Merchants' Mag.*, XVI, 95.

[2] *Engineer's Rept., Second Ann. Rept. Board of Directors of the St. Louis and Iron Mountain Railroad*, p. 25.

[3] *Western Journal and Civilian*, III, 242.

[4] *Ibid.*, X, 424.   [5] *Ibid.*, VIII, 139.

[6] *Second Ann. Rept. Board of Directors of the St. Louis and Iron Mountain Railroad*, p. 14.

[7] *Ibid.*   [9] Stevens, *Missouri, the Center State*, I, 200.

[8] *Ibid.*, pp. 22–23.   [10] *Missouri Geol. Surv.*, II, 306.

[11] *Hunt's Merchants' Mag.*, LIII, 335.

of iron ore in Missouri had been about 100,000 tons. In the following decade, during which the railroad was opened, the first large development of the Iron Mountain district took place, and the production for the decade was 310,000 tons. In the sixties the tonnage doubled, amounting to 625,000, and in the year 1870 316,000 tons were produced in the state.[1] Of the total output of the state to this date the Iron Mountain district yielded more than nine-tenths. Two flourishing towns sprang up, Iron Mountain and Pilot Knob. The people of the neighborhood flocked in to work in the iron mines, even as they had left their farms in lead-mining booms.[2] Immigrants from abroad were also attracted, especially the English and Germans. In Iron Mountain there were as many as a thousand operatives at a time. The new railroad diverted the shipping business from Ste. Genevieve to St. Louis, which also developed an important iron industry. By the middle of the century the furnaces at the mines were beginning to feel the exhaustion of wood fuel and the lack of coal.[3] St. Louis therefore, which had coal near at hand, received larger and larger shipments of ore and correspondingly smaller shipments of pig iron, the proportion in 1875 being three to one.[4] As late as 1880 an orator, eulogizing St. Louis, named it "the city of the Iron Crown."[5]

Production averaged somewhat less than 300,000 tons of ore per year until 1887,[6] after which there was a rapid decrease due to the mining of the cheap ores of the Lake Superior district and to the partial exhaustion of local deposits.

Other industries.—Manufactures other than those of mineral products were few, small, and supplied pioneer needs, or produced a compact article for export. Grist mills were one of the earlier necessities of pioneer communities. They were operated usually by water power. It was a matter of little difficulty to build a log or masonry dam across the smaller creeks and so to impound enough water to operate a mill wheel.[7] Bryan, of the Femme Osage Colony, had erected such a water mill by 1801.[8] In 1823 there were nine grist mills in Cape Girardeau County, which ground, in that year, 61,675 bushels of grain; at the same time mills in Jefferson County used 30,000 bushels; there were also five mills

[1] Winslow, *Missouri Geol. Surv.*, II, 324.

[2] *Hunt's Merchants' Mag.*, XVI, 94.   [3] Muench, *Staat Missouri*, p. 49.

[4] Allen, *Missouri, a Discourse at the Centennial Exposition*, p. 20.

[5] Stevens, *Missouri, the Center State*, p. 201.   [6] Winslow, *loc. cit.*

[7] *Hist. of Franklin and Jefferson Counties*, p. 220.

[8] Stevens, *op. cit.*, p. 115.

in Ste. Genevieve County and two in Madison.[1] In 1827 Cooper County had ten mills.[2] Many mills did custom carding and supplied the housewife with rolls for her spinning wheel.[3] These water mills also sawed timber for local use.

Distilling on a commercial scale was introduced into the region by Americans, who nad found it the only feasible means of marketing grain from the frontier. A considerable part of the whiskey was sold at St. Louis for the Indian trade.[4] Israel Dodge built a still near Ste. Genevieve in 1795.[5] Another was erected between Plattin and Joachim creeks in 1801.[6] In 1823 Cape Girardeau had thirty-one stills producing 17,800 gallons of distilled spirits; Jefferson County made 29,000 gallons; Madison 3,800; and Ste. Genevieve converted $900 worth of grain into whiskey worth $11,912.[7] The census of 1840 listed thirty-five stills in Cape Girardeau County, eight in Cooper, eight in Madison, seven in Cole, and smaller numbers in the other counties.

A number of other industries converted bulky products of the frontier into articles sufficiently valuable to bear cost of transportation to distant markets. Hides and oak bark supplied the requisites for the tanning of leather. In 1823 Cape Girardeau County had four tanyards,[8] while Cooper County had seven in 1827.[9] According to the census of 1840, there were in Cape Girardeau County twelve, in Cole, Franklin, and Perry each four, in St. Francois five, and in Washington County three, tanyards. Hemp was made into tow cloth and ropes,[10] used largely in river shipping, at rope walks in Ste. Genevieve and Franklin.[11] A tobacco factory was organized at Franklin in 1821.[12]

TRADE AND TRANSPORTATION

This region produced an unusually large number of the necessities of pioneer life: flour, meal, meat, lard, sugar, and salt for the table, wool,

[1] *Digest of Accounts of Manufacturing Establishments* (Washington, D.C., 1823).

[2] Tax list in *Missouri Hist. Soc. MSS.*

[3] *Third Ann. Agric. Rept. of Missouri*, p. 320.

[4] Stoddard, *Sketches of Louisiana*, p. 228.

[5] Record Books, Secretary of State, *Survey No. 2067.*

[6] Houck, *Hist. of Missouri*, II, 258.

[7] *Digest of Accounts of Manufacturing Establishments.*

[8] *Ibid.*

[9] Tax list in *Missouri Hist. Soc. MSS.*

[10] Schoolcraft, *View of Lead Mines*, p. 172.

[11] Houck, *op. cit.*, III, 187.   [12] *Ibid.*

cotton, and flax for cloth, leather for shoes and harness, wood for many purposes, iron for the blacksmith's needs, and lead and gunpowder for hunting. The articles therefore which had to be imported were few. These were principally manufactured goods, such as cutlery, nails, tools, plow irons, glassware, drugs, dry goods, and some groceries.[1] Lead, salt, iron, whiskey, flour and grain, tobacco, live stock, and animal products were the principal articles of export.[2] For all of these there was satisfactory demand ordinarily. These articles also possessed the merit of being marketable under the tedious and careless methods of transportation then in use. The city of St. Louis, the lead mines,[3] and, later, the iron mines, absorbed part of the surplus, especially of agricultural products. The greatest commercial asset of the region was its water routes, which provided transportation in all four directions of the compass. On the whole, therefore, the commercial situation was advantageous.

Trade was carried on at first chiefly by the producers, who took their surplus to market and returned with goods in exchange.[4] Gradually methods changed with the development of a class of professional merchants.

Before the introduction of steam, navigation was principally by boats of three types: canoe, flatboat, and keelboat. Canoes or piroques were small, narrow boats, made in various ways, and were used especially on the smaller streams. Perhaps the crudest type was the hollow sycamore log, its ends chinked up with clay, used by Boone in shipping salt down the Missouri.[5] Flatboats, built of heavy sawed planks, were employed as in other parts of the Mississippi Valley to convey goods downstream,[6] usually to New Orleans, where both cargo and craft were sold. Keelboats were superior to the other types, for they were often of larger capacity and could be propelled upstream.[7] Because of their unwieldy nature and their weak motive power all these craft were

[1] Schoolcraft, op. cit., pp. 44–45.

[2] Brackenridge, Views of Louisiana, p. 156; Stoddard, Sketches of Louisiana, p. 214; Hist. of Franklin and Jefferson Counties, p. 220; Darby, Emigrants' Guide, p. 142; View of the U.S.A. (London, 1820), p. 668.

[3] Schoolcraft, op. cit., p. 38; Wetmore, Gazetteer, p. 168.

[4] Stoddard, op. cit., p. 230.

[5] Cooper, in Campbell, Gazetteer, p. 242.

[6] Niles' Register, XXI, 336.

[7] Hall, The West, Its Commerce and Navigation, pp. 111–14.

difficult to handle in narrow, swift, or sinuous parts of the river channel.[1]

The first steamboat to ascend the Mississippi above the mouth of the Ohio arrived at St. Louis in 1817.[2] The swift current of the Missouri and its more difficult channel made it appear questionable whether that stream could be navigated by steam.[3] The question was answered in 1819, when the first steamboat landed at Franklin.[4] On the Mississippi steam navigation was established securely within a brief period.[5] On the Missouri the development of steamboating was slower, due to the character of the stream and the stage of development of the region. On both streams, but more especially on the Missouri, cheaply constructed rafts and flatboats, floating downstream, laden with produce, were familiar sights for years after steam navigation was introduced.[6] Parker, in 1835, reported passing hundreds of them.[7] In that year there were two boats making regular trips between St. Louis and Franklin on the Missouri.[8] In 1836 there were 140 arrivals of steamboats at Rocheport, Boone County, by September 8.[9] In 1854 more than 300 steamers a year were said to have landed at Boonville, which by this time had become the most important river port above St. Louis.[10]

The introduction of the steamboat increased the efficiency of the larger water routes greatly and thereby improved economic conditions along them. (1) The cost of transportation was reasonable. In 1831 freight from St. Louis to New Orleans was 37½ cents per one hundred pounds, return rate, 62½ cents; from Franklin to St. Louis, 25 cents,

[1] Several rocky narrows on the Mississippi were feared especially by early boatmen, notably those of Grand Tower above Cape Girardeau (Hall, *Statistics of the West*, pp. 48–49; Schultz, *Travels*, II, 81–85; Flagg, in *Early Western Travels*, XXVI, 89; also note by editor on same page). This "is a noble and massive pyramid of rock, rising perpendicularly out of the bed of the river, in which it forms an island. Around it the river foams and boils, throwing from its base a kind of spiral current across the river. Opposite 'the Tower' is another bold bluff, on the Illinois shore, called the 'Devil's Oven.' This, too, throws off another sweeping current, and between these currents the passage is difficult, and at some stages of the water, dangerous" (Flint, *Recollections*, p. 95). The (Grand) Chain of Rocks at Commerce was another dangerous obstruction (Schultz, *Travels*, II, 82, 85).

[2] Carr, *Missouri*, p. 132.   [4] *Missouri Hist. Rev.*, I, 310.

[3] Houck, *Hist. of Missouri*, III, 198.   [5] Schoolcraft, *View of Lead Mines*, p. 44.

[6] Baudissin, *Der Ansiedler im Missouri Staate*, p. 26.

[7] *Trip to the West and Texas*, p. 93.   [9] Wetmore, *Gazetteer*, p. 44.

[8] Bromme, *Missouri*, p. 39.   [10] Oelshausen, *Staat Missouri*, p. 163.

return, 75 cents.[1] Especially the competition of the flatboat reduced the downstream freight rates. Cabin passage from St. Louis to New Orleans in 1831 was $20.00; return, $25.00. Deck passage was only $5.00, but involved the obligation of carrying wood on board. The rates varied with the season, the depth of the water, and with other conditions,[2] and they usually were less on the Mississippi than on the Missouri because of greater competition on the former. (2) A regular shipping business was created, which freed the shipper from the task of taking his own goods to market, as had been necessary previously in most cases. (3) By providing a means of passenger transportation the steamboat increased immigration. (4) Prices improved, partly because of the increased demands of immigrants, partly because of the reduced cost of marketing.[3] (5) As a result of the latter, there was an increase not only in the volume of trade but in the number of commodities which were produced. Especially as St. Louis developed into an important market products of the most varied sort were shipped into it from the surrounding region.[4] (6) River landings became flourishing centers of trade. On the Mississippi the growth of Cape Girardeau was stimulated,[5] and on the Missouri that of Boonville, Franklin, and Jefferson City. Steamboat landings which had a large tributary territory soon developed into towns of importance, such as Washington and New Haven in Franklin County. (7) A considerable number of people, living along the rivers, supported themselves by supplying the steamboats with fresh provisions and with cordwood.[6] (8) The steamboat formed a link in the Santa Fe trade.[7]

During the period in which traffic was by river New Orleans was the great market of the region. Most bulky commodities, such as groceries, were shipped by this port.[8] The next largest trade was with the East by way of the Ohio. Lead and salt especially were exported over this route.[9] Because of the limited market which New Orleans afforded and the difficulty and expense of shipping bulky goods across the Appalachian Mountains, a circular trade developed. According to Schoolcraft, "lead is taken down the Mississippi in boats to New Orleans, and there either

[1] Baudissin, loc. cit.   [2] Ibid.

[3] James, in Early Western Travels, XIV, 148; Bek, German Settlement Soc., pp. 68–69.

[4] Ann. Rev. Comm. St. Louis (1854), p. 4.

[5] Flagg, in Early Western Travels, XXVI, 87; Wetmore, Gazetteer, p. 51.

[6] Baudissin, op. cit., p. 30.   [8] Schoolcraft, op. cit., p. 44.

[7] See p. 134.   [9] Stoddard, Sketches of Louisiana, p. 230.

sold, or shipped to Philadelphia or New York. The dry goods with which this country is supplied are principally purchased at Philadelphia, and waggoned across the Alleghany Mountains to Pittsburgh, and thence taken down the Ohio and up the Mississippi in boats."[1] Another account states that "the merchants at that early date made all their purchases of dry goods in Philadelphia and of groceries in New Orleans. They went to Philadelphia once or twice a year, proceeding up the Ohio by way of Pittsburgh, thence by stage on the National Road to destination. Their purchases were then shipped around to New Orleans and reforwarded by boat up the Mississippi River."[2]

Land travel consisted largely of short wagon hauls from interior points to river ports. The roads from the lead mines to the river were established in this way.[3] Little care was expended on roads. They were located along high ground if possible to secure good drainage. The construction of a road consisted merely in the felling of enough trees to enable the passage of a wagon, or in the blazing of a trail,[4] and in general it was found cheaper to make a new road than to repair an old one.[5] Bridges were almost unknown, although the region contains many streams.[6] After 1850 plank roads were constructed along a few lines of heavy travel. The difficulty of ascending the Missouri led to the opening of an important road between St. Louis and the Boonslick, to the north of the broken country along the Missouri. This is now the great cross-state highway, still known as the "Boonslick Road." Another important form of land traffic, which involved considerable distances, was the driving of large droves of mules, horses, and other live stock to distant markets, especially to the Red River and other southern points.[7]

The most famous overland trade of the state was that with Santa Fe, which later contributed greatly to the growth of the cities on the Missouri-Kansas border.[8] This trade had its origin in Franklin, where the first important expedition was assembled in 1822[9] by a company from the Boonslick. Their first venture showed the feasibility of the route; they found the country to the southwest open and level and abounding

---

[1] Schoolcraft, *loc. cit.*   [2] *Souvenir of Ste. Genevieve.*

[3] See p. 84; *Hist. of Franklin and Jefferson Counties*, p. 394.

[4] Baudissin, *op. cit.*, p. 31.   [5] Schoolcraft, *Travels*, p. 238.

[6] Schoolcraft, *View of Lead Mines*, p. 42; Houck, *Hist. of Missouri*, I, 371.

[7] Schoolcraft, *View of Lead Mines*, p. 35.

[8] See *Missouri Hist. Rev.*, VI, 1, and *Missouri Hist. Coll.*, II, No. 6.

[9] Wetmore, *Gazetteer*, p. 86.

in the grass necessary to sustain their teams.[1] Because of the strong contrast in climate, the difference in mineral resources, and the remoteness of Sante Fe from manufacturing districts, the trade was prosecuted successfully from the outset. Santa Fe supplied the Missouri country with specie, mules, and skins,[2] and received in return in the main manufactured articles, which were brought up the river from St. Louis. Whiskey, it is averred, was an important item; it was bought from Missouri distilleries at 40 cents a gallon, diluted with an equal volume of water, and sold in Taos for three dollars.[3] Both Franklin and Boonville soon were engaged largely in this traffic. These towns lay so far west that routes from there to the southwest avoided the rugged hill sections of the Ozarks. Their situation on the extremity of a bend to the southwest of the Missouri River made them two of the nearer river ports to the Santa Fe country.

As time passed roads and rivers inevitably became insufficient for the needs of the growing region. Canals were out of the question for most parts of the Ozarks because of topographic conditions. Sporadic efforts were made to improve the smaller rivers, so as to render them more useful.[4] Adequate improvement of transportation conditions, however, waited on the construction of railroads.

Railroads were built parallel to the Missouri and Mississippi rivers almost simultaneously. In contrast to most early railroads, local needs were not the determining factor in the construction of the Missouri Pacific Railroad. The road was planned as a great trunk line to connect the Far West with the Mississippi Valley. In 1849 a bill was introduced into the United States Senate "to provide for the location and construction of a Central National Road from the Pacific Ocean to the Mississippi."[5] St. Louis was then the first gateway of the West because of its position at the mouth of the Missouri River, and was chosen as the eastern terminus of the road. From here it was built along the flood plain of the Missouri River, reaching Jefferson City in 1856.[6] Beyond Jefferson City, because of the changed direction of the river and the lower elevation of the upland, the railroad in pursuance of its westerly course left the valley. As the Missouri Pacific Railroad

---

[1] *Niles' Register*, XXIII, 177.

[2] *Ibid.*, XXV, 230; XXVIII, 356; XXIX, 100, 127–28.

[3] Turley, in Stevens, *op. cit.*, I, 125.

[4] *Western Journal and Civilian*, I, 52; IV, 178–82.

[5] *Geol. Rept. of the Southwest Branch of the Pacific Railroad*, p. iii.

[6] *Ibid.*, p. xv.

passed through what was then the best-developed part of the state, its completion was not followed by large-scale immigration nor radical economic changes. It traversed a fairly wealthy section in the direction in which the country was developing and in which there was most traffic. It therefore enjoyed a large business from the outset and soon supplanted the Missouri River as the leading artery of commerce across the state.

The Iron Mountain Railroad, begun in 1853[1] and opened to De Soto in 1857,[2] was built for two principal reasons: (1) As suggested by its name, to be a "means of bringing into active and extensive usefulness the ores of the Iron Mountain and Pilot Knob";[3] (2) to establish rail connections "south to some point on the Mississippi below the influence of low water in summer, or the effect of ice in winter."[4] Between St. Louis and Helena, Arkansas, it was claimed, "navigation in summer is sometimes embarrassed by low water and sandbars; and in the wintertime, it is frequently obstructed by floating ice."[5] It also was argued that this route would enable St. Louis to establish trade relations with Europe by way of the Gulf more advantageously than through the Atlantic ports.[6] (3) Another reason is suggested by the requirement of the charter that it be so located as to serve the lead-mining region of Potosi. To reach the iron and lead deposits a difficult route through the crystalline knobs was taken, which would not have been necessary otherwise.[7] Access to the St. Francois region was secured by ascending Joachim Creek for almost its entire length. The road today carries neither iron nor lead in important amounts, but it still follows the route imposed by these resources of a past day. The road was completed first to Pilot Knob, with a branch to Potosi. Its principal freight consisted of metals and metallic ores, in the order given in the table (p. 136). Lumber also was carried to a considerable extent, but as the road passed through a very poor agricultural area, except for the basins of Fredericktown soils, the shipments of farm products were small.

In part because of heavy operating expenses through the hilly region, the limited demand for the few commodities produced in its territory,

[1] *Western Journal and Civilian*, X, 424.

[2] *Fifth Ann. Rept., Board of Directors of the St. Louis and Iron Mountain Railroad*, p. 5.

[3] *Western Journal and Civilian*, VII, 296.

[4] *Fifth Ann. Rept., Board of Directors*, p. 14.

[5] Waterhouse, *Resources of Missouri*, p. 63.

[6] *Western Journal and Civilian*, VII, 294–95.   [7] *Ibid.*, VIII, 408–22.

and the fact that the iron deposits did not equal the expectations that
had been held of them, the Iron Mountain Railroad was unable to meet its
expenses so long as its terminus was at Pilot Knob.   It therefore became
a necessity to extend it south into more productive territory.[1]   Several
places competed for the terminus of the extension, chiefly Belmont,
Missouri, Memphis, Tennessee, and Helena, Arkansas.   A memorial
from the citizens of Memphis argued that "Memphis is at the head of
perpetual navigation on the Mississippi.   There the river has never been
obstructed within the memory of any living soul.   It always is navigable
for the largest class of steamers.   At Columbus [opposite Belmont],
however, such an event is not a phenomenon.   The river has been gorged
with ice for days together."[2]   Belmont, however, across the river from
the northern terminus of the Mobile and Ohio Railroad,[3] was chosen

PRINCIPAL FREIGHT CARRIED IN 1874-76*

	Pounds in 1874	Pounds in 1875	Pounds in 1876
Iron ore....................	234,818,000	240,981,000	239,118,000
Pig and bloom iron..........	30,182,000	24,155,000	20,145,000
Lead, zinc, and iron ore.......	17,916,000	21,930,000	24,162,000
Barytes....................	5,360,000	5,381,000	4,961,000

* Summarized from directors' reports.

ultimately in 1867 because it was the shortest line which would connect
with a channel supposedly navigable the year around, as well as with a
railroad to the South.   The interest of St. Louis was enlisted by the
argument that the new Illinois Central Railroad was bringing Chicago
as close to Cairo as St. Louis then was by the water route.   The remedy,
it was pointed out, would be found in the construction of the Belmont
branch.[4]   The line was built in 1868, beginning at the place where Bismarck was laid out in that year.[5]   The road never realized the expectations of its promoters, as: (1) its terminus was an obscure river town;
(2) it was necessary to ferry across the river all goods intended for further
rail transportation; (3) it connected with an independent railroad system, which soon extended its terminus to St. Louis; (4) the shortness
of the haul between St. Louis and Belmont made it unprofitable gener-

[1] Seventh Ann. Rept., Board of Directors, p. 5.

[2] Ibid., p. 14.   [3] Waterhouse, op. cit., p. 53.

[4] Bucklin, Reconnaissance of a Route for the St. Louis and Columbus Railroad.

[5] Hist. of Southeastern Missouri, p. 446.

ally for commodities shipped by river to break bulk there. The road affected Cape Girardeau adversely by cutting off most of its hinterland.

A few years later the main line of the Iron Mountain Railroad was extended south from Pilot Knob down the Black River Valley, and so into Arkansas and the Southwest, and became one of the more important trunk lines entering St. Louis. As a result of this extension Poplar Bluff became important, and lesser centers, such as Piedmont, Ironton, and Williamsville, developed.

Because of the accessibility of these border regions from the Mississippi and Missouri rivers, railroad construction stimulated rather than revolutionized development. It aided especially the development of crop growing at the expense of stock farming, the establishment of a arge-scale lead industry, and the rapid exploitation of timber resources.

CHAPTER IX

SETTLEMENT OF THE SPRINGFIELD PLAIN

ROUTES OF IMMIGRATION AND PIONEER LOCATIONS

The western border of the Ozarks, although more favored in resources, was settled many years later than the eastern and northern borders. The reasons were: (1) The region lies two hundred miles west of the Mississippi Valley, and it therefore had to wait until emigration had moved well beyond this river. (2) It was accessible by no large streams, the only navigable ones being the Osage, White, and Neosho. All of these are small and connect with the Mississippi by very circuitous routes. (3) To the east is the rough Ozark hill country, which was a barrier to direct immigration. (4) The region was mostly prairie and hence was not considered desirable, nor was it generally suited to early settlement. (5) Its great mineral wealth was not known until after the middle of the nineteenth century.

The earlier settlements were on the headwaters of the White River. The first permanent location on record was at Delaware town, on the James fork of White River in Christian County, seven miles east of Billings. Here a small community was formed in 1822 by a number of families which had "left their homes in Ohio, traveling in a keel boat down the Muskingum, Ohio, and Mississippi rivers, to the mouth of the Arkansas, thence ascending that river, the White River and James Fork."[1] Their line of approach is a fair example of the devious routes by which settlers reached the region. The first settler in Newton County likewise came from the South, probably by the Neosho River, having started from Tennessee and followed the Arkansas River upstream.[2] The southern margin of the Springfield Plain received the earliest settlers because (1) the White and Neosho River country had an excellent reputation for game. Thus the "country of the Six Bulls" (corrupted from boils, or springs) was known in Tennessee about 1820 as a famous hunting-ground.[3] (2) At some seasons the navigation of the White and of the Neosho was not a difficult matter. (3) The Arkansas Valley was settled at an early date and from it settlements extended up

[1] Campbell, *Gazetteer*, p. 137.
[2] *Hist. of Newton and Lawrence Counties*, p. 218. [3] *Ibid.*, p. 197.

its tributaries. The White River Valley afforded splendid sites for home-steads. Due to the form and size of the valley these were not numerous, however, and so a thin chain of settlement extended upstream rapidly. The southern margin of the Springfield Plain was most accessible from Tennessee, which was the source of the great majority of the early immigrants.

Another early route into this region followed the even crest of several long divides across the Ozarks. This formed a continuous upland trail, except at the crossing of the Gasconade.[1] Later it became an important highway from St. Louis to Rolla, Lebanon, Marshfield, Springfield, Mount Vernon, and Neosho,[2] and still later it was followed closely by the St. Louis and San Francisco Railroad. A third line of immigration, used more largely than the last, skirted the northwestern margin of the Ozark hill country and used either the Osage River or overland trails from Jefferson City and Boonville. The first land travel in the northern section of the Springfield Plain was around the Osage-Gasconade hill belt by the Missionary Trail from Jefferson City to an Indian mission at Harmony in Bates County, established in 1821.[3]

The Osage River had been used by French traders at an early, unknown date, and subsequently by American hunters. Beginning about 1830 it became an artery of immigration. By 1837 keelboats of forty tons' burden had been taken up the Osage well beyond the limits of the Springfield Plain.[4] Warsaw is the oldest and was long the largest town on the river. It developed from Bledsoe's Ferry, established in 1831,[5] and was long second in importance only to Springfield among the communities of southwest Missouri. The town was ordinarily at the head of navigation for steamboats, and here as well all land travel to and from the Missouri River crossed the Osage. The roads from Boonville to Fort Smith, Arkansas, and from Jefferson City to Bolivar and Springfield ran southwest from the Missouri River so as to avoid the rough Osage-Gasconade hills, and crossed the river at this point.[6] Warsaw thus became a distributing point, at first for the immigration bound for the northern section of the Springfield Plain and later for the trade of this region.

[1] *Ibid.*, pp. 218–19.

[2] Broadhead, *Missouri Hist. Rev.*, VIII, 91.

[3] Campbell, *Gazetteer*, p. 389; Parker, *Missouri as It Is*, p. 184.

[4] Wetmore, *Gazetteer*, p. 40.

[5] *Encyclopedia of the History of Missouri:* Benton County.

[6] Broadhead, *loc. cit.;* Wetmore, *loc. cit.*

The earlier settlements, as in most other prairie regions, were located in valleys at the edge of the timber.[1] One of the early settlers thus expressed the condition which determined the choice of a location: "No man in those days would settle in this country unless he had a spring of running water. The next thing of importance to him and for which he sought was timber, and coming from a woodland country in Tennessee and North Carolina, where they didn't know how to make a field unless they hewed it out of the forest, they would go down on a spring branch and clear three or four acres for a field, which would cost them more labor than it would have to build a forty-acre field in a prairie."[2] As late as 1839 the following opinion was expressed by an intelligent traveler: "The land is cultivable only along the water courses. The farther one penetrates westward, the more arid the soil becomes, and soon the lands which produce trees, ... alone are suited to agriculture: the finer the forests are, the richer is the ground; but in the prairie, cultivation is no longer possible."[3]

Springfield, settled in 1822–23, became the most flourishing town on the western border.[4]   It was located on the margin of Kickapoo Prairie, one of the finest and largest bodies of farm land in the Ozarks, and controlled the trade of this prairie.   The site of the village was determined by an excellent spring and power site.   Here also the roads from Warsaw and St. Louis crossed, the former skirting the western margin of the dissected country, the course of the latter determined by watersheds, both meeting at Springfield because of topographic conditions.

NATIVITY OF THE EARLY SETTLERS

The pioneer stock of the Springfield Plain was much like that of the other border sections.   In the southern part of the region, previous to the development of mining, Tennesseeans were strongly preponderant.[5] In 1888 a biography of settlers of Newton County listed forty-eight natives of Tennessee, Kentucky being the second state, with twenty-two.[6] This was also the only part of Missouri in which natives of Arkansas

---

[1] Hubble, *Personal Reminiscences of Springfield*, p. 25; *Encyc. of the Hist. of Missouri:* Barry County; Campbell, *Gazetteer:* Cedar, Christian, Dade counties.

[2] Hubble, *op. cit.,* p. 23.

[3] Tixier, *Voyage*, p. 88.   [4] Hubble, *op. cit.,* p. 7.

[5] Wetmore, *Gazetteer*, p. 76; Hubble, *op. cit.,* pp. 6, 7, 11, 14, 19; *Encyc. of the Hist. of Missouri:* Lawrence County.

[6] *Hist. of Newton and Lawrence Counties.*

were met with to any extent.[1] The nativity of the people of the southern section was influenced by the White and Neosho rivers as dominant routes of immigration.

PIONEER OCCUPATIONS

The pioneers were for the most part farmers, who distinguished themselves from their contemporaries of the Missouri and Mississippi borders by greater attention to stock raising.[2] An emigrant's guide of 1849 recommended the region "only to those who wish to raise cattle on a large scale."[3] Cattle and corn were the principal products of this region, which as early as 1832 was said to export the meat of thousands of cattle annually.[4] By 1850 Greene County had more cattle and more hogs than any other Ozark county and ranked second in sheep. The census of that year shows that more cattle were kept in this section of Missouri than in any other in proportion to the acreage of improved land. The importance of the stock industry was due chiefly (1) to the distance to market, the lack of transportation facilities, and the fact that stock could transport itself. Cattle were driven from Lawrence County, for example, not only to St. Louis, but even to New Orleans.[5] (2) Animal products formed a stable and concentrated article of export, for which there was demand, especially in the southern markets, and they could bear the cost of long wagon hauls and boat transportation under the inexpensive method of stock raising then practiced. Salt meats, cured hides, tallow, and lard figure prominently in the early exports.[6] In 1854 the exports of Warsaw were: bacon, 11,994 pcs.; hams, 204 cks.; shoulders, 159 cks.; lard, 630 bbls.; pork, 200 bbls.; 150 hides; leather, 30 rolls; wheat, 5,550 bu.; deerskins, 144 bales; 2,230 furs; beeswax, 33 bbls.[7] (3) As long as settlements were confined to the margin of the prairies every farmer had, almost at his back door, excellent and abundant pasturage. (4) Moderate winter temperatures and light snowfall made it unnecessary to house stock. (5) The grass-growing clay soils were not immediately available for cultivation, because the first settlers

[1] Biographical lists in *Hist. of Newton and Lawrence Counties; Encyc. of the Hist. of Missouri:* Dade County.

[2] Compendium of the sixth census.

[3] Schmölder, *Wegweiser für Auswanderer*, p. 96.

[4] Oelshausen, *Staat Missouri*, pp. 167, 168, 169, 170; Baird, *View of Valley of Mississippi*, p. 240.

[5] *First Ann. Agric. Rept. of Missouri*, App., p. 86.

[6] Baird, *loc. cit.*   [7] *Ann. Rev. Comm. St. Louis* (1854), p. 52.

did not possess the necessary equipment for cultivating them. (6) Corn, abundantly produced by the rich soil, was used to best advantage in the feeding of stock.

As in the other sections of the highland, corn was by far the most important crop. Greene County tripled its production of corn between 1840 and 1850, and in the latter year led all Ozark counties. The Springfield soil quickly showed its adaptation to corn culture. Whatever prejudice against prairies existed at the outset was dispelled quickly by the magnificent crops of this grain which they grew. "Whoever has seen Kickapoo and Grand Prairies in their pride and the crops which the farmers grew upon them will not doubt that here it is good to live."[1] Crops were on the whole less diversified than in the other border sections. Wheat was not grown extensively in early years because adequate markets for it were lacking. Tobacco was not an important crop, probably because of the lack of virgin woodland soil. The region was too remote to attract wealthy planters and therefore the culture of hemp and flax was not developed largely.

Mills were erected under advantageous conditions, as there were many streams of moderate size, of steady flow, and of vigorous current, due to the number of large springs and the elevation of the region. The first grist mills probably were built at the beginning of the decade from 1830 to 1840.[2] By 1840 there were more than a score of grist mills and a number of saw mills,[3] especially in the pine forests[4] on the headwaters of White River.[5] By this time also a few tanneries had been established, and five counties had sixteen distilleries.[6]

The greater part of the Springfield Plain had the Missouri River as its outlet, chiefly through the port of Boonville. This town, now an ordinary county seat, then controlled the trade even of far southern Lawrence County.[7] Its former period of large river commerce was due to the fact that it was the nearest river port, with good roads, for all southwest Missouri, and even for a portion of Arkansas and the Cherokee Nation.[8] The Osage River penetrated farthest into the region and was of some commercial importance to it.[9] In 1859, 8,000 tons of freight were

---

[1] Muench, *Staat Missouri* (1859), p. 212.

[2] Hubble, *Personal Reminiscences*, p. 8; *Encyc. of the Hist. of Missouri:* Christian County.

[3] Compendium of the sixth census.   [6] Compendium of the sixth census.

[4] Oelshausen, *Staat Missouri*, p. 168.   [7] Campbell, *Gazetteer*, p. 303.

[5] Wetmore, *Gazetteer*, p. 38.   [8] Barker, *Hist. of All Western States*, p. 433.

[9] *Western Journal and Civilian*, IV, 86–90.

sent from St. Louis to Osage River points.[1]   At high water boats ran to Osceola,[2] but ordinarily not beyond Warsaw.[3]   The position of Warsaw at the usual head of navigation, combined with the fact that here the overland traffic to and from the Missouri River crossed,[4] made it a flourishing trading center.   In 1854 it was called the principal commercial point for about fifteen counties in southwestern Missouri.[5] Only the extreme southern counties used the roundabout routes of the White and Neosho rivers as outlets.   In 1851 Barry County appropriated a sum for the improvement of White River.   In 1854 the General Assembly of Missouri voted moneys for the same purpose.   Of Stone County, which is traversed by White River, it was reported in the seventies: "Up to the late war, all the trading of the people was carried on in a very primitive manner; the numerous streams of the country afforded ample facilities for boating, and freighted flat boats might often be seen drifting quietly down the river, the grain piled high in the centre of the broad bottomed craft."[6]   From Newton County goods were shipped down the Neosho River through the present state of Oklahoma to the Arkansas River and so to the Mississippi.   There is record of three flatboats of lead having been shipped to New Orleans by this route in 1851.[7]   Connections with St. Louis and Kansas City, now the most important markets of the region, were then wanting for the most part.

DEVELOPMENT SINCE 1850

The western border entered the second phase of its development about 1850, when lead mining began.   From the earliest times lead had been found in scattered lumps in this region, as in other parts of the Ozarks.   It had been mined to a small extent in Greene and Webster counties in the early forties,[8] and near Joplin in 1848.[9]   The first discovery at Granby, in Newton County, was made in 1849.[10]   In 1850 six men are said to have raised 100,000 pounds of lead at this place in four months.[11]   The great deposits of the Granby field were discovered in 1854.[12]   In the fall of that year there was not a house on the site of

[1] Parker, *Missouri as It Is*, p. 187.
[2] Oelshausen, *Staat Missouri*, p. 169.
[3] *Ibid.*, p. 166.
[4] Wetmore, *Gazetteer*, p. 41.
[5] *Ann. Rev. Comm. St. Louis* (1854), p. 52.
[6] Campbell, *Gazetteer*, p. 609.
[7] De Bow's *Review*, XI, 89.
[8] Shepard, *Missouri Geol. Surv.*, XII, 181.
[9] Winslow, *Missouri Geol. Surv.*, VI, 281.
[10] Parker, *Missouri as It Is*, p. 95.
[11] Oelshausen, *Staat Missouri*, p. 167.
[12] Parker, *loc. cit.*

Granby, and only one shaft had been sunk.[1]   In 1857 a single small shaft averaged $1,400 per month.[2]   About one thousand miners had collected from all parts of the world,[3] and Granby was a mining camp in full boom.[4]   Hundreds of log cabins had been built, and the place had the appearance of a prairie-dog town, it is said, with its mounds of earth thrown up from hundreds of shafts in and around the town.[5]   In 1860, 4,000 miners were engaged.[6]   It is estimated that since the opening of the district there have been more than 5,000 shafts sunk.[7]

Transportation was still a serious problem, but as lead brought from 5 to 6 cents per pound[8] it was profitable to transport it even under the crude conditions then existing.   "The lead of the southwest was hauled long distances in wagons to the markets, or to river points.   Some went as far north as Boonville, on the Missouri River, and a large amount was hauled to Linn Creek, on the Osage river, while another large portion was hauled to Fort Smith, on the Arkansas river, and then transferred by boat to New Orleans, St. Louis and other markets."[9]

The discovery of lead in this remote section first aroused the interest of the state as a whole in its southwestern part.   A project soon was formed to develop the region by constructing the Southwestern Branch of the Pacific Railroad, later named the Atlantic and Pacific Railroad. To secure the best location for this line the State Geological Survey was created.   The report of Swallow, published in 1858, called widespread attention to the prospects of mineral wealth.   Construction of the railroad was undertaken and continued until the outbreak of the Civil War, which found it completed only to Rolla.

The war not only checked economic development but caused the dispersal of a considerable part of the population.[10]   This region, because of its smooth surface, formed a good passageway between the Missouri and Arkansas valleys, and thus witnessed the severest fighting in Missouri.   It was levied upon by regular troops of both sides, and it was ravaged repeatedly by marauding parties.   The live stock was largely driven out of the country and little land was cultivated.   The Granby

[1] Swallow, *Geol. Rept. of the Southwestern Branch of the Pacific Railroad of Missouri*, pp. 36-37.

[2] *Ibid.*   [3] *Ibid.*   [4] Parker, *op. cit.*, p. 97.

[5] Swallow, *loc. cit.*, plate opp. p. 36; Richardson, *Beyond the Mississippi*, p. 210.

[6] Stevens, *Missouri, the Center State*, I, 53.

[7] Buckley and Buehler, *Missouri Bur. Geol. and Mines*, Ser. 2, IV, ix.

[8] Winslow, *op. cit.*, p. 290.   [9] *Ibid.*

[10] *Encyc. of the Hist. of Missouri:* Barry County.

lead mines were deserted part of the time; at other times they were worked either by Confederate or Federal forces.[1]

The recovery of the region after the war was rapid. Christian County, which in 1865 was nearly depopulated, is said to have had 9,000 inhabitants in 1872, one-third of whom returned after the war, the remainder having immigrated.[2] In 1870 the railroad was completed from Rolla to Springfield and the mining region, and about at the same time the extraordinary mineral deposits of the Joplin district were discovered.[3] In 1870 there was not a single house at Joplin. In February, 1871, there were received at that place 80,000 pounds of lead per month. The *Joplin Index* said in 1872: "We thought this basis was sufficient for healthy growth, but this small beginning soon grew to 500,000 pounds per month, and during the last three months it has not fell [*sic*] short of 1,500,000 pounds, thus scattering in our city every month, over $40,000."[4] In 1874 Joplin was a city of 3,000 people, with 1,000 miners and 13 furnaces. Oronogo, Webb City, and Cartersville were laid out in quick succession.[5] In the meantime a satisfactory process had been developed for the treating of zinc blende.[6] As a result Joplin in 1872 began to ship out zinc ore, and, the price rising rapidly from $3 to $15 per ton, continued to work its zinc ores at an increasing rate until by 1880 zinc was nearly as valuable a product of the Jasper County district as lead.[7] In this latter year Jasper County produced 10,878 tons of lead ore and 21,304 of zinc.[8] The utilization of zinc revived the decadent mining industry of the Granby region, which yielded zinc to the value of $2,096,000 in the period from 1873 to 1893 and thereby surpassed its mineral production of the first twenty years.[9] From 1893 to 1904 the output of zinc was three and one-half times as valuable as that of lead. From the first decade of production southwestern Missouri has held first place in the world's zinc output. In addition to the Joplin and Granby districts other deposits were discovered from time to time, notably that at Aurora, which was opened in 1886. By 1891 Lawrence County, in which Aurora lies, was second among the counties of the state in zinc production and

---

[1] *Missouri Geol. Surv.*, VI, 291 ff.

[2] *Eighth Ann. Rept. State Board of Agric.*, p. 246.

[3] Stevens, *op. cit.*, I, 55.

[4] *Eighth Ann. Rept. State Board of Agric.*, p. 311.

[5] *Missouri Geol. Surv.*, VI, 291 ff.; Stevens, *op. cit.*, I, 59.

[6] Bain, *U.S. Geol. Surv.*, *Twenty-second Ann. Rept.*, Part II, p. 62.

[7] *Missouri Geol. Surv.*, VI, 291 ff.

[8] *Ibid.*, 298.   [9] Buckley and Buehler, *op. cit.*, pp. 3–4.

third in lead.[1]   In all camps, except Oronogo, there has been a steady increase in the relative importance of the zinc output from year to year. The development of the southwestern mining region has continued almost to the present day, partly as a result of discoveries of new ore bodies and partly because of the continued rise in the price of zinc.

The growth of the mining camps created a good home market for agricultural products.   The completion of the Atlantic and Pacific (Frisco) Railroad afforded an outlet to St. Louis.   About 1880 the Missouri Pacific and the Kansas City, Fort Scott and Memphis railroads were built into the Springfield region from Kansas City.[2]   The former isolation was thus broken down rapidly and effectively.   Farming experienced a marked invigoration.   The prairies, at first despised, presently were considered "the most valuable agricultural land in southern Missouri.   The ease with which they can be cultivated, through the introduction of labor-saving machinery, has given them a marked preference over the timbered lands."[3]   In 1867 Jasper County's principal hay product still was "taken from the prairies,"[4] but in 1880 this county had 205,000 acres of improved land, five times as much as in 1860.[5]   By 1880 the proportion of improved land to total land area had become higher in this region than in the longer-settled northern and eastern borders of the Ozark Highland.   In this year Jasper, Greene, Benton, Dade, Lawrence, Polk, Worth, and Cedar counties each produced more than a million bushels of corn,[6] whereas twenty years previously Greene County alone had produced such an amount.   The soil was excellently adapted to wheat growing, and as soon as railroad transportation was available the cultivation of this grain assumed large proportions. As early as 1872 Springfield possessed fifteen busy mills.[7]

In the development subsequent to the Civil War settlers from northern states had a dominant influence.   Illinois, Iowa, southern Wisconsin, and northern Missouri were well settled at that time.   Southern Missouri, after it was provided with railroads, was an inviting field for immigration from older states, since large areas of good, cheap land were available, and farm conditions were similar to those of the prairie states of the Middle West.   When railroads linked the region to the Missouri

---

[1] *Missouri Geol. Surv.*, VII, 614 ff.   [2] *Ibid.*, 614.

[3] Missouri State Board of Immigration, *Handbook of Missouri* (1881), p. 11.

[4] *Third Ann. Agric. Rept. of Missouri*, p. 305.

[5] Census of 1880.   [6] *Ibid.*

[7] *Eighth Ann. Rept. State Board of Agric.*, p. 281.

River and eastern points, a large immigration into the Springfield Plain took place, which was part of that great body of northern settlers who previously had appropriated north Missouri, Illinois, and Iowa.[1] Settlers from the North continued to come for several decades. In this connection it is interesting to note that Springfield probably was the first center of Congregationalism in Missouri. At present southwest Missouri is in almost every way more like the northern part of the state than is any other section south of the Missouri River.

[1] *Ibid.*, pp. 246, 357.

CHAPTER X

SETTLEMENT OF THE OZARK CENTER

The plateau and hill regions of the central Ozarks were settled last, in part because of their poverty, but principally because of their isolation. Only on the periphery, where river valleys established connection with the outside world and furnished good land, were settlements made contemporaneously with those of the Ozark borders. By 1811 the frontier had retired sixty miles west of the Mississippi[1] to the margins of the Courtois Hills. This region of scanty resources served as a barrier which deflected the major immigration to the north. On the east, where stream valleys led back into the hills, a limited number of people found homes in the occupation of valley lands. Successively the eastern, northern, and western borders were settled. Even after all the border regions were well populated the settlements of the interior remained few, small, and scattered, and considerable areas were still unoccupied. Figs. 23 and 24, showing the distribution of population in 1820 and 1830, represent the beginning of this peripheral movement of population around the Ozark Center. Gradually there was a slow immigration into the central regions, the process of settlement being slowest in the Courtois and the Osage-Gasconade River hills and longest delayed on the remote Arkansas border. The region has experienced no marked periods of rapid growth, except after the Civil War, and nothing that may be called a boom. Settlement has been by gradual and unobtrusive infiltration.

Many of those who came were unable or unwilling to meet the competition of life in more progressive regions. The Ozark Center has held few prizes to stimulate the ambition of its people, most of whom have lived uneventful lives and therefore have made little local history. The region has been cut off by its hills from the rest of the state, and has developed small interest in outside affairs. Few men have gone from it to take a strong hand in the affairs of the state. It has been a minor factor in shaping the policies of the state government, except in so far as counties settled by large delegations of Tennessee or Kentucky hill people have been bulwarks of the Republican party. The paucity

[1] Brackenridge, *Views of Louisiana*, p. 113.

of important events, the want of pride in local affairs, and the character of the people all are reflected in the scarcity of written accounts of the history of the region.

HUNTER FRONTIERSMEN

The principal pioneer groups of this region were of different types from those of the border sections. Probably the largest class were hunters predominantly; a smaller number came to farm in the valleys and to raise stock; others were attracted by the pine timber, saltpeter, and iron.

The region inevitably became a haven for the frontiersman who lived by his gun and traps, giving only incidental attention to agriculture. As the more accessible and richer portions of the country were occupied, men of this class were crowded out by their unfitness for ordered occupations and by their devotion to the chase. Of the eastern border it was said in 1819: "Hunting is every year becoming less an object. Those, therefore, who are attached to this kind of life are almost imperceptibly withdrawing further into the woods."[1] To these men the hills of the central Ozarks were by no means an undesirable region. They cared little for fertile soil and less for transportation facilities. Here was a healthful country, abundant game, springs of cold, clear water, patches of bottom land sufficient to produce the small amount of corn and cotton which they needed, and that elbowroom which men of this stamp desired. In many places lead and gunpowder could be produced with little trouble.[2]

Of the sections which were considered especially desirable by this class of frontiersmen, the White River country ranked first. It is indeed still a pleasant country for the hunter and fisherman. Here as early as 1790, at the junction of the James and White, a white man made his

---

[1] Schoolcraft, *View of Lead Mines*, p. 36.

[2] An interesting instance of the manner in which the early hunters lived on the resources of the country is the following: "When Uncle Sampson Barker was a boy he went out in a hollow of Taney County almost anywhere and picked up some fragments of lead ore. He selected a stump, white oak preferred. The hole he filled with light wood. He struck a flint or touched a match, if he happened to have one of those new-fangled things called lucifers. He piled on the ore and went away. When the homemade smelter had cooled off, Sampson went back, raked the lead out of the ashes and molded his bullets. Uncle Sampson Barker lived to be one of the oldest hunters in the White River region. He never thought of going to the store for cartridges, even when fixed ammunition became cheap, but down to the end of the century smelted his lead and molded his bullets" (Stevens, *Missouri, the Center State*, I, 43).

home.[1]   In 1811 this region was spoken of "with rapture by those who have seen it. . . . . Hunters agree in declaring that on the waters of this river, a country may be chosen, at least one hundred miles square, not surpassed by the best parts of Kentucky."[2]   The estimate of the country was undoubtedly that of the hunter, not of the farmer.   The springs, streams, and woods were reported to be of extraordinary excellence.[3] Of this region it was said in 1818 that "the furs and peltries are taken down the river at certain seasons in canoes, and disposed of to traders, who visit the lower parts of the river for that purpose.   Here they receive in exchange for their furs, woolen clothes, rifles, knives and hatchets, salt, powder, lead, etc."[4]   At this time a slender chain of pioneer cabins extended for 300 miles along the White River, from Batesville, Arkansas, to Forsyth, Missouri.[5]   Other early locations were on the Black River, in Reynolds County,[6] and at Poplar Bluff, where the combination of wooded hills and swamps made a good hunting-ground.[7]   At this time the northern interior regions of the Ozarks seem to have been less well known,[8] the Niangua River, however, receiving favorable comment "for the number of bears which range in the woods."[9]

Numerous accounts have been left of the life and character of these people.   They were not recruited from any one class nor from any one section,[10] although they were mostly of southern origin, like the other settlers of this period.   For the most part they "either embraced hunting from the love of ease or singularity, or have fled from society to escape the severity of the laws, and to indulge in unrestrained passion."[11]   Their life was adjusted perfectly to their primitive surroundings.   "Insulated by a pathless wilderness, without the pale of civil law, or the restraints upon manners and actions imposed by refined society, this population are an extraordinary instance of the retrogression of society.   So far as is not necessary for animal existence, they have abandoned the pursuit of agriculture."[12]   As late as 1859 the inhabitants of the Arkansas

---

[1] Campbell, *Gazetteer*, p. 609; Schoolcraft in 1818 found no families above Beaver Creek (*Tour into the Interior*, pp. 43–67).

[2] Brackenridge, *Views of Louisiana*, p. 101.

[3] *Ibid.*   [4] Schoolcraft, *op. cit.*, pp. 249, 250.

[5] Pettibone, in *Missouri Hist. Colls.*, Vol. II, No. 1, pp. 47–50.

[6] Campbell, *Gazetteer*, p. 477.   [7] *Ibid.*, p. 83.

[8] Brackenridge, *op. cit.*, p. 102; Beck, *Gazetteer*, p. 336.

[9] Dana, *Geog. Sketches on the West Country*, p. 293.

[10] Schoolcraft, *op. cit.*, pp. 174–75; see also his *Tour into the Interior*.

[11] *Ibid.*   [12] *Ibid.*

border were characterized as half wild,[1] certainly somewhat too sweeping a generalization.

Their occupations were described thus: They support themselves by hunting the bear, deer, buffaloe, elk, beaver, racoon, and other animals. . . . . They also raise some corn for bread, and for feeding their horses, on preparing for long voyages into the woods, or other extraordinary occasions. They seldom, however, cultivate more than an acre or two, subsisting chiefly on animal food and wild honey. . . . . When the season of hunting arrives, the ordinary labors of a man about the house and corn-field devolve upon the women. . . . . They in fact pursue a similar course of life with the savages; having embraced their love of ease, and their contempt for agricultural pursuits, with their sagacity in the chase, their mode of dressing in skins, their manners, and their hospitality to strangers.[2]

This class of frontiersman, so numerously represented in the Ozark hills, formed little attachment to the place of their habitation. They were said to "continue there, until the game has disappeared, or the proper claimant of the land comes and 'warns them off.'"[3] The nomadic habits of the frontier were developed to the highest degree in this foot-loose group. The general type is well described by Flint: "Next to hunting, Indian wars, and the wonderful exuberance of Kentucky, the

[1] Muench, *Staat Missouri* (1859), p. 74; (1865), p. 55.

[2] Schoolcraft, *loc. cit.;* similarly Featherstonhaugh, *Excursion,* I, 337. An account of early Howell County has it that "the country at that time abounded in millions of deer, turkeys, bear, wolves, and small animals. I remember as my father was moving west . . . . that we could see the deer feeding on the hills in great herds like cattle, and wild turkeys were in abundance. Wild meat was so plentiful that the settlers easily subsisted upon the flesh of wild animals until they could grow some tame stock, such as hogs and cattle. This country was then almost a 'land of honey.' Bees abounded in great numbers and men hunted them for the profit they derived from the beeswax. When my father first located, beeswax, peltry and fur skins almost constituted the currency of the country. I remember that a short time after my father located, a gentleman came to my father's house and wanted to buy a horse and offered to pay him in beeswax and honey." In hunting expeditions, honey and beeswax were as much sought after as deer skins. Not infrequently the hunters returned laden with freshly killed deer skins, filled with wild honey in the comb. The women then separated the honey from the beeswax, molded the beeswax into cakes, and helped to prepare the deer skins. Honey supplied the household sweetening; beeswax and skins were marketed. Taxes were commonly paid with skins. "I have seen collectors leading a horse for the purpose of carrying his fur skins. I have seen the horse completely covered with fur skins so you could see no part of him but his head and hoofs and tail" (Monks, *Hist. of Southern Missouri and Northern Arkansas,* pp. 8–11).

[3] Baird, *View of the Mississippi,* p. 238.

favorite topic is new countries. They talk of them. They are attached
to the associations connected with such conversations. They have a
fatal effect upon their exertions. They have no motive, in consonance
with these feelings, to build with old Cato, 'for posterity and the im-
mortal gods.' They only make such improvements as they can leave
without reluctance and without loss."[1] This class was typical, of course,
of almost every frontier. It existed in greater purity, however, in the
Ozark hills, and remained longer there than in most sections, because
of the small and belated competition from agricultural immigrants.
As Missouri developed, many men of this type moved west with the
frontier.[2] Others retreated into the hills south of the Missouri. Since
the Ozark hills were almost unoccupied agriculturally for years after
the surrounding regions had been converted to farming uses, this section
long served as a refuge to the hunter frontiersman. Thus many became
detached from that westward moving frontier of which they had been
a part and remained in the hills. They gradually accepted agricultural
habits,[3] with varying degrees of success,[4] or formed a local proletariat,
working at teaming, tie hacking, clay digging, and other occasional jobs.

EARLY LUMBERING AND MINING

The pine forests of the Gasconade, and later those of the Arkansas
border, attracted numbers of people. In 1818 Nicholas Van Zandt
wrote of the Gasconade: "Lumber is rafted down this river for more than
60 miles during high water."[5] Schoolcraft, traveling across the Ozarks
in 1818-19, observed that the sawmills on the Gasconade constituted the
only settlements in that region.[6] He wrote: "On this stream are already
situated several saw mills, where boards and plank are cut for the St.
Louis market."[7] As the party of Major Long passed up the Missouri
River in 1819, they found that most of the settlements along it were
supplied with pine timber from sawmills on the Gasconade.[8] This was
the nearest source of pine lumber for the St. Louis district,[9] and as a

[1] Flint, *Recollections*, pp. 204-5; see also Featherstonhaugh, *op. cit.*, I, 336 ff.

[2] Muench, *Staat Missouri* (1859), p. 74; (1865), p. 55; Baird, *loc. cit.*

[3] Campbell, *Gazetteer*, pp. 609, 617 (account of the Yocum family); Muench,
Staat Missouri (1865), p. 55.

[4] Ball and Smith, *Missouri Bur. Geol. and Mines*, Ser. 2, I, 20.

[5] *Full Description of the Military Lands*, p. 102.   [6] *Tour into the Interior*, p. 15.

[7] *View of Lead Mines*, p. 164; see also p. 172.

[8] James, in *Early Western Travels*, XIV, 137.

[9] Beck, *Gazetteer*, p. 232; Thwaites, *Early Western Travels*, XVIII, 33-34.

result there soon developed a profitable business of rafting pine planks and timber from the upper Gasconade.[1] In 1823 it was said: "Formerly, lumber was brought at great expense from the Alleghany and Ohio rivers. At present it can be sent down the Gasconade to St. Louis, and the other towns along the river, for one-fourth the price."[2] The first settlements in Texas County were made by men who built sawmills on the Big Piney.[3] Here there were in 1823 "already six saw-mills erected, which are kept continually employed."[4] In 1831 it was said that from this country a "great supply of plank and timber, of that kind is brought to St. Charles and St. Louis."[5] In 1852 the Gasconade Valley was still considered chiefly important for the supplies of pine plank and timber which it furnished to the country below.[6] At about this time the more remote forests of the Arkansas border were first exploited, as most of the Gasconade lumber had been cut. There were then more than a dozen small mills in Ozark County, "some capable of cutting upwards of 2,000 feet per day." Fig. 17 is a map illustrating the principal "pineries" of Ozark County about 1855 and the location of mills. A large portion of this lumber was conveyed by ox teams to Springfield, Bolivar, and even to Linn Creek, on the Osage.[7] By 1867 the southern part of the Courtois Hills, including Carter County, had become an important producer of pine lumber.[8]

The saltpeter caves of the cavernous limestone formations were perhaps the best-known resource of the interior districts in early days. As was the case in Kentucky and Tennessee, they were eagerly sought and supplied a needed commodity to the frontier. The number of saltpeter caves is said to have been greatest along the Gasconade River.[9] The deposits were for the most part bat guano and earth, impregnated with the feces of bats and birds that had their homes in the caves.[10] Bradbury wrote of the saltpeter industry in 1810 as though it had been established some time. He said: "In order to obtain the nitre, the earth is collected and lixiviated; the water, after being saturated, is boiled down and suffered to stand till the crystals are formed. In this manner, it is no

[1] Pattie, in Early Western Travels, XVIII, 33.   [3] Parker, Missouri as It Is, p. 404.

[2] Beck, Gazetteer, p. 282.   [4] Beck, Gazetteer, p. 232.

[5] Flint, History and Geography of the Mississippi Valley, p. 302.

[6] De Bow, Industrial Resources, II, 62.

[7] Shumard, Repts. Geol. Surv. of Missouri (1855-71), pp. 201-2.

[8] Eighth Ann. Agric. Rept. of Missouri, pp. 54-56.

[9] Encyc. of the Hist. of Missouri: Gasconade County.

[10] See Stevens, Missouri, the Center State, I, 170.

uncommon thing for three men to make a hundred pounds of saltpetre in one day." In the spring of 1810 a man and his two sons made 3,000 pounds on the Gasconade in a few weeks.[1] Not later than 1816 settlers near Waynesville, Pulaski County, made gunpowder by mixing saltpeter with charcoal, produced locally, and sulphur. They found a ready market for their product among the hunters and trappers of the region.[2] On Current River, at Ashley's Cave, Schoolcraft observed in 1818 that "great quantities of this article are annually collected and manufactured by Colonel Ashley, of Mine à Burton, and transported to his powder-manufactory, in Washington county."[3] In 1837 it was said: "The mineral is either sent down the river, or consumed in the manufacture of gunpowder, for which there are several mills."[4] One of the last records of the use of these deposits for gunpowder dates from the Civil War, during which it is said considerable quantities were made at Friedes Cave, Phelps County.[5] Most of what remained of the deposits after the war has been consumed as farm fertilizer.

The mining and manufacture of iron near St. James in Phelps County was the largest mineral industry of the interior. In 1826 Massey, one of the most famous pioneers of Missouri, opened the "Meramec" ore bank and in 1829 the Meramec Iron Works.[6] "A little settlement sprang up here, and in 1835 it contained about 50 families."[7] In spite of the poor transportation facilities the iron industry prospered, and before the opening of the Iron Mountain district supplied manufactured iron to almost all parts of the state.[8] A number of people found employment in hauling iron to Hermann, the shipping-point on the Missouri River, and in returning with provisions for the iron works. Because of this traffic the main highway of Gasconade County is still known as Iron Road. The furnace was operated until 1860[9] and the mine until 1891,[10] to which date it had produced 375,000 tons. The company also developed other properties in this vicinity. In 1819, before the Meramec Works were put into operation, a bloomery had been built on Thicketty Creek, Crawford County, the ore being hauled in ox carts from the adjacent hills and smelted in a crude stone stack. Midland,

[1] In *Early Western Travels*, V, 247.   [2] Campbell, *Gazetteer*, p. 455.

[3] *Tour into the Interior*, p. 10; see also *View of Lead Mines*, p. 43.

[4] Wetmore, *Gazetteer*, p. 74 (quoted from Beck).

[5] *Encyc. of the Hist. of Missouri*.   [7] Campbell, *Gazetteer*, p. 433.

[6] Shumard, *op. cit.*, p. 238.   [8] Wetmore, *Gazetteer*, p. 69.

[9] *Missouri Bur. Geol. and Mines*, Ser. 2, X, 289.

[10] *Ibid.*, p. 295.

in Crawford County, was at one time a flourishing iron-making community, with 300 men engaged at the furnace, nearly 100 at the ore banks, and about 300 cutting wood and making charcoal.[1] An iron furnace was also built in 1849 at the Scotia mines in Crawford County.[2] An early furnace farther west, in Camden County, is said to have represented an investment of $50,000,[3] a sum not equaled by any present-day industry of the county. Other furnaces were put into blast and other mines were opened from time to time. They performed a valuable service during the pioneer period in supplying iron at moderate prices to a considerable part of the state. Iron was made in these small plants until the deposits of ore were exhausted, or until their operation was made unprofitable by the great cheapening of iron through the development of rail transportation and of a large-scale industry in the East.

CROP FARMING, STOCK RAISING, AND PERMANENT SETTLEMENT

Agricultural settlers, in so far as they can be differentiated from the preceding types, entered the region first from the East by ascending the larger valleys. In 1815 a settlement was made on the Meramec in Crawford County.[4] On the Fourche à Courtois a number of plantations had been established by 1818.[5] In Wayne County Spanish grants were made along the St. Francois River. In 1823 settlements in Wayne County still were confined largely to this stream, the upland being in general undesirable.[6] In Ripley County the first permanent settlement was made in 1819 on the Current River.[7] At this date there were settlements also on Eleven Points River in Oregon County.[8] These valley settlers were in the main distinctly farmers, who removed from the limestone basins of the St. Francois area and the Mississippi River counties. On the north the Osage River was the principal line of approach, as it afforded the best means of transportation through the northern hill region.[9] The slip-off slopes along the intrenched meanders were attractive sites for settlement, affording water transportation, good farmland, and security from floods. A rather enthusiastic account of 1839 says: "This river, which twenty years ago was deemed to be in exclusive possession of the savages, is now bordered by thriving settlements. . . . .

[1] Stevens, *Missouri, the Center State*, I, 203.   [3] Nason, *op. cit.*, p. 311.

[2] *Ibid.*   [4] Parker, *Missouri as It Is*, p. 239.

[5] Schoolcraft, *Tour into the Interior*, p. 5; *View of Lead Mines*, p. 51.

[6] Beck, *Gazetteer*, p. 257.

[7] Campbell, *Gazetteer*, p. 479.   [8] *Ibid.*, p. 407.

[9] Ball and Smith, *Missouri Bur. Geol. and Mines*, Ser. 2, I, 19.

A steamboat plies regularly between the Osage and the settlements near the mouth of the Missouri and the country is rapidly filling up with farmers."[1]

Generally settlement began with the valley lands, then the prairie margins were occupied, and later the open prairies, whereas most of the hillsides remain unimproved to this day.   Of Howell County in 1844 it is said: "The country at that time was very sparsely settled.   The settlements were confined to the creeks and rivers, where were found plenty of water and springs.   No place at that time was thought worth settling unless it had a spring upon it."[2]   In the north the date of entry of land depended to a very considerable degree on the distance from the Missouri River, as this was the only outlet for the region.   There was also extremely close accordance of drainage lines and early settlement. In contrast to the border regions no preference was shown for small valleys as against the larger ones.   In this section almost all streams have sufficient fall to make them reasonably free from malaria.   On the Osage malaria was somewhat prevalent,[3] but conditions were not very serious.   The settlers built their houses by preference well up on the valley sides,[4] and here for the most part they lived securely and prosperously.   Only on the southeastern streams near the margins of the area were conditions of health in general bad.

Fig. 26 illustrates the order of entry for the lands in Hickory County, which is situated largely in the Central Plateau.   The first settlements were in the southeastern corner, in the Elkton Prairie region.   This tract is assigned most properly to the Springfield Plain.   It contains excellent soils of the Springfield-Lebanon groups, has good water accessible in the small valleys, and was also within a convenient distance of timber.   It is still probably the most prosperous section in the county.   The next entries were on the Pomme de Terre River, which bisects the county north and south, and on the smaller creeks.   In this decade there were also notable entries on the prairies which occupy the interstream areas. The decade 1850–60 witnessed the purchase of almost all of the remaining prairie land.   This rapid entry was due in part to the Graduation Act and the inducements it held for speculation.   The dissected country marginal to the Pomme de Terre River and the poor Clarksville soils of the eastern extremity were entered slowly in the succeeding years.   This map probably suggests too strongly the early occupation of prairies in

[1] *Niles' Register*, LVI, 224.   [2] Monks, *op. cit.*, p. 7.
[3] Tixier, *Voyage aux Prairies Osages*, pp. 256–57.
[4] Ball and Smith, *Missouri Bur. Geol. and Mines*, Ser. 2, I, 19.

Hickory County.   Old settlers maintain that early settlements were not on the prairie but at its margins.   Much of the prairie land probably was not improved for years after it was entered.   The early purchase of such large areas of the prairie, however, indicates clearly that even at that time the merits of the land were appreciated, although the pioneer still found it more convenient for a number of years to remain in the familiar location on the side of a valley.   In Pulaski County the small prairie uplands, especially on the northwest, were entered similarly at an early date.   In Dallas County, Buffalo Head Prairie was one of

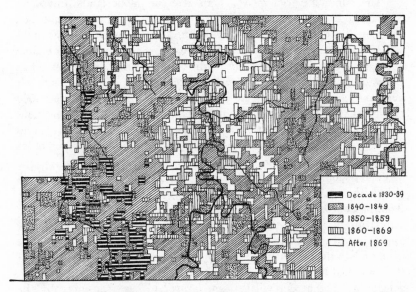

FIG. 26.—Order of land entries in Hickory County (prepared from *Land Entry Book*, County Clerk's Office, Hermitage).

the earlier settlements.   The same is true of most of the prairies of the Central Plateau.   Except in the southern portion, settlers located on the prairies before 1840.   The time and rate of settlement seem to have been determined, not so much by the woodland or prairie character of the land, but by the desirability of the soil.   The Iberia and better grade of Lebanon soils were settled before the Civil War, while many of the tracts of Howell upland soils with their stony surfaces were not entered until lately.   Most of the prairies were long, narrow strips with wood and water accessible at short distances.   They provided excellent grazing for cattle, of which many were kept in this section, and their sod was not so difficult to break as that of the larger prairies.   Moreover, the principal highways followed these ridge lands.   They therefore did not repel settlement as did the large prairies of the western and northern parts of the state.   The central counties of the Arkansas border were last to be settled because they possessed no large tracts of first-class soil, and were shut off from markets, not only by a considerable stretch of difficult wild country, but also by the swampy lowlands of southeastern Missouri and northeastern Arkansas.   In Douglas County, for example, little land was entered before 1870.

The minimum price of $1.25 an acre for public lands proved an obstacle to the settlement of the poorer tracts, as most of the land then was not considered worth the price.   Land entries were greatly stimulated by the passage of the Graduation Act in 1854.   In the year ending June 30, 1858, 1,890,000 acres of public land were sold under this act in Missouri.   Of this number 1,140,304 were disposed of at $12\frac{1}{2}$ cents per acre and 227,940,000 acres at 25 cents.   These lands were described chiefly as pine lands, limestone districts, and mineral, i.e., other non-agricultural lands.   The land office at Jackson alone sold 1,009,335 acres at $12\frac{1}{2}$ cents and 85,999 acres at 25 cents,[1] largely in Shannon and other counties of the Courtois Hills.[2]

The region suffered a check during the Civil War fully as severe as the southwest.   This was true especially of plateau counties near the Arkansas border, settled by Tennessee hill people who were northern sympathizers.   The settlements were weak and the broken country along the streams gave easy refuge to the lawless bands,[3] as it had done from time to time previously.[4]   In 1865 Oregon County complained that it "contained less than two hundred families, and half of them without a male head; that our villages and farms had been consumed by the torch of the jayhawker; . . . . that our mills, stock and grain were all swept away."[5]   In Howell County only fifty families remained at the close of the war.[6]   On the other hand it is recorded that "Stone County suffered little during the late Civil War on account of its topography,

---

[1] Parker, Missouri as It Is, pp. 173–74.   [2] Ibid., p. 382.

[3] Ball and Smith, Missouri Bur. Geol. and Mines, Ser. 2, I, 20.

[4] "About 1833 there was formed in St. Louis, with headquarters at Waynesville, in Pulaski County, an organization known commonly as the Bank of Niangua.   It had a president, cashier, clerks, board of directors, and for some time paid enormous dividends.   The organization was a band of counterfeiters, and had in the mountains of Pulaski County a cabin where the counterfeiting was done" (Encyc. of the Hist. of Missouri: Bank of Niangua).

[5] Second Ann. Rept. State Board of Agric., p. 292.   [6] Campbell, Gazetteer, p. 255.

which put a formidable barrier in the way of marauding parties."[1] It seems that the White River country was too difficult of access even for bands of bushwhackers and jayhawkers.

Agricultural immigration previous to the war had been overwhelmingly from Tennessee and Kentucky. Some of the southeastern counties to this day are inhabited chiefly by Tennesseeans,[2] and it is no rare thing to find some remote valley in which every inhabitant is descended from Tennessee stock. The ancestor of one of the pioneers of Howell County came from Ireland and settled in South Carolina. His descendants removed to Alabama, thence to Tennessee, Illinois, and Arkansas successively, drifting with the stream courses. The final removal was from Arkansas to Missouri.[3] Of the representatives from the central Ozarks to the state legislature in 1872, ten were from Tennessee, six from Kentucky, three were natives of Virginia, two of North Carolina, and one of Hungary.[4] Many of the settlers were hill people from central and east Tennessee, drawn from the poorest classes.[5] Some of the counties of Tennessee which contributed largely were Monroe, Polk, Sumner, Smith, and Grainger. Of the immigrants to the Osage Valley it was said: "The uncertainty of the navigation of the Osage has prevented the staple growing immigrants from settling in its valley and consequently it has been left open to the smaller farmers . . . . not having much produce to ship."[6] A few of the prairie farmers were slave-owners,[7] but most of the people kept no slaves and opposed slavery. The hill people of the Alleghany Plateau found here conditions not unlike those of their homes but much better in many respects, especially as regards soil, water, and accessibility. Because this region was adapted to their tastes and was free from the competition of the wealthier and more efficient farming classes of other sections they moved into it in large numbers.

After the war the immigration of southern hill people slackened, while home seekers of small means came from many northern states, especially to the prairies of the Central Plateau. To this immigration Indiana, Illinois, Ohio, Pennsylvania, and the New England states contributed

[1] *Ibid.*, p. 609.

[2] See biographical section, *Hist. of Southeastern Missouri* (1888).

[3] Monks, *op. cit.*, pp. 5–6.

[4] Pratt, *Pen Pictures, House of Representatives* (1872).

[5] Featherstonhaugh, *Excursions*, I, 337.

[6] *Western Journal and Civilian*, I, 51.

[7] Ball and Smith, *Missouri Bur. Geol. and Mines*, Ser. 2, I, 20.

most.[1] The better lands farther east had been taken up. The Homestead Act (1862) enabled men of little or no means to establish themselves in reasonable comfort on these lands.[2] The Atlantic and Pacific Railroad (Frisco) was in operation and opened a large tract of land previously difficult of access. Moreover, the road had been financed largely by a land grant and the company advertised its lands vigorously.[3] These lands were placed on sale at reasonable prices, and large quantities were sold, beginning with the seventies.

Until the last quarter-century stock raising was the most profitable occupation. For many counties it was almost the only business from which cash returns could be secured because the poor roads and the distance to market prohibited other exports. In 1866 Dallas County reported: "Cattle are driven to market from this county to St. Louis and other markets. Large droves are bought up and driven to Iowa, Illinois, and to other portions of this state."[4] This statement could be applied equally well to many of the interior counties until recently. Polk County was early noted for its stock.[5] Of Oregon County it was said in 1859 that "the inhabitants cultivate enough corn for bread and live happily and simply by the chase and stock-raising."[6] As long as there were not too many people engaged in raising stock the business was profitable, even in the hilliest sections. The combination of fertile lands for the growth of corn and hay and of land suited for pasturage was appreciated early as the principal advantage of this region.[7] For the most part, however, stock raising was by grazing on the wild land rather than by the feeding of hay or grain. Cattle were turned out on the free range of the public domain after the fashion first practiced by the French. "A man could raise all the stock in the way of horses and cattle that he could possibly look after; the only expense was salting and caring for them."[8] The nutritious bluestem grass grew on the prairie, and on the slopes of steep hills,[9] and the habit of burning it in the fall made grazing good even in the timber. It was claimed as late as 1881, with some exaggeration, that this was "a range for stock unsurpassed

[1] *Eighth Ann. Rept. State Board of Agric.*, pp. 273, 292, 296, 376, 423.

[2] *Ibid.*, p. 296.

[3] *Lands on the Atlantic and Pacific Railroad* (1871).

[4] *Second Ann. Rept. State Board of Agric.*, p. 246.

[5] Oelshausen, *Staat Missouri*, p. 170; Muench, *Staat Missouri* (1859), p. 214.

[6] Muench, *op. cit.*, p. 215.   [8] Monks, *op. cit.*, p. 11.

[7] Wetmore, *Gazetteer* (1837), p. 70.   [9] Oelshausen, *op. cit.*, p. 6.

at least for quality; a region well-watered, well-timbered and shaded, clothed with nutritious grasses."[1] To some extent the practice prevailed of driving cattle south in winter to the canebrakes of Arkansas, thus entirely avoiding the cost of feeding.[2] Hogs were raised with equal ease and at less cost on the abundant mast but were somewhat more difficult to market.

The method pursued in raising stock was cheap, well adapted to the conditions then existing, and required almost no labor, but it did not tend to produce stock of high quality. In Crawford County it was stated that "the method has been to let cattle run through the summer and get fat; sell off what can be spared and keep the rest on the very least possible amount of 'roughness' that will subsist an animal and keep strength enough in the body to begin with in the coming spring; in this way it takes one-third of the summer to recover the losses of winter starvation. I have no doubt but one-half the entire neat cattle of this county, with horses, mules, sheep and hogs go through the winter season with no more food than would be required to feed them well two weeks."[3] The average weight of a cow was given at 375 pounds or less, and that of a four-year-old steer at 475. "Hogs are perhaps the most neglected of any kind of stock. The common breed of the country, the 'pointer,' is the almost universal hog here, and a meaner one cannot be found in any country." Its average weight was said not to exceed 135 pounds.[4]

With the extension of settlement and continued stock raising the range deteriorated rapidly. Close grazing killed out the bluestem grass. The cessation of fires caused the grasses to be displaced by a growth of weeds, prairie grass, sassafras sprouts, and post-oak runners.[5] Grazing continued to be good longest in the southern border counties, which were settled last. With pasturage reduced in area and quality, a decrease in the number of stock became necessary, and this resulted either in greater attention to crop growing and lumbering or in a progressively reduced standard of living. This readjustment, in part, is still taking place.[6]

The other pioneer occupations did not differ materially from those of the border regions, except in a few respects. (1) Because of their isolation the people of this region were forced to be self-sufficient to a

[1] *Handbook of Missouri*, p. 24.   [2] *Ibid.*
[3] *First Ann. Rept. State Board of Agric.*, App., p. 61.   [4] *Ibid.*
[5] *Eighth Ann. Rept. State Board of Agric.*, p. 225.
[6] Marbut, *Soil Reconnaissance*, pp. 19–22.

larger extent and for a longer period than the pioneers of the border regions. As a result cotton growing, household spinning and weaving, and other pioneer industries were common long after they had been abandoned in other sections.[1] In 1867 homemade farm implements were still in general use.[2] (2) Mining was less important than in the other sections. Iron was by far the most valuable mineral product. Lead was worked here and there, mostly at odd times. Crawford County produced lead to the value of $202,000 before 1880 and Miller County to the value of $178,000.[3] For a time great things were expected of the copper deposits of Shannon County, of which the government reserved seven townships. Copper was produced as early as 1837; one mine is said to have yielded $50,000 worth, all told, but the industry never realized more than a small part of the expectations of those who developed it.[4] (3) The region is unusually well supplied with mill sites, and water mills were constructed in almost every neighborhood. Not only were the rapid, clear, hill streams so used but the springs afforded splendid power for driving primitive water wheels. The great Bryce's Spring, the spring at Hahatonka,[5] the one at Waynesville, and many others were so used. They were not often affected by droughts nor endangered by floods and usually furnished more power than was needed. (4) Production on the whole was less efficient than in the border regions. The people who appropriated this region were for the most part poor and accustomed to low standards of living, and they found in it little to raise these standards. By moderate labor they could secure enough to supply their small wants. By additional labor they gained little more, working in the fashion to which they had become accustomed. One man made about as much as his neighbor and both were satisfied. Because of the lack of transportation facilities there was little stimulus to the production of a surplus. In Ripley County in 1867 the hoe was enumerated among the principal agricultural implements.[6] This quality of being contented with little was described graphically in 1859 as follows: "Until our people [Crawford County] are educated up to the

[1] On the production of cotton see *First Ann. Agric. Rept. of Missouri*, App., p. 64.

[2] *Third Ann. Agric. Rept.*, p. 337; *First Ann. Agric. Rept.*, App., p. 60.

[3] Winslow, *Missouri Geol. Surv.*, VI.

[4] Bain and Ulrich, *U.S. Geol. Surv., Bull. No. 267*, pp. 9–10.

[5] An early appreciation of this splendid mill site is in Swallow, *First Ann. Rept.. Geol. Surv. of Missouri*, p. 205.

[6] *Third Ann. Agric. Rept.*, p. 337; *First Ann. Agric. Rept.*, App., p. 60.

point where they can value a sheep higher than a dog, and agriculture and manufactures better than opossum and coon hunting, I suppose our annual crops of nutritious grains will grow to 'waste their fragrance on the desert air,' and our rapid streams send their babbling waters to cool the mean whiskey . . . . , instead of making cheap clothing for our ragged people."[1]

[1] *First Ann. Agric. Rept.*, App., p. 59.

CHAPTER XI

GERMAN IMMIGRATION

The latest infusion of blood into the region, on a large scale, has been by German immigration. Excepting the French it has contributed the only appreciable number of non-English people, the Swedish colonies of the southwest and the Polish and Bohemian settlements of Franklin and Gasconade counties being nearly negligible in comparison. The larger part of the rural German population of Missouri is located in the Missouri and Mississippi border regions of the Ozarks, in compact settlements. Here the German immigration has displaced largely the earlier American settlers. The process of German settlement has duplicated in the main that of the original settlement of the region. The groups of Germans, who located at various places at different times, exhibit to a high degree common racial characteristics, which have been modified only in part by their present environment. This individuality of the German stock has expressed itself prominently in the development of the region which they occupy.

WHITEWATER DUTCH

The earliest compact settlements of Germans were made before the end of the eighteenth century by the so-called Whitewater Dutch, under the leadership of Bollinger.[1] This was the only German colony in Missouri which was on the extreme frontier.[2] It was established about Whitewater Creek in Cape Girardeau and Bollinger counties, remained isolated for a considerable period, and so preserved for a time the racial traits almost unchanged.[3] These colonists were, however, not reinforced by other German immigrants. Historically, this immigration was part of the great movement of settlers from the South into the new West, not directly a movement from abroad. Most of them were natives of North Carolina, and they were not in communication with other German groups in the West, nor with Germany. When, therefore, they became surrounded by Anglo-American settlements they gradually lost their racial identity. In physical characteristics there is nothing to distinguish them at present from their neighbors. Typically they are tall,

[1] The name of Bollinger County is still given the German pronunciation.

[2] Flint, *Recollections of the Last Ten Years*, p. 233.   [3] *Ibid.*, p. 232.

spare, and sharp-featured. They retain nothing of their original language or customs but still the consciousness of their extraction. They hold themselves in general quite aloof from the German immigrants who came a half-century later. They are still in part Lutherans and have been much less mobile than the Anglo-Saxon stock of the region, remaining commonly in their ancestral seats. These are as a rule the best farms of that section.

IMMIGRATION FROM 1830 TO 1850

The next period of German immigration commenced about 1830 and continued until after 1850.[1] The dominant type during this time consisted of educated men, many of them of gentle birth. They were largely exiles from Germany, voluntary or involuntary. The Napoleonic wars had been followed by a constitutionalist movement, which was supported especially by university circles. This "Jungdeutschland" movement was suppressed by a reactionary government, and many of those who participated in it were forced to flee or chose to leave the country. Following the years 1832–33 and 1848–49 thousands of Germany's ablest men, young and old, left their native land and a large part of them came to America. A second group, a small one, came to the New World because it had tired of a convention-ridden civilization. The spirit of romanticism then was strong in many quarters, and there were some who put into practice, more or less consistently, the principles of Rousseau in the wilderness of the West. A third group consisted of religious Separatists, for whom the free and full development of their ideals depended on escape from the repressive hand of an established church. In all of these classes ideal rather than economic considerations were dominant. For all of them the frontier was the best place to realize these ideals, each group hoping to build its community uninfluenced by established institutions. Others, probably the largest single class but not the most influential, came solely to better their fortunes. A few were unruly spirits who wished to escape the surveillance of society. The Germans of Missouri of 1834 were described as a "group of Westphalian hired hands, who had established themselves after a poor fashion, and a mottled aristocracy, consisting of German counts, barons, scholars, pastors, planters, and officers."[2]

[1] A good summary of German immigration is by Kargau, in *Missouri Hist. Colls.*, Vol. II, No. 1, p. 23.

[2] Eickhoff, *In der neuen Heimat* (2d ed.), p. 337; accounts of the character of early immigrants are to be found, *ibid.*, pp. 337–39, and in Körner, *Das deutsche Element in den Vereinigten Staaten*, pp. 299–350.

The determining factor in directing many of these Germans to Missouri was the publication of a book, entitled *Reise nach den westlichen Staaten*, by Gottfried Duden. During 1824–25 this man lived on Lake Creek, in Warren County. He wrote in glowing terms of the beautiful Missouri Valley, the wooded uplands, the mild climate, and the charm of pioneer life. He seems to have experienced two abnormally mild winters. At any rate, unintentionally, he led many to expect a climate almost Italian in its moderation. The volume contains few misstatements, but had unfortunate results through the emphasis placed by the author on his own experiences in Missouri. The publication of this geographic romance bore almost immediate fruits.[1] Those who were dissatisfied with Germany hoped to find in the region a new home similar to their German one, but without its social and geographic drawbacks.

By the end of the year 1832 there were at least thirty-three German families established on the Missouri and twenty in the old Boone settlement on the Femme Osage. On this first list were a number of noblemen and others who later became well-known figures in the state. Directly in response to the propaganda of Duden the Emigration Society of Giessen sent over, in 1834, a colony which became located at the home of Duden, in the vicinity of Dutzow, Warren County.[2] "All flocked at first to the place where the philosopher of the wilderness had lived, and here there was soon formed a settlement composed of the most varied German elements."[3]

The nucleus having been formed, many others came to various parts of the Missouri Valley,[4] the Missouri River serving as distributary. The vicinity of Pinckney, Warren County, attracted many.[5] Some located many miles above, as the two counts Baudissin, at Portland in Callaway County. Washington was settled by an emigration society from Berlin,[6] and in 1838 the largest single colony was located at Hermann. This group was sent out from Philadelphia. Its agent came west with instructions to select a site on a navigable river. He chose the site of Hermann, in part because of the German settlements already established north of the river, in part because a large block of public land was available there, in part because the romantic location on the loess bluffs of the Missouri reminded him of his south German home and

[1] Löher, *Deutsche in Amerika*, p. 277.

[2] Muench, *Staat Missouri* (1859), p. 8; Löher, *op. cit.*, p. 278.

[3] Muench, *ibid.*, p. 19.   [4] Flagg, *The Far West*, II, 19.

[5] Zimmermann, *Missouri Hist. Rev.*, IX, 41; Oelshausen, *Staat Missouri*, p. 148.

[6] Bek, *German Settlement Society of Philadelphia*, p. 46.

suggested the possibility of hillside horticulture, and largely because he was an inexperienced judge of farmland and of town sites.[1] Two hundred and thirty persons arrived in the first year, recruited from all parts of Germany, Alsace, and Switzerland.[2] On the Mississippi River Border German immigrants entered Cape Girardeau County in 1833–34 and in 1835 or 1836 a Swiss colony was located at Dutchtown.[3]

The earliest settlement in Missouri for the purpose of securing religious solidarity was at Westphalia, Osage County. Here Catholics from Muenster selected a location on Maries Creek in 1833 and founded a village. In 1844 there was a second large immigration, reinforced in 1849 by political refugees. Around this center other Catholic settlements formed shortly, including Taos in Cole County, Richfountain, Loose Creek, Luystown, Frankenstein, and others in Osage County.[4] Other Catholic settlements were those of 1840 at New Offenburg and Zell in Ste. Genevieve County, attracted apparently by the French Catholics resident near by. This nucleus expanded rapidly, especially by immigrants from the lower and upper Rhine,[5] until Ste. Genevieve County possessed a German-speaking majority. In 1839 Protestant Separatists, the so-called Stephanists, came to Perry County and founded, in a short time, the German villages of Wittenberg, Altenburg, and Frohna.[6] Their choice of rough hill lands was most unfortunate and was due to the inefficiency of their leader in matters of practical judgment.[7]

These, in the main, were the early nuclei of German settlement in Missouri outside of St. Louis. Mostly, they proposed to preserve the German language and institutions and many of them had definite religious or social ends. They possessed, therefore, a homogeneity which carried most of them safely through the difficult period of readjustment. The colony settlements introduced a degree of social organization previously unknown in this section. Their social and economic advantages helped to attract later immigrants. Because of the number of early settlers who were men of education, others of the same sort were attracted from time to time. To establish these colonies it was necessary to select locations which were unoccupied in the main. These were either at some distance from the large rivers, as Westphalia, or consisted of land

[1] *Ibid.*, pp. 38–46; Schmölder, *Wegweiser für Auswanderer*, p. 94; Löher, *op. cit.*, p. 287.

[2] Bek, *op. cit.*, pp. 59, 74.   [3] *Hist. of Southeastern Missouri*, p. 282.

[4] MS of Father Helias d'Huddeghem, in *St. Louis U. Collection.*

[5] Schmölder, *op. cit.*, p. 96.

[6] *Hist. of Southeastern Missouri*, p. 282.   [7] Schmölder, *op. cit.*, pp. 59, 142–44.

that was not considered especially desirable, as at Hermann, Dutzow, Wittenberg, and New Offenburg.

The chief geographic bases of German settlement in Missouri, besides the frontier location, were the accessibility of the region from Europe by way of New Orleans and the Mississippi River, the low cost of land, and the similarity of soil, climate, and vegetation to conditions in their native country. This immigration antedated the construction of western railroads and also, in the main, of canals between the Great Lakes and the Mississippi Valley. The state of Missouri was reached more easily, therefore, than the states farther north and also more easily than large tracts of more desirable land farther east. The majority of the new-comers established themselves on the river hills. The bottoms, both of the Missouri and of the larger creeks, were farmed by older American settlers. In 1859 the distribution was thus characterized: "In the older, especially the German settlements, all of the good river hill land is occupied. The Americans to make large plantations, seize upon the bottoms first, and then the prairies, and leave room in the so-called hills for the German."[1] The reasons for their location are as follows: (1) On the river bluffs the German immigrants found cheap land. (2) This land was near the older settlements and convenient to river transportation. (3) These locations were said to be preferred by the Germans because they were most healthful.[2] The Dutzow settlement was recommended because of its elevated position.[3] An emigrants' guide, published by one of their number, warned especially against locating in the bottoms before acclimatization had taken place.[4] (4) As charm of location was an important factor in determining the site of Duden's frontier retreat, so subsequently those romantically inclined found, along the bluffs of the Missouri, sites that needed but ruined castles to duplicate the valley of the Rhine. This romantic factor seems to have determined a number of locations.[5] (5) Much of the land was better than its reputation. It was said: "The Americans reproach the Germans for selecting the very poorest land."[6] A German settler, however, after nearly twenty-five years of experience on a river-hill farm, felt no regrets. He said that, whereas the pioneer American farmer often ruined such farms in a little while, the German founded here the most valuable plantations.[7] Most

[1] Muench, *Staat Missouri* (1859), pp. 29–30.

[2] Zimmermann, *Missouri Hist. Rev.*, IX, 41.

[3] Schmölder, *op. cit.*, p. 92.

[4] Muench, *op. cit.*, p. 27.   [6] Zimmermann, *loc. cit.*

[5] *Ibid.*, pp. 29–30.   [7] Muench, *op. cit.*, p. 29.

of this hill land was veneered with loess but had been avoided by the American because of its uneven surface. The German, however, who was accustomed to careful farming on a small scale was able to cultivate the hill soil so as to avoid erosion and was willing to expend upon it the additional labor which its topography required. Properly tilled, the bluff lands yielded excellent regular returns. The settler was able, therefore, not only to establish himself at small outlay, but to save a surplus and later to buy more desirable lands.

The expectations of the early settlers were disappointed in numerous respects, and in time the less steadfast were weeded out. (1) "Scarcely had the Germans taken foot, when hard times, lasting through several years, set in, ... times too severe for a part of the German element who had come with highest hopes."[1] (2) Settlers who came expecting to find the conditions which Duden had portrayed found themselves disillusioned.[2] (3) Some of the communal colonies were mismanaged and the participants lost part or all of their possessions. The Stephanists discovered that the apostolic simplicity of communistic living was ill-adapted to the American West. (4) The most serious handicap lay in the training and aptitude of those settlers who possessed education and social station. Some of the wealthier attempted to set up fine estates and lived as gentlemen of leisure, with the result that their fortunes were dissipated. The great majority set out to live in accordance with the democratic ideals which they professed, but they lacked adaptability to frontier conditions. Men undertook to do the hard labor of clearing and cultivating who had never lifted an ax nor held a plow. One who knew his way through the mazes of the heavenly constellations, and continued in his log cabin his astronomical studies, would lose his way in his own neighborhood. Even if their bodies became hardened to the task, in many cases they were unable to develop the necessary farming sense. Others tired of the Arcadian simplicity which they had come so far to find. Thus in large part the intellectuals failed. "Not many held out under the hardships of pioneer life. Sooner or later they sought and found for the most part in the cities occupations better suited to their abilities."[3] Some helped in the development of cities such as Washington, Boonville, Jefferson City, and Hermann. Most of them went to St. Louis, and many there retrieved brilliantly their previous failure. Those who remained and forged ahead were mostly of the peasant class and were inured to hard labor and scant living.

[1] Muench, *op. cit.*, p. 19.   [2] Oelshausen, *Staat Missouri*, pp. 147–48.
[3] Muench, *Mississippi Blaetter*, June 15, 1915.

An important step toward the success of the German settlements was the introduction of wine-growing at Hermann by immigrants from the Rhine. In 1845 there were 50,000 vines at this place; in 1846, 150,000; in 1848, 500,000; and in 1849, 700,000. In the last-mentioned year it was predicted that the wine crop of a few townships in Gasconade County would be of greater value than the hemp crop of the state.[1] The success of grapes at Hermann led to the extensive planting of vineyards at Ste. Genevieve, at Boonville, and in Franklin, Warren, and St. Charles counties.[2] The vineyards were located on loess hillsides,[3] which afforded warm soil, excellent drainage, and protection from unseasonable frosts. They were supposed by vintners of the time to benefit by their nearness to a large stream. The climate was said to be better than in the Rhine country because of the sunny fall weather, which permitted the grapes to ripen with high flavor.[4] Previous to the introduction of the grape, Hermann, with its mediocre farmland, had been losing by emigration. The splendid harvest of the year 1848 caused people to seek again this place,[5] and thereafter the community flourished. In 1856 a yield of 100,000 gallons was reported for Hermann at a profit of $300 per acre and of 6,000 gallons for Boonville.[6] In 1857 Hermann claimed a production of 80,000 gallons[7] and in 1858 of 25,000 gallons, which was said to be an average yield.[8] The price, originally about $2 a gallon, had fallen by 1858 to $1.25,[9] which still enabled very profitable production. In spite of the vicissitudes of grape culture Hermann adhered to this occupation. A large wine trade was built up; a local wine cellar became one of the sights of the state; and Hermann wines became known throughout the country.

LATER IMMIGRATION; SPREAD OF THE GERMAN SETTLEMENTS

After 1848–49 the immigrants were mostly of the peasant class, recruited from north, south, and middle Germany, Switzerland, and Alsace, and they came for the primary purpose of bettering their economic condition. The large surplus rural population of Germany

---

[1] *Western Journal and Civilian*, III, 53–54.

[2] Muench, *Staat Missouri*, p. 138.

[3] Swallow, *Geol. Rept. of Southwestern Branch of the Pacific Railroad of Missouri*, p. 10.

[4] Baudissin, *Der Ansiedler im Missouri Staate*, pp. 89–90.

[5] *Ibid.*

[6] Swallow, *op. cit.*, p. 18.   [8] *Ibid.*, XL, 128.

[7] *Hunt's Merchants' Mag.*, XXXIX, 385.   [9] *Ibid.*

resulted in rapid emigration, which spread over many states in this country, and of which Missouri, containing numerous established German settlements and much cheap land, received its share. In 1860 there were 95,000 people of German birth in the state, of whom Franklin County had 4,951; Gasconade, 3,137; Cape Girardeau, 2,843; Jefferson, 2,112; Cole, 2,069; Osage, 2,057; Cooper, 1,923; Perry, 1,800; and Ste. Genevieve, 1,231.[1] Figures including those born in America of German parentage would be considerably higher. Large-scale immigration ceased nearly fifty years ago. Land became too high-priced for indigent immigrants. Moreover, the development of industries in Germany subsequent to 1870 furnished occupation for the surplus rural population.

The expansion of the German settlements has been in the main by compact growth along stream courses and from poor to better land. The immigrants were clannish and settled amid the older German communities of eastern Missouri. These people worked harder and lived on less than the Americans, and so gradually accumulated wealth with which they bought out their American neighbors, who were owners of rich bottoms or prairie land. Muench described the process of expansion in 1859 thus: "The Germans located first along the valleys, intruding themselves between the Americans, here and there accumulating greater numbers, so that settlements wholly or mostly German were formed, which expanded more and more in all directions. The Americans either find it to their advantage to sell their land to the Germans, or do so because they do not like to live among the Germans."[2] The American of the early days felt slight attachment to his homestead and was usually ready to seek a new home farther west. It was said of him: "The whole country is the fatherland to which he is attached; the place of habitation is of subordinate importance."[3] The German, on the other hand, was decidedly not a frontiersman and was willing to pay a good price for the privilege of living near his countrymen.[4] This process of displacement continued until nearly the whole Missouri River Border and a large part of the Mississippi River Border were occupied by settlers of German stock.

By 1859 the German settlements of Washington and Hermann had become important towns; Jefferson City was half German, and Boonville

[1] Census of 1860.   [2] Muench, op. cit. (1859), p. 76.
[3] Oelshausen, op. cit., p. 67.
[4] Baudissin, op. cit., p. 161; Zimmermann, loc. cit.

one-fourth.[1] German was taught in the schools of Hermann, Washington, and Jefferson City.[2] By this time many German farmers had purchased Missouri River bottom farms.[3] In time they occupied the great majority of farms in the Missouri flood plain as far as the Boonslick country, into which they penetrated only in Cooper County. Similarly the creek bottoms and ridge lands near the Missouri passed into German hands. St. Charles, Franklin, Warren, Gasconade, and Osage counties became overwhelmingly German. In 1888 a biographical record of Gasconade County[4] included 131 men of German birth or parentage as against 9 native Americans. In Franklin County there were enumerated 168 of German stock against about one hundred of all other sources. Cole County was estimated to be half German in 1875.[5]

Except for a large colony on the prairie at Cole Camp in Benton County[6] the German settlements did not extend much beyond the river tier of counties. In Crawford and Phelps counties they are found on the headwaters of the Bourbeuse, and in Maries County they have occupied most of the bottom farms of the Big and Little Maries. Their expansion south from the Missouri ceased at the edge of the rough country, as had that of the original American immigration at an earlier date.

In the Mississippi River Border they acquired a majority in Ste. Genevieve, Cape Girardeau, and Perry counties, and a strong minority in Jefferson County. In this region they occupied most of the Springfield and loess lands and a large part of the Hagerstown and alluvial lands. In the vicinity of Farmington and Fredericktown numerous families settled in the rich basins of Fredericktown soil, and thereby introduced after a time a German element into these two cities. Farther west the poor land of the igneous knobs and flint hills blocked further expansion.

As the river districts became densely populated they in turn founded daughter-colonies farther west, where land was cheaper. Most of these were in the loess districts of Jefferson and Saline counties, western Missouri, and in Brown County, Kansas. Later southwest Missouri, especially the fertile prairies of Lawrence County, received a considerable immigration from the river counties. At present St. Louis is attracting many, but the percentage which is leaving the farm for the city is not

[1] Muench, *op. cit.*, p. 205.

[2] *Ibid.*, pp. 164–65.   [3] *Ibid.*, p. 27.

[4] *Hist. of Franklin and Jefferson Counties.*

[5] Muench, *Staat Missouri* (1875), p. 140.   [6] *Ibid.*, p. 136.

so great as among the Anglo-American stock. The large infusion of German blood into the river counties of the state is shown in Fig. 27.

Stability remains the most distinguishing characteristic of the German stock. Where Germans have located in most cases they have remained. The selling of real estate is not a thriving business in their communities. Property is handed down from father to son, and in many

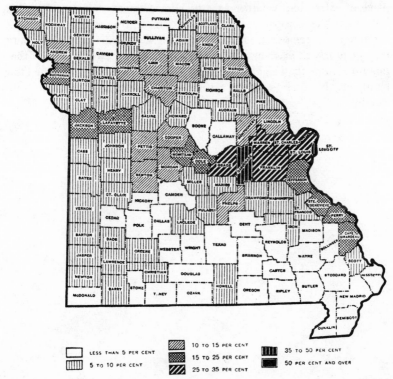

FIG. 27.—Distribution of population in Missouri of foreign birth or parentage. This figure does not show racial extraction beyond the second generation (*Thirteenth Census, Statistical Atlas,* plate on p. 166*b*).

cases the descendants of the original entrymen still retain the land. Because of this stability of ownership their improvements surpass in durability, if not in elegance, those of any other group of farmers. They build by preference of stone or brick. Where good stone is available, as at Westphalia and Hermann, one sees not only stone houses, but stone barns, sheds, and fences. Their towns, built of high houses situated directly on the streets, which are paved and carefully kept, have decidedly an Old World appearance. They still have the reputation of being the most careful farmers and are rather slow to adopt innovations, but they are ready to make changes the merit of which is fully demonstrated. They retain in large part the faith of their fathers, as they do their language. The degree of racial tenacity is not dependent upon the place of extraction, whether Low or High German, Swiss or Prussian, but upon the compactness and isolation of the settlement. Rural communities, remote from railroads, as Westphalia and Altenburg, may be nearly as pronouncedly German as they were at the date of their founding, more than eighty years ago. The railroad towns, on the other hand, are by their superior accessibility losing their German traits rapidly.

PART III

RECENT ECONOMIC CONDITIONS

CHAPTER XII

THE UNIMPROVED LAND AND ITS USES

DISTRIBUTION AND OWNERSHIP

The greater part of the Ozark Highland consists of unimproved, so-called wild land, covered with forest or brush. This land either has steep slopes or is so remote from lines of transportation that it has not been profitable to clear it. As shown in Fig. 28, all the larger streams,

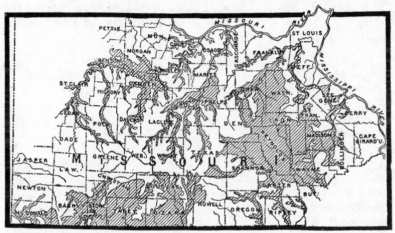

FIG. 28.—Land too rough for field cultivation. Shaded areas indicate majority of surface too rough (Marbut, *U.S. Bur. Soils, Field Reports,* 1911).

except the Mississippi and Missouri, are bordered by a wide belt of rugged hill country, which in the main is unsuited to field cultivation. The areas of wild land are largest in the Courtois Hills and in the Osage-Gasconade Hills. Next in order are the White River Hills and the

¹ All statistics in Part III, unless otherwise noted, are from the *Thirteenth Census.* Personal observation in detail does not extend beyond the year 1916. Since then economic values, here as elsewhere, have been greatly disturbed. The economic conditions brought about by the recent war are not considered here. They have of course been serious, especially in the draining off of population to industrial centers outside of the Ozarks. Changes have been less revolutionary, however, than in less isolated districts. Occupations are essentially unchanged, and even prices have been less affected than elsewhere.

177

St. Francois region.   In the Clarksville soil areas of the Courtois and Osage-Gasconade regions probably not much more than 1 per cent of the land is cleared.   Areas half a dozen miles square have no upland clearings larger than five or six acres.   On some of the ridges in these sections one can travel a dozen miles without seeing a field or a house.   Fig. 29 represents the distribution of cleared land in a small Clarksville soil area of the eastern border.   The clearings are limited to coves in valleys and a few ridge crests.   Though small and discontinuous, they are more numerous than in similar areas in the interior of the Ozarks. The table below shows the small amount of improved land in the hill sections as compared with the border regions and the Central Plateau. The Springfield Plain has the least unimproved land of any part of the Ozarks.   Percentage of total area of improved farm land for selected counties is as follows:

	Percentage			Percentage
Missouri River Border		*St. Francois and Courtois Regions*		
Cooper	76	Madison		21
Cole	51	Washington		20
Franklin	47	Iron		14
Gasconade	38	*Osage-Gasconade Hills*		
Mississippi River Border		Pulaski		27
Cape Girardeau	60	Camden		25
Perry	53	*White River Hills*		
Jefferson	40	Stone		27
Ste. Genevieve	34	Taney		16
Springfield Plain		*Central Plateau*		
Lawrence	74	Polk		52
Greene	71	Webster		48
Jasper	67	Dallas		44
Newton	55	Howell		30
St. Francois Region		*Central Plateau and Courtois Hills*		
St. Francois	33	Oregon		22
Courtois Hills		Ripley		19
Crawford	24	*Central Plateau and White River Hills*		
Wayne	19	Ozark		19
Reynolds	11			
Shannon	10			
Carter	9			

The greater part of the wild land belongs to farms, which contain as a rule a far smaller combined acreage of fields and cleared pastures than they do of woods (Figs. 31, 32).   Especially in the poorer counties the woodlands belonging to farms form forests miles in extent, in which many individual holdings are included. The unimproved land is held in small esteem. Land is valued usually according to its agricultural productiveness, and land not suited for cultivation brings a nominal price, rarely in excess of five dollars an acre and often much less. Farmers not uncommonly state as the size of their farms the acreage of cleared land, the rest being considered negligible, although it may be much the larger part.

Fig. 30 shows the percentage of land area in farms. In Carter and Reynolds c o u n t i e s the percentage is only 27.5. In these counties large tracts, in a number of instances tens of thousands of acres, are owned by nonresidents. Companies have bought l a n d for lumber, for mineral prospects, or merely for speculative purposes. Most of it was secured very cheaply, some under the Graduation Act for $12\frac{1}{2}$ cents per acre and some at sheriff's sales, on the assumption that any land purchased at such prices must be a profitable investment. In some of the hill counties there remain small areas of public land.

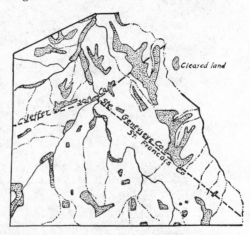

FIG. 29.—Relation of cleared land to forest in a portion of the Clarksville soil area. Clearings are of two types only, those on ridge tops and those on valley floors.

TIMBER AND ITS USES

Timber is the most important resource and the chief product of the wild land. In the Courtois Hills forest products exceed farm crops in value.

Pine timber, long the most valuable forest product, is approaching exhaustion rapidly, due to its exploitation for nearly a century. The large pine forests of early days have long since disappeared and are succeeded mainly by oaks. In remote parts of the southern counties small stands on poor uplands have escaped destruction. In Douglas

County, on the state boundary, there is a pine forest which was estimated some years since to contain 1 per cent of the timber of the county.[1] In 1904 pine was estimated to represent 8 per cent of the timber of Taney County, which is in one of the most difficultly accessible parts of the Ozark Highland.[2]   In recent years the cutting of pine timber has been perhaps most extensive in the rough hills of Reynolds, Shannon, and

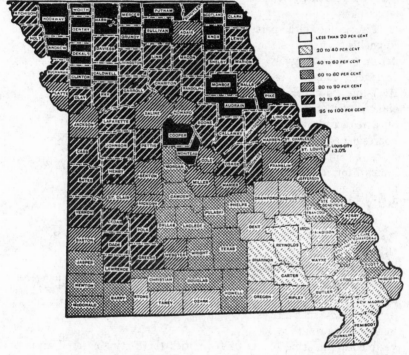

FIG. 30.—Percentage of land in farms in Missouri (*Thirteenth Census, Statistical Atlas*).

Carter counties, with Birch Tree, Winona, and Grandin the leading lumber camps.[3] This southern part of the Courtois Hills is tapped by logging railroads which connect with the main line of the Iron Mountain Railroad. These roads are extended from time to time into areas of uncut timber. Their construction has not been so difficult a matter as the broken topography would indicate. The roads have been built

[1] *State of Missouri* (1904), p. 382.
[2] *Ibid.*, p. 526.   [3] *Ibid.*, p. 517.

invariably along the even crests of the old peneplain, and, although their courses are sinuous, expensive grading is not necessary. According to the very fragmentary figures which are available, Reynolds and Shannon counties are still the leading producers of lumber, their shipments in 1912 amounting to 30,244,000 and 21,020,000 feet respectively, mostly pine lumber.[1] The stationary mills are able to maintain themselves only where lumber may be floated down from large areas or where it is carried

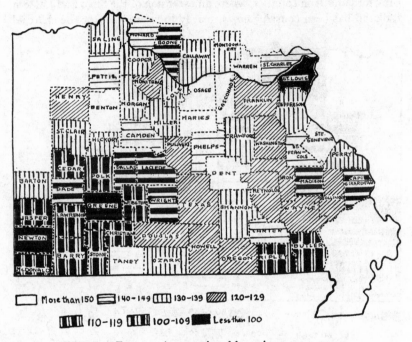

FIG. 31.—Average size of farms in acres

in by logging railroads. As all these favored locations have been exploited to a considerable degree, the days of large operators are drawing to a close rapidly. Pine lumber is being cut to an increasing extent by small portable mills which can operate economically on small tracts at great distances from the railroad.

The predominance of oak timber in the Ozark forests is becoming more marked from year to year, partially because of its resistance to fire and its success in coppicing and consequent survival in cut-over

[1] State Bureau of Labor Statistics, *Missouri, 1912, 1913, 1914.*

tracts. The other kinds of timber, such as hickory, walnut, sugar maple, tulip tree, and gum, are chiefly in very mixed stands, in small groves on the lower valley slopes. The high value of walnut and tulip wood has resulted in the removal of much of this timber.

The exploitation of the hardwoods is carried on for the most part by small occasional operators, as the mixed sizes of most of the timber do not favor the logging off of large tracts. A conspicuous exception is in Crawford and Iron counties, where an extension of the Sligo and Eastern Railroad has been constructed, primarily to secure fuel for the charcoal

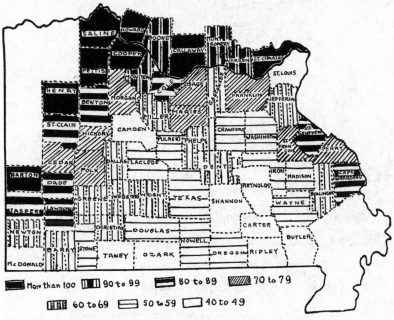

FIG. 32.—Average number of acres of improved land per farm

furnaces at Sligo. Here clean cutting is practiced. The small timber is used for charcoal, the larger is cut into ties and saw logs. A late development in clean cutting on a large scale is by the elaborate wood-distilling plant at Midco, Carter County.

Ties are the most important hardwood product of the Ozarks. They are cut preferably from white or post oak, but other oak also is used extensively. All sections except the Springfield Plain are important producers. In 1912 twenty-five counties reported shipments in excess of 100,000 ties each. According to figures compiled by railroad-station agents, Douglas County shipped in this year 1,500,000 ties; Crawford, 837,000; Ripley, 808,000; Wayne, 750,000; Iron, 536,000; and Stone, 500,000.[1] Production is largest at present in the more isolated sections, as the continued demand, especially by railroads operating in the prairie country to the north and west, has resulted in the rapid depletion of tie timber in the more accessible counties. The possibility of floating ties out has made tie cutting profitable at long distances from a railroad. The returns of the industry are paid out mostly for labor in cutting and hauling. Ties at rail points in 1914 brought commonly twenty-five to forty-five cents each, but on the stump rarely more than ten cents and in many cases only five. The difference paid the cost of making and transportation and the commission of the contractor. Ties are made in three ways: (1) in winter, by farmers who thus find occupation on their wood lots for an otherwise non-productive season, (2) at sawmills, usually as a by-product, from timber too small to be used for saw logs, and (3) by "tie hackers." These work either in the employ of tie contractors or independently. They usually build shacks in the forest, where they live in primitive and lonely fashion. Tie hackers are looked down upon by the farming population and often are a somewhat lawless element. When the tie timber has been exhausted at one locality, they move to another, rarely remaining at one place more than a few years. They accumulate few possessions and develop slight social inclinations. Finished ties either are hauled by wagon to a railroad station, usually much to the detriment of the roads, or are floated down a stream. Often they are piled high along the banks of small creeks, and when the stream rises sufficiently the ties are pushed in hurriedly, so that they may be carried out to a larger stream before the water recedes. Plate XV a is a scene from Crawford County; all available hands are helping, although it is Sunday, usually observed strictly, in order to get the ties down the fast-falling creek. On the river ties are made into rafts and floated many miles to a convenient railroad point. The rafting of ties is especially important on the Osage River, largely to the railhead at Bagnell.

Poles, posts, and mine props are produced according to demand. The largest shipments of poles and posts were from Douglas County, which sent out 2,000,000 in 1912.[2] The local demand for telephone poles and fence posts is supplied easily in nearly every vicinity. In addition cedar posts are shipped to distant markets, principally from the glade lands. Mine timbers are cut from small stock. Because of

[1] *Missouri, 1912, 1913, 1914.*   [2] *Ibid.*

the abundant supply and low price, usually about two cents a linear foot, they are produced only in those border counties which are near mining regions. The Missouri River Border sends large numbers to the coal mines of northern Missouri.

Cooperage is produced in stave mills in many places. As good oak lumber is required, the mills rarely remain at one place more than a few years, after which they seek a new location where the large timber has not been cut. According to available statistics the industry of 1912 was prosecuted most vigorously in Bollinger County, which shipped out 1,116 cars of cooperage. Cape Girardeau shipped 372 cars and Reynolds 104.[1] In a few places specialty wood products are made of oak lumber, such as flooring for railroad cars and telephone and telegraph brackets. A number of handle factories create a local demand for second-growth hickory.

In addition to the fuel produced for the Sligo iron industry, charcoal is made especially in Jefferson County, which shipped 284 cars in 1912; Osage, 72; Cole, 55; and Pulaski, 28. These counties have direct rail connections with St. Louis and Kansas City, where charcoal finds ready sale. The charcoal is made mostly from small timber. Wood is the only fuel used on most farms and is also employed much more largely than coal in most villages and small cities.

HUNTING AND TRAPPING

Hunting and trapping are no longer of much commercial significance, the professional hunter and trapper being virtually extinct. In remote sections hunting is still an important part of farm life. By his gun and traps the native of the hills secures a considerable part of his supply of fresh meat as well as peltry to trade in at the country store. In many of the hill sections the settler still asserts, regardless of state laws, the right of the frontiersman to hunt when, where, and how he pleases and maintains the same freedom for his hunting associate, the hound. The more poorly developed the country the greater is the number of hounds kept. In many cases these procure the principal part of their food from the forests, and are therefore very destructive, especially of young game and eggs. Potentially the Ozarks are a magnificent game preserve for the fast-disappearing wild life of the Middle West. Before this can take place, however, the native of the hills must realize more fully that he can no longer be a law unto himself and that he must restrain his gun and his dogs in accordance with the game laws of the state.

[1] *Missouri, 1912, 1913, 1914.*

In the mind of many natives of the Ozark Center laws of trespass do not exist for the wild land. Whatever land is not farmed is considered semipublic property, in which one may hunt and graze his stock and which may supply in some cases the household needs of fuel. The natives will not hesitate to lay ax to a bee tree or to one on which a raccoon has taken refuge. Foreign landowners who attempt to exclude them from the free passage and use of wooded lands commonly meet with strong resentment and occasionally with resistance. It has happened that a large cut-over tract, which was fenced for pasturage, has had its fences cut to shreds repeatedly because the neighboring small farmers felt that they had a right to pasture their stock on it. This attitude is a relic of pioneer days, when the settler, at best, held title to forty or eighty acres and derived most of his livelihood from the public domain.

THE FREE RANGE

A large part of the wild land still constitutes a free range. Stock law, which makes the owner responsible for all unconfined stock, has been introduced only in the better parts of the border regions, and usually only after a spirited contest between the farmers interested in crop raising and the poorer farmers of the old régime. Elsewhere whatever land is not under fence is free to anybody's stock. Most of the range is very poor, especially for cattle. The grass-covered hills of the early days have been replaced for the most part by a dense growth of oak sprouts. The ceasing of grass fires, the clearing of smooth land, and the over-grazing of the remaining area have caused the famous bluestem pasture grass of the early days to become nearly extinct. In a few remote sections of the southern counties cattle still do well on the range. The nature of the range in most parts, however, is such that the production of beef of good quality is out of the question. In spite of the poor grazing the small amount of care which stock requires on the free range still makes it the principal factor in stock production in the interior sections. As long as the stock finds enough feed for subsistence the farmers will not trouble to fence and seed pastures. As long as cattle roam at will accidental breeding prevents the grading up of stock to any great degree. This pioneer custom therefore is incompatible with progressive agriculture.

For the raising of hogs conditions are much better, as the abundance of acorns and other mast makes the average range fairly good. The region produces few fat hogs, because of the small amount of corn which is fed, but yields a very fair bacon type, which is produced at almost no cost. In a typical case a farmer sold $500 worth of hogs, to which he had fed altogether only twelve bushels of corn and which had received almost no care. The half-wild hog of the hills is of lighter weight and worth less than the corn-fed hog. In 1909 the average value of a hog in corn-producing Cooper County was $7.60; in the oak forests of Shannon only $4.20. The range hogs are remarkably free from disease, and it is claimed that they seldom are attacked by cholera.

Stock usually is marked in early spring, the mark of the owner having been recorded at the courthouse. Thereafter the animals receive little attention, except an occasional salting, until winter. Bells are attached to the leaders of the herd so that the farmer can locate his animals. Nearly everywhere, even in the most isolated woods, one hears the tinkle of bells, which are attached to cattle, horses, sheep, and turkeys. In some sections cattle still are driven to distant townships or to a neighboring county when the grazing at home becomes scant.

PROMOTION SCHEMES

The large areas of cheap land have given rise from time to time to promotion schemes. For this business the region possesses unusual inducements. The Ozarks are near large centers of population. They have an attractive climate, especially to northern people. The region has a certain reputation for fruit growing. The pleasant scenery delights city people who think of country life in romantic terms. In the hands of skilful manipulators, well-selected illustrations and half-truths are elaborated artfully from these points of attraction. Visions of comfortable country homes are held out to city clerks and tradesmen who have tired of the precariousness and routine of their present occupations. Fruit orchards, chicken farms, cattle and hog ranches, are the favorite projects promoted. Usually the very poorest land, which even the natives have avoided, is chosen. This is either laid out in small tracts of five to forty acres, or a stock company sells shares in a very large tract. In either case the profits are figured on the basis of a high per acre productiveness. In this way land has been sold for fruit orchards on which trees could have been planted only by blasting holes, and chicken ranches have been promoted in inaccessible localities where the production of grain is an impossibility and even grass grows with difficulty. Some of the land which has been sold for purposes of intensive farming is so rough that it is impossible to drive a wagon over it. If properly managed, the companies clear many hundred per cent, and the investor is left with a tract of land that is nearly worthless because it is poor and is too small to be put to any practical use. Much of the land is sold for taxes after the owners are disillusioned. In numerous cases the owner, who has not seen the land, has decided to quit his position and move to his "farm." By the time he is established on the place a large part of his savings is gone, and in the course of a short time the remainder is lost in the hopeless effort to produce a living there. Finally the settler is reduced to doing odd jobs in the vicinity at very low wages, or, if fortunate, returns to the city to begin over. The promotion of these schemes has not only unloaded on the region families who have become its wards, but has discredited the Ozarks entirely in the minds of many people, in spite of their not inconsiderable possibilities of successful development.

CHAPTER XIII

FARMING CONDITIONS

SIZES AND VALUES OF FARMS

With the exception of Atchinson County in northwestern Missouri, which contains one of the largest farms in the world, the largest average farms of the state are in the Mississippi and Missouri borders of the Ozarks. In 1910 Ste. Genevieve County led with an average of 186.8 acres, then came Osage with 172, Warren with 171, and Gascónade with 163.8 (Fig. 31). The average size for the state was 124.8 acres. The largest acreages are in counties which contain fair-sized areas of moderately good farmland adjacent to larger areas of rough hill land. The farmers of these counties cultivate about the same number of acres as those of the other border sections or a somewhat smaller acreage, but their farms are larger because there is more rough land. The smallest farms of the Ozarks are in the Springfield Plain, where non-agricultural land is least in amount. In Greene County, which contains not only a high percentage of good land but also has developed truck and fruit farming, the average farm has only 86.9 acres.

Fig. 32 shows the average acres of improved land to each farm, and supplements Fig. 31. Of forty-two counties of Missouri having more than one hundred acres improved per farm, only one, Cooper, is included in the Ozark region, and it is decidedly intermediate in character between highland and prairie plains. Of the twelve counties in the state averaging less than fifty acres improved to the farm, nine are in the Ozarks, two in the swamp district of southeast Missouri, and the remaining one is St. Louis County. Of those in the Ozarks, five are in the Courtois Hills, three in the White River Basin, and one in the Osage-Gasconade Hills. The small improved acreage in these counties is the result of the following factors: (1) The small amount of cultivable land available in compact bodies makes large fields impossible. (2) The hill land requires more labor in cultivation than prairie or bottom land and does not admit so readily of the use of machinery. (3) The difficulty of marketing field crops from the more remote sections discourages production and so tends to keep down the acreage of tilled land. (4) Poor yields from poor soils are not conducive to large-scale farming. (5) Many farms have been opened recently and the size of their clearings is still small.

In parts of the Ozark Highland there is a marked increase in improved land from year to year, indicating that the frontier stage is not yet past. In Carter, Laclede, Maries, Miller, Oregon, Ripley, Shannon, Webster, and Wright counties this increase has been 25 per cent or more from 1900 to 1910. The increase has been approximately 35 per cent in Maries County, where the Rock Island Railroad made accessible at that period a large area of fairly smooth upland, which previously was remote from lines of transportation. In general, the extension of cultivated land is greatest at present in the Central Plateau, where there still remain many tracts of smooth upland, mostly of cherty Howell soil, which if cleared make fairly satisfactory fields and pastures. These tracts, for the most part, are at points most distant from rail transportation. Plate XV *b* illustrates such a clearing in Howell County. In the southern part of the Springfield Plain, especially in McDonald and Newton counties, there has been extensive clearing of land lately, in part because of the building of the Missouri and North Arkansas Railroad, in part because of the attention which fruit and truck growing is receiving in this section. In the Missouri River Border the increase for the decade ranges from 3 per cent in maturely developed Cooper County to 15 in Gasconade County, which has benefited considerably by the building of the Rock Island Railroad through its southern end. In the St. Francois region the extension of farming area has been almost nil because the rich limestone soils of the Fredericktown basins have been under cultivation a long time and the igneous rock soils are pemanently non-agricultural. Because of the extension of mining operations St. Francois County has even registered a slight decrease in its farm area. In the border counties the increase in cleared land is mostly by the addition of small patches to existing fields or farms. In the remote sections, especially of the south, however, one may still see numerous recent homesteads, which consist of small log houses standing in the midst of a forest of dead trees, between which corn has been planted. Plate XVI *a* shows the first crop of corn in a clearing that has been made by cutting out the brush and saplings and by girdling the larger trees.

Values of farmland vary with fertility of soil, proportion of cultivable land, and facilities for marketing. As shown in Fig. 33, the highest land values of the state are in the suburban districts of the large cities, in the rich northwestern counties, and in the loess counties of the Missouri Valley below Kansas City. Cooper, Jasper, and Greene, alone of the Ozark counties, exceed the average value of Missouri farmland. In Cooper County, with its loess soils and large stock industry, which belongs as much to the prairie region as to the Ozark Border, the average value of farmland in 1910 was $56.45 per acre, and of all property per farm $10,513. Jasper County, with excellent local markets at the mines, had an average acre value of $52.25 and a farm value of $7,500. Greene County was third in per acre value with $44.73. At the other extreme are Ozark, Taney, and Shannon counties. Ozark County contains a large amount of very rough land, especially on the south; it is also in

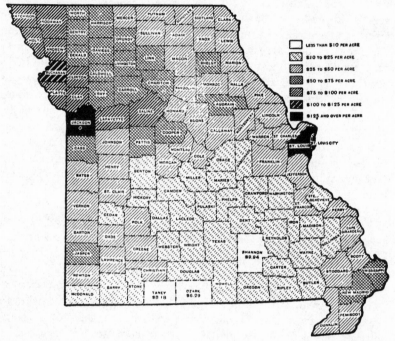

FIG. 33.—Land values in Missouri, 1910 (*Thirteenth Census, Historical Atlas*)

one of the most inaccessible sections of the Ozarks and therefore has been little developed. It is doubtful, however, whether the county will remain in last place, as it has possibilities of development on its extensive upland "flat woods." In Taney County farmland is cheap because of the thin, easily eroded Berryville soils and the rough topography. Shannon County is in the heart of the Courtois flint hills. The primitive condition of agriculture in Ozark County is attested strikingly by an average farm value for the county as a whole of $1,662. In this respect Ripley County is second, with a value of $2,043.

CROP GROWING

The total value of all crops produced in any Ozark county in 1909 exceeded $1,920,000, the value for the average county in Missouri, only in the following counties:

Missouri River Border

Cooper........................... $3,096,121

Franklin.......................... 2,934,343

Springfield Plain

Greene............................ 2,846,349

Jasper............................ 2,573,369

Lawrence.......................... 2,557,447

Newton............................ 2,045,894

Mississippi River Border

Jefferson......................... 2,195,193

Cape Girardeau.................... 2,194,803

The Courtois Hill region, including the entire area of Reynolds, Ripley, Shannon, and Carter counties, produced in the aggregate only a little in excess of one average county.

The extremes of corn production in the Ozarks in 1909 were:[1]

County	Bushels	County	Bushels
Cooper.	3,006,339	Iron.	232,239
Greene.	2,019,622	Carter.	239,930
Jasper.	2,006,001	Madison.	323,145
Dade.	1,810,770	Taney.	370,562
Polk.	1,664,850	Stone.	441,171
Moniteau.	1,658,078	St. Francois.	450,869

The Ozark Border regions, with their more fertile lands and much larger farm areas, are much heavier producers of corn than is the Ozark Center. The superiority of the Ozark Border over the Ozark Center is brought out more particularly by the following per acre yields (1905–14) in bushels:[2]

[1] The figures given by the State Board of Agriculture for the ten-year period 1905–14 are: Cooper, 2,700,000; Greene, 2,077,000; Jasper, 2,014,000; Polk, 1,667,000; Franklin, 1,600,000; Lawrence, 1,589,000; Carter, 239,000; Iron, 298,000; Reynolds, 331,000; Madison, 422,000; Shannon, 427,000; St. Francois, 432,000.

[2] *State Board of Agric. Yearbook*, 1916.

Missouri River Border
Cooper.................... 34
Franklin.................. 30
Moniteau.................. 29

Mississippi River Border
Cape Girardeau............. 32
Perry...................... 31
Jefferson.................. 32

Springfield Plain
Greene..................... 27
Jasper..................... 26
Lawrence................... 26

Central Plateau
Texas...................... 20
Wright..................... 23
Dallas..................... 23

Hill sections
Reynolds................... 21
Shannon.................... 21
Douglas 21
Ozark...................... 19

Yields in the Springfield Plain are somewhat more likely to be cut down by dry weather than in the other border sections. Fig. 33 represents the yield of corn per square mile of improved farmland for all counties entirely or in part within the Ozarks. This shows the relative importance of corn-growing in various sections, as only equal areas which are put to productive farm use are compared and the waste land is disregarded. The heavy production on the northwestern margin of the Ozarks corresponds to the most extensive area of loess soils. In proportion to the area farmed the southeastern region, which includes four of the poorest counties of the state, comes in second place. Considering only the area of improved land, the entire Ozark Center ranks high. On this basis Camden County, in the poor flint hills of the middle Osage Basin, belongs in the same class with wealthy Cooper County. Of the total acreage in cereal crops, which in the Ozarks is nearly equivalent to the total area of land under field cultivation, corn occupies a much higher percentage in the Ozark Center than in the Border. Thus in the border regions corn is grown on the following percentages of the total cereal area: Cooper 54, Osage 45, Cape Girardeau 52, Perry 46, Greene 59. In the central regions, on the other hand, the following extremely high percentages are found: Taney 82, Camden 87, Carter 91, and Reynolds 94. In the poorest part of the state therefore the greatest relative attention is paid to the cultivation of corn. The principal reasons are: (1) It is to be noted that the southeastern hill counties, as well as Camden County, lie in the two most intricately dissected regions of the Ozarks, the Courtois and the Osage-Gasconade Hills. In both of these regions most of the farmland is in valleys, which include the large and very fertile river bottoms of the Osage, Black, Current, and St. Francois. These lands are suited splendidly to corn culture. (2) Corn is the traditional crop of the hill farmers; it was produced by their grandfathers, and, being conservative because they are hill people, they continue to grow it. (3) With their few, cheap tools and the inefficient cultivation which is customary on the hill farms, it is probably the most satisfactory crop. There are still some farmers, although not many, whose stock of tools consist of a one-horse plow, a homemade harrow, and a few hoes. (4) Many sections are too distant from the railroad to haul grain to the station. In such localities corn growing is combined with stock raising

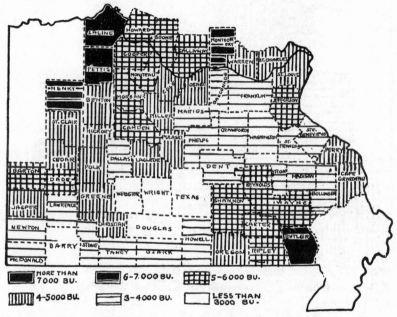

FIG. 34.—Yield of corn per square mile of improved farmland

to the best advantage. (5) Corn is the grain of most general utility for household use and stock. Flour, bran, and shorts are not readily procurable in remote sections. A typical cornfield of the Central Plateau is shown in Plate XVI b.

Wheat is grown most largely in the border sections, as shown in Fig. 35. In the state statistics Franklin ranks second among Missouri wheat-growing counties for the period 1905–14. The figures are: Franklin, 1,016,000 bushels; Jasper, 807,000; Lawrence, 794,000; Cooper, 740,000. In 1909 Franklin led the counties which belong in major part to the Ozarks with 933,000 bushels, Lawrence following with 874,000.

Carter, Reynolds, Butler, and Shannon counties, of the Ozark Center, produced less than 10,000 bushels each.   In the hill counties very little is produced, in part because of the difficulty of marketing, in part because of the difficulty of preparing the seed bed adequately, and largely because the farmers are accustomed to grow corn.   The greatest attention to wheat raising is paid in the eastern counties of the Missouri River Border. These contain on the whole less loess and bottom land than the western

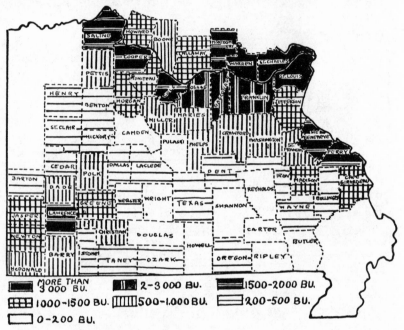

FIG. 35.—Yield of wheat per square mile of improved farmland

counties on the Missouri River, and more of the Union, Lebanon, Howell, and other second-class clay upland soils.   They are therefore not suited so well to the growing of corn but are probably adapted equally as well to wheat culture.   The heavy production of wheat in counties, such as St. Charles, Franklin, Warren, and Gasconade, is due, moreover, in large measure to the preponderance of German farmers, who are specialists in the growing of small grains.   On the Mississippi River Border conditions are similar.   Here too there is a large German population, and the extensive areas of upland soils of the Springfield, Hagerstown, and Fredericktown groups are well suited to wheat.   On the limestone prairies of the southwest wheat is an important crop but much less so than corn. This land has a "stronger" soil than have the uplands of the other border regions. The attention which stock raising receives in the district also tends to make corn rather than wheat the principal crop. There is of late an increase in wheat culture on the prairies of the Central Plateau, the soils of which are somewhat deficient in humus and are better suited to wheat as a basic crop than they are to corn.

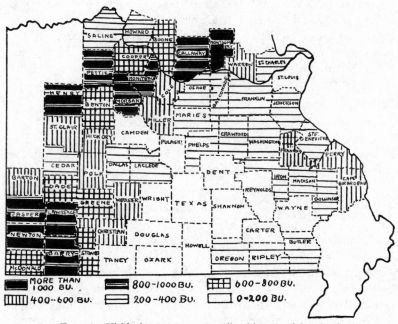

FIG. 36.—Yield of oats per square mile of improved farmland

Oats are not produced extensively (Fig. 36); whereas for the state as a whole their acreage is half that of wheat; for the Springfield Plain, the principal producing region in the Ozarks, the ratio is little better than one to three. In the Missouri River Border the ratio is less than one to five. Largely because crop rotation in corn farming is not practiced commonly in the Ozark Center, a field of oats is a rarity in this section. As a whole oats are not a profitable crop in southern Missouri, being grown chiefly in rotation with corn. As a rule the grain is of lighter weight than in more northern states. Yields are low, being less than twenty-five bushels on the average in Greene, the county of largest production.

In the production of hay the Ozark Center compares very favorably with the border sections (Fig. 37). In 1909 Polk County, a large part of which belongs to the Central Plateau, led the entire Ozark section in total yield, with 47,042 tons from 45,001 acres. On the basis of production per unit area of improved farmland Carter County takes first place, with Reynolds and Camden counties devoting nearly as much attention to hay farming. The greater relative importance of hay in the interior sections is due (1) to the importance of stock raising, (2) to the insufficient agricultural labor available and the ease of production of a meadow crop, (3) to the grass-growing qualities of the upland clay soils and bottom lands of the interior, and (4) to the fact that the mediocre soils of the interior produce grass nearly as well as do the better and higher-priced lands of the Ozark Border. In 1909 average yields in tons per acre for selected counties were:

Ozark Center		Ozark Border	
Laclede	0.93	Greene	1.09
Crawford	1.01	Franklin	1.21
Polk	1.05	Cooper	1.22
Carter	1.12	Cape Girardeau	1.27

The grade of hay produced in the interior counties is poor on the whole and consists of timothy, mixed with a large proportion of wild grasses.

Almost no clover is grown in the interior of the Ozarks, in part because of backward conditions in general, and in minor part because some of the soil is deficient in lime. Of the 47,042 tons of hay grown in Polk County only 863 were clover. In the more progressive border regions the value of clover has been well recognized, and in the Missouri and Mississippi River borders more clover is produced than in any other part of the state. Franklin, with 14,581 tons in 1909, and Jefferson with 14,195, are the leading clover-growing counties of Missouri. Yields nearly as large are reported from Cooper and Cape Girardeau counties. The need of rotation with clover has been felt most keenly in the old northeastern counties of the Ozarks, as the land here, in large part not of the highest fertility originally, has become depleted by long cropping. In Jefferson and Franklin counties the extension of dairying is in part responsible for the high clover production. As a whole the German farmers have taken to the growing of clover most readily, largely because they more than any other group consider their farms their permanent homes. In the last few years the growing of alfalfa has made rapid strides, the bottom lands being found generally suited to this crop without previous inoculation. The results are too recent to show appreciably in census figures, but at present there are few sections of the northern and eastern borders in which small fields are not numerous and increasing rapidly. Alfalfa is also finding favor among the better stock raisers of the interior sections, fine fields of it being found in such remote sections as Taney and Ozark counties. Because of their rapid growth cowpeas are planted usually in June or July in the wheat stubble. They should form an important rotation crop for forage and soil restoration but are

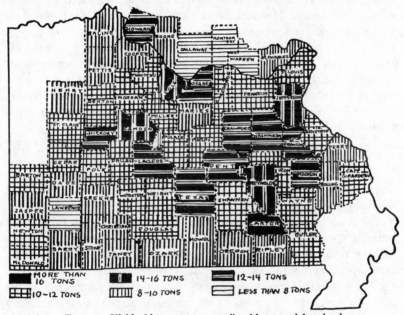

Fig. 37.—Yield of hay per square mile of improved farmland

not grown to any large extent, except on the poorer uplands of the border regions. Most of the alluvial, loess, and limestone soils are well adapted to legumes. In most places where they do not succeed the corrective is at hand in abundant outcrops of limestone. The general introduction of leguminous crops into the farm husbandry appears therefore to be only a question of time.

Millet is a crop of some importance on the poorer lands and is grown especially in dry seasons, when the young corn has failed. Sorghum is grown chiefly in the Ozark Center. Texas County led the state, reporting, in 1909, 43,510 gallons of syrup. Other important producers are

Dallas, Miller, Polk, Moniteau, and Cape Girardeau counties. The cane grows well on rather poor land, gives high returns per acre, and in the more remote sections sorghum syrup still serves as the common household sweetening.

Tobacco growing is nearly extinct. Most of that produced at present is for home consumption. Cooper alone of the Ozark counties yielded more than 50,000 pounds in 1909. Cotton is grown in the southern counties, principally on bottom land. The cotton-growing counties lie at the northern limit of production, in the same latitude as the southeastern lowlands of Missouri, in which cotton is one of the chief crops. In 1909 Ozark County produced 1,066 bales; Taney, 861; Oregon, 744; Ripley, 617; and Howell, 183. Cotton growing, however, receives far less attention on these bottom lands than it does in the southeastern lowlands, partly because the Ozark valleys are more subject to early and late frosts, due to the inflow of cold air from the surrounding hills, and partly because the Ozark districts contain almost no negro population.

ANIMAL INDUSTRIES

Over large areas stock raising is the dominant occupation. In the Central Plateau and in a large part of the hill sections the value of animal products commonly exceeds the value of all crops. In the border regions, on the other hand, the reverse is true. Comparative figures for selected counties are given in the table (p. 199). If figures were available on the value of field crops marketed as such, they would establish the fact that animal products are the leading output of Ozark farms in all sections with the exception of the northeastern and eastern counties and a part of the Springfield region. The greatest relative importance of animal industry is in the interior. This is due to (1) poor transportation conditions, which constitute one of the most serious economic problems of the region, (2) the combination of bottom lands which grow corn and hay, and of upland pastures, (3) the excellent springs, (4) small amount of labor required under primitive conditions in vogue, and (5) the inherited interest in this occupation. Plate XVII a shows a seeded pasture in the interior of the Ozarks which is in striking contrast to the more common wild pastures. The stock farmer, alone of the occupants of the Ozark Center, is not seriously handicapped by isolation. A good stock farm, no matter how far it is from a railroad, may command a hundred dollars per acre for its bottom land. There are silos in valleys more than twenty-five miles distant from the nearest railroad. Many of these farms sell nothing but animal products, and are improving year by year in fertility and equipment.

Fig. 38 shows the number of cattle kept per square mile in the Ozark Highland and in the adjacent counties. The corn- and hay-growing counties of the west and northwest are the largest producers and yield also the best grade of stock. In these sections the animals are fattened for market and receive in general the same treatment as in the corn belt of Iowa and Illinois. Next in importance is the Central Plateau, where the extensive grasslands are the chief factor in production

AGRICULTURAL PRODUCTION, 1909

	All Animal Products	All Crops
Central Plateau:		
Polk.....................	$2,490,000	$1,850,000
Howell..................	1,600,000	1,270,000
Webster.................	1,420,000	1,220,000
Wright..................	1,340,000	1,070,000
Dallas..................	970,000	950,000
Hill sections:		
Camden.................	950,000	910,000
Crawford...............	850,000	960,000
Shannon................	680,000	590,000
Stone..................	680,000	620,000
Wayne..................	660,000	920,000
Pulaski................	630,000	750,000
Springfield Plain:		
Greene.................	2,510,000	2,850,000
Lawrence...............	1,520,000	2,560,000
Missouri River Border:		
Cooper.................	2,430,000	3,100,000
Franklin...............	1,790,000	2,930,000
Mississippi River Border:		
Cape Girardeau..........	1,340,000	2,200,000

(Plate XVII *a*). The low rank of the eastern and northern border counties is due in part to the good grain markets which they possess, in part to the development of dairying rather than of meat production, and in part to the German population, which in this region is becoming interested only slowly in stock raising.

In spite of the great natural advantages the dairy industry has not been developed extensively in most parts of the Ozarks (Fig. 39). Jefferson County, perhaps the poorest county of the Ozark borders, ranks first, with dairy products valued at $386,000 in 1909. This figure has since been far surpassed. The redemption of this county from poverty has been accomplished by dairying. The nearby St. Louis market has given the incentive to the industry. The county contains a great deal of hill land, which furnishes fair pasturage. It also has sufficient land suited for growing corn and hay, and has good water. To the west of St. Louis, Franklin County is beginning to develop similarly. The southwestern counties supply Springfield and the mining districts with dairy products. Excepting these sections there are very few dairies in the Ozarks. Physical conditions for dairying are good in all sections,

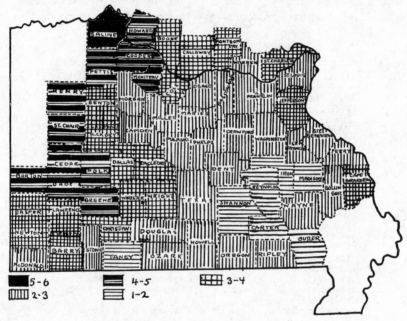

FIG. 38.—Number of cattle per square mile

as shown by examples of individual success,[1] but the problem of market-ing and the lack of organization retard development. The difficulty of transportation has as its effect the conversion of the farm surplus of milk into butter. If butter is estimated to be worth on the average 16 cents per pound in 1909, Douglas County sold $53,000 worth of butter out of a total of $56,000 in dairy products. For Ripley County the respective figures are $40,000 and $43,000; for Oregon, $57,000 and $61,000, and so on. On the other hand regions with good market con-nections sell chiefly milk and cream. The butter produced in Jefferson

---

[1] *Forty-sixth Ann. Rept. of the State Board of Agric.*, pp. 403–5.

County was worth only one-fourth of the total value of dairy products and that in Greene County about one-half.

Fig. 40 shows the number of hogs kept in 1909. The distribution of hogs corresponds rather closely to the production of corn, and the industry is therefore best developed in the Boonslick region of the northwest. The counties in the interior which make the best success of hog raising are the ones possessing rail transportation. Thus the main line

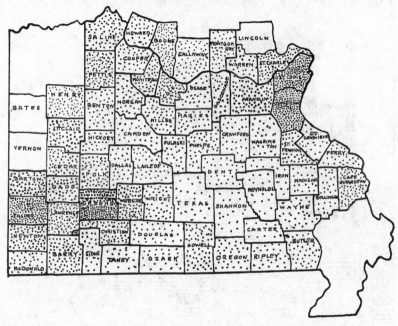

Fig. 39.—Dairy products. Each dot represents $2,000

of the Frisco is outlined by a chain of counties producing more hogs than their more inaccessible neighbors. Hogs cannot transport themselves so well as cattle, and are not produced so extensively in remote sections.

Although the country is well adapted to the production of sheep, this industry has attained no great importance. In the Ozark Center the danger from dogs and the fact that sheep lose themselves in the forests are serious handicaps. Laclede County led in 1909 with 26,600. In this and other counties there are also numerous herds of goats (Plate XVII *b*). They are shipped in mostly from the southwest, are turned into brushy pastures during summer, and are then sent usually to market at St. Louis.

As the goats destroy the brush and saplings the land is afterward used most commonly as pasture for cattle or sheep. The introduction of goats therefore is followed in most cases by an increase in the number of other live stock.

Draft animals in the border region are of medium weight and fair quality. In the Missouri Valley mule breeding continues to be important. In the hill regions horses and mules are of inferior grade. Because of the steep slopes, the sharp gravel, and the small amount of feed they

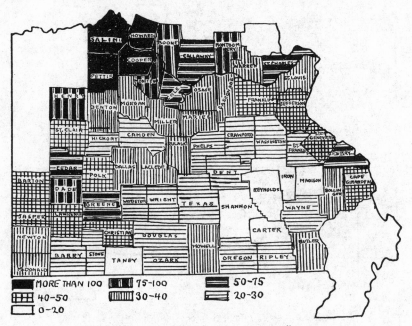

FIG. 40.—Number of hogs per square mile

receive, there has been evolved a light, wiry, and sure-footed strain which is well suited to the needs of the poorer farmers. In much of the hill country the average horse or mule is well below a thousand pounds in weight. On the Central Plateau some attention is given to horse breeding, largely because of the long wagon hauls that are necessary in most parts to reach shipping-points, in part because the smooth prairies make the employment of good draft animals profitable. Plate XVIII a shows a horse show at Licking, a small village on one of the most isolated prairies.

Poultry raising, as shown in Fig. 41, is dependent not so much on fertility of soil as upon marketing facilities. In this region, however, poultry raising for market is not profitable unless most of the feed is produced on the place. There are few exclusive poultry farms. Poultry in the Ozarks is a by-product of general farming and subsists mostly on what otherwise would be wasted on the farm. In receipts from the sale of poultry and eggs Jefferson County leads the state, although it is not a large county and is poor in comparison with north Missouri counties.

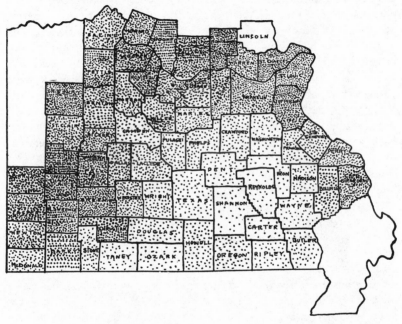

FIG. 41.—Value of poultry and eggs. Each dot represents $2,000

Franklin County is a close second. The money received in Jefferson County from poultry and eggs in 1909 was more than that from its wheat crop. The eastern counties of the Missouri River Border, which are less fertile than the western ones and at the same time have easy access to large markets, engage largely in the production of poultry and eggs. Where the cattle and hog business prospers, farmers do not have time or inclination to devote themselves to the raising of poultry. In the less favored counties, however, the poultry business is in many cases the deciding factor which makes the farm show a profit instead of a deficit. Turkeys are most numerous in the hill sections, where these birds, which are efficient foragers, find almost their entire sustenance in the woods from spring until fall. At the latter season they are fattened on corn and then shipped or driven to market in large numbers.

TRUCK AND FRUIT FARMING

The growing of vegetables for market is not pursued extensively except in the southwest. The largest single producer in 1909 was Greene County with an output worth $210,000. There are numerous market gardens also in the neighboring counties of Jasper, Newton, Barry, Webster, and Lawrence, all of which have good local markets in the Joplin mining region and at Springfield. The southeast is favored also in the production of early vegetables for northern markets, because it has an early spring, a warm cherty soil which drains well and can be worked early, and good rail connections with the north. Many vegetables are grown in this section as filler crops between rows of small fruits, which are an important product (see below). Canning industries have been extablished recently, and extend the demand for vegetables over a longer period. In the vicinity of St. Louis, Jefferson and Franklin counties have added truck farming to their other intensified farming interests. Jefferson County especially is favored in the growing of various vegetables by its large areas of sandy soil.

Although the Ozarks have been advertised extensively as the "land of the big red apple," they take second place to the great loess belt of western Missouri, of which Cooper County is the eastern extremity. In four adjoining counties of the Ozarks, Greene, Wright (each with 210,000 bushels in 1909), Texas, and Webster, the most numerous apple orchards are to be found. It is not apparent that this region possesses advantages over other sections of the Ozarks other than the fact that an early start has made the vicinity of Springfield a well-known center for apple buyers and that transportation facilities are better than the average. Apples, especially winter varieties, do well on all the clay and loam soils of the highland and are grown as a rule on less thin and stony soils than are peaches. Plate XVIII b shows a typical apple orchard. They are located usually on smooth land, and labor-saving machinery is employed largely in their care.

In peach growing a group of southeastern counties is first in the state and constitutes one of the important commercial districts of the country. The following yields are given for 1909: Oregon County, 117,000 bushels; Howell, 78,000; Texas, 68,000; Bollinger, 60,000. Both soil and climate are adapted to the production of fruit of sweet flavor and high color, which enters the markets after the Georgia peaches are gone and before the Michigan fruit is ripe. The trees grow mostly on Howell soil, which is warm and well drained because of its high chert content. The reflection of light from the chert fragments probably contributes to the high color of the peaches. The district lies far enough south to escape most of the late killing frosts. The orchards are located mostly on the upland near the edge of a valley, thus providing air drainage which protects them from unseasonable frosts. As in the case of apples, commercial orchards are not located on rough land on which machinery cannot be employed to good advantage. Although the fruit has been known to do well in this section for a long time, its successful production on a commercial scale has had to wait for organization of the growers. The largest growers' association has shipping stations at Pomona, Koshkonong, Brandsville, and Thayer. About five thousand people are at present employed during the picking season. They are in part professionals following the crop season north, but largely natives from the surrounding hills who desert their poor farms temporarily for the peach orchards to make a few dollars less hard-won than by growing corn on their thin lands. For a time there is great activity; every one is busy during the day, and at night traveling shows reap a rich harvest. Thereafter the region relapses into quiet until the next season.[1] Plate XIX *a* shows a commercial orchard at picking time.

Recently Missouri strawberries have entered the metropolitan markets, and at present about two dozen places, centering about Neosho and Monett, are engaged in growing and shipping an annual crop worth from $500,000 to $1,000,000. The cherty soil so employed warms up quickly and maintains a favorable moisture condition. Most of the strawberry land is smooth and easily cultivated. The season lasts about a month, from the middle of May to the middle of June, and bridges in part the interval between the southern berries and those from Michigan. To place the fruit on the market promptly, the railroads operate "strawberry specials" to Kansas City and Chicago.

CONDITIONS OF RURAL LIFE

Conditions of life in the Ozark Border are in sharp contrast to those of the Ozark Center. The border farms are richer, more numerous, less scattered, and in closer contact with the outside world than are the farms of the hill and plateau sections.

[1] Bureau of Labor Statistics, *Missouri, 1912, 1913, 1914*, pp. 67–71.

Farm improvements are generally ample and in good condition in the border regions. Most of the dwellings are two-story frame houses, built on the conventional plan of western farm dwellings. In the German sections they are built largely of stone or brick. The prairies of the Central Plateau are similar to the borders in the character of their homes. Elsewhere in the interior one finds most commonly low structures, which, by their long, built-in porches, show the architecture of the old South. Many houses still are built of logs and range from crude one-room cabins of rough-hewn, ill-fitted logs to structures built of carefully squared logs, joined so well that almost no "chinking" is required (Plate XX). In contrast to the factory-made and often garish home furnishings of the border farms, the isolated farm of the interior valleys is still fitted largely with homemade articles. Many of the better-class homes resemble those of more eastern sections of several generations ago. Hickory chairs and walnut worm bedsteads are in common use. The housewife still knows how to knit rag rugs and to weave coverlets of various designs. Quilting is a cherished art in which time-honored patterns are used that were evolved on the frontier, or were brought from the southern seaboard. The gun still hangs over the fireplace, ready for use, and in a corner the spinning wheel may be seen occasionally, as there are some who still card their own wool and spin it into thread for jeans.

Barns as a rule are not large in any part of the highland, except in the northwestern counties. On the poor farms of the hill regions they are wretched sheds. Here the little hay that is cut is left in the cock, corn remains in the field or is put into log cribs, stock seeks its own shelter, and small grains are not produced. A barn therefore is an improvement of slight value to the hill farmer. The spring house (Plate XIX b) is still the favorite place for keeping perishable food. Most cove farmers keep their butter and milk in the cavernous openings from which springs issue. Rail fences are almost universal, except in the Springfield Plain and on the prairies. Plates XXI and XXII a show contrasted types of farms on the prairie and in the hills.

As external circumstances change slowly in the central region, so thought and custom have become crystallized through isolation. There are no political upheavals in the Ozark Center; its voters can be relied on to vote "regular" and to oppose changes in the existing order. The church is the one great social institution of the hill regions, and preaching and prayer meeting are attended regularly by nearly all. Entertainments are of the old-fashioned sort, such as spelling matches, quilting bees, and dancing to the fiddle. The classic of the frontier, "the Hoosier schoolmaster," could still be matched in parts of the Ozarks today. The speech of the people is full of homespun epigrams and contains a number of obsolete expressions which are probably imported from the hills of Tennessee. In short, whereas the people of the Ozark borders live much in the fashion of the surrounding prairie states, the interior is still in many respects a remnant of the frontier and has preserved conditions of life which in most other regions belonged to past generations. In this respect it is similar to the hills of Kentucky and Tennessee, but as the isolation of the Ozarks has been less effective the degree of retardation is less. The backward condition of the interior regions is heightened by the fact that the settlers came originally from eastern Tennessee or Kentucky, and were in a backward state at the time of their immigration to Missouri.

In the hill sections there is a sharp difference between the farmer of the larger valley and the farmer of the hillside or small cove. The former usually enjoys a reasonable prosperity, the latter too commonly lives in abject poverty. The valley people are on the whole well built, alert, frank, and intelligent. The hill farmers are largely of the shambling, furtive, and shiftless type that is associated popularly with "hill billies." They go barefooted most of the year, old and young of both sexes smoke and dip snuff, and they marry when hardly out of childhood. Most of the ancestors of both groups came from the same regions of Tennessee and Kentucky. In part the present hill farmers are descended from the poorer immigrants who located on the less desirable land. In numerous instances, however, valley farmers and hill farmers are from the same stock and have become differentiated since settling in Missouri by reason of a strongly contrasted environment.

Where bottom lands and prairies lie in close proximity, they afford interesting economic and social contrasts. The bottom lands are almost invariably much richer than the adjacent prairies. The prairie farms, however, make a surer crop because they are never flooded. They are also cultivated more easily because of the more compact form and level surface of their fields and usually are more healthful. For these reasons the prairie farms in many sections are better cared for than the bottom farms and bring a higher price, considering their fertility. An additional factor, and probably the most important one which makes the prairie land more in demand, is its accessibility. Most bottoms are much less than half a mile wide, and are flanked on both sides by a belt of rough, almost uninhabited, country, which most likely is several miles in width. A neighborhood in the bottoms is therefore linear, the houses being strung along the valley at distances usually in excess of half a mile. On the prairie, however, roads lead in all directions and there are neighbors all around (Plate XXI). Moreover, the main roads are located almost invariably upon the upland, so that the prairie farmer may live in touch with the outer world, whereas the valleys are served by side roads, traveled ordinarily only by a few people of the vicinity. The one region therefore enjoys a fair amount of community life, whereas the other may be extremely isolated. This isolation has a somewhat discouraging effect on the husbandry of the valley farmer, as he lacks the stimulus derived from the competition and comment of numerous neighbors and from an exchange of opinions. The most serious effect of isolation, however, is upon the farmer's family, which commonly tires of the lonely life. Because of the wishes of his family the valley farmer in many instances disposes of his place after a time and removes to a section where there are more social relations.

School conditions throw light on the contrasted social conditions of the Ozark Center and Border. In six counties in Missouri the average attendance per pupil enrolled was less than 75 days for the school year 1912–13. These counties and the average number of days in attendance are: Douglas, 69; Reynolds, 69.5; Camden, 70.9; Bollinger, 71.2; Stone, 73; Carter, 74—all of the Ozark Center. In contrast to these conditions an agricultural county of north Missouri, Holt, showed a record of 123.9 days and some of the Ozark Border counties the following: Franklin, 109.4; Jefferson, 107.1; Barry, 107.5. None of these has any large part of its pupils in city school districts. Including Butler County there are eighteen school districts in the Ozarks, each of which has a total assessed valuation of less than $10,000. In Ozark, Pulaski, Phelps, Texas, and Wayne counties not a single one-room district (this includes all rural schools as well as the smaller villages) is assessed as high as $50,000. In many of these poorer schools the teacher has been employed at $25 a month, and in at least one case at $20.[1]

[1] *Sixty-fourth Missouri Report of Public Schools.*

CHAPTER XIV

MINING AND MANUFACTURING

IMPORTANCE OF MINING INDUSTRY

To Missouri's normal mineral output of $50,000,000 the Ozark Highland contributes more than three-fifths. The value of all minerals produced in the Ozarks is nearly half as great as that of all agricultural crops. Half of the mineral values of the state consist of lead and zinc, both of which are mined exclusively in the Ozarks. In addition the region yields clay, limestone, granite, baryte, iron ore, tripoli, copper, silver, and coal. More than half the total mineral output of the highland is from the southwestern district, comprising Jasper, Newton, and Lawrence counties, and most of the remainder from the southeastern counties, St. Francois, Washington, and Madison. The places of principal production of the various minerals are shown in Fig. 42.

Mining in general probably does not benefit the region to the extent which similar earnings along many other lines do, because (1) the net profits of mining are largely taken out of the region, and (2) the wage-earners themselves do little to build up the community. Ordinarily they do not become permanent citizens but drift away after a time, and their savings go with them. Mining has aided development principally in the following ways: (1) The taxes enable the carrying out of extensive public works, especially the construction of good roads. Jasper and St. Francois counties have some of the best roads in the state built by these means. (2) The mining towns furnish excellent markets for the surrounding agricultural sections. (3) The miners spend freely and thus create good business for the merchants. (4) In so far as royalties are paid to owners of land, the stable indigenous population shares in the profits. (5) The mineral deposits attract railroads, which in turn aid the general development of the mining districts and of the territory lying between the mines and the markets.

SOUTHWESTERN MINING REGION

The southwestern region still leads the country in normal times in the production of zinc. Its output of raw ore in 1912 was worth $13,000,000. In addition there was produced about $2,100,000 worth of lead ore, mainly as a by-product. Of the total, almost 95 per cent came from

Jasper County.[1]   Values of zinc concentrates in 1915 were $18,585,454; of lead, $1,805,782.   The total ore values for the district in 1917 were placed at $25,000,000.[2]   The outbreak of the war in 1914 created an enormous demand for zinc.   Old mills were reopened, low-grade producers from the "sheet ground" areas were greatly stimulated, tailings were re-worked, improved methods of recovery were introduced, and, above all else, the district experienced an enormous expansion of area by the opening of new mines.   This expansion was almost entirely westward and northward and lay, therefore, for the most part beyond the

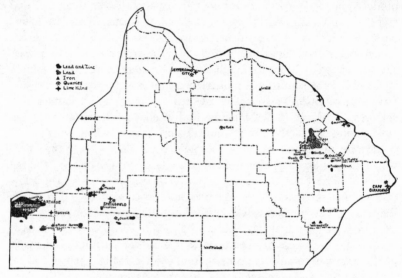

FIG. 42.—Principal areas of mineral production

boundaries of the state.   Joplin, the metropolis of the district, has thereby been placed in a distinctly marginal position to the zinc and lead region.   Prices in 1916 rose three to five times the normal ore values, and development assumed in places a frenzied character.   In 1917 a sharp recession in spelter prices took place without a reduction in the high costs of mining, and the older mining districts in Missouri began to suffer heavily.

Joplin, with a population of 32,073 in 1910, is the metropolis of the zinc region.   Probably 100,000 people live within a ten-mile radius of this

[1] *Twenty-sixth Ann. Rept. Bur. Mines, State of Missouri.*

[2] *Eng. and Min. Jour.* (1918), p. 70.

place. Other cities built up principally through mining development are Webb City (11,817), Carthage (9,483), Carterville (4,549), Oronogo (1,912), Carl Junction (1,115), Purcell (997), and Duenweg in Jasper County; Aurora (4,149) in Lawrence County; and Granby (2,336) in Newton County. The number of cities is not equaled by any other equal area in the state. The concentration of population has resulted in a net of interurban electric lines. Mining has made Joplin one of the most important railroad centers of the state, and thereby has attracted wholesale merchants, selling to a large territory in the southwest, as well as numerous manufacturers. Joplin itself has for some time been a less important producer than some other sections, but it has retained commercial control of the district, as the earliest great center. Mining centers are numerous and for the most part small, as the ore is widely distributed and not suited to the erection of a few large mining establishments. Instead, there is a host of small producers, resulting in an extraordinarily large number of small mining centers. This situation facilitates continued control of the business of the district by Joplin, which is becoming more and more a commercial city rather than a mining town. The manufactures are in large part connected with the mining industry, important products being mining machinery, dynamite, and white lead. Smelters using zinc ore from this region are located at Nevada and Rich Hill in Missouri, and at Pittsburg, Weir City, Iola, Gas City, La Harpe, and other places in Kansas. Spelter is also shipped to Illinois. Since twice as much coal as ore is required in smelting, the ore for the most part is shipped to places at which there is cheap fuel. Zinc smelters have developed therefore in the oil and gas fields of Kansas and at coal-mining centers in Missouri and Illinois.

Because of the age of the district and its uninterrupted profitable production, the cities have an air of stability not common to mining sections. For the same reasons the mining population is mostly American, having been resident in the region in many cases for several generations.

SOUTHEASTERN MINING REGION

In southeast Missouri St. Francois County dominates the mining industry even to a larger extent than Jasper County does in the southwest. The production of Madison County, which ranks second, is less than 2 per cent of the total for this region. Production by modern methods dates from about 1865, when systematic underground mining of disseminated lead deposits was begun at Bonne Terre. In 1888 shafts were sunk at Doe Run and resulted in a strong boom. In 1890 the Mississippi River and Bonne Terre Railroad was opened and a smelter was built at its terminus on the river at Herculaneum. The ore was transported to this point, where cheap coal is available. The opening up of this railroad solved the vexing fuel problem and inaugurated large-scale development. Doe Run experienced a short period of prosperity, the workings being practically abandoned in 1896. The town is at present largely in ruins. The greatest development began in 1892, when the first shaft was sunk in the Flat River field; about at the same time operations commenced at Desloge.[1] In 1902 the Federal Lead Company entered the field, sinking shafts at Flat River, Elvins, and Central. The St. Francois district yielded from 1869 to 1906 lead concentrates valued at $59,870,000.[2] From 1907 to 1915 their value amounted to $85,207,971, probably in excess of all production prior to 1907.[3] In 1915 alone the concentrates were valued at approximately $12,000,000. In 1912 mining companies controlled 42,000 acres of land in St. Francois County which contain ample reserves for a number of years.[4] As in the Joplin district, both production and development work were enormously stimulated by the Great War. There exist possibilities of extension of the area producing lead from disseminated ore, especially into Washington County, at the scene of the original lead mining in Missouri.

The ore bodies are more deep-seated than in the southwestern region, and the quantity available in the same area of mining operations is as a rule greater. Mining equipment is therefore on a larger scale and of a more permanent character than in the Joplin region. A few large companies dominate the field completely, have built large power plants and mills, and even, in considerable part, towns in which the miners live. In this section is the largest lead-mining corporation on the continent, the St. Joseph Lead Company, which produced in 1917 ore approximating $18,000,000 in value and paid nearly $5,000,000 in dividends in that year.

The rapid mining development has resulted in a phenomenal increase of population in St. Francois County, which is equaled by no other Ozark county during the same period. In 1880 the county had 13,822 people; in 1890, 17,347; in 1900, 24,051; in 1910, 35,738. The increase since then has been even more rapid. In 1880 the population was approximately the same as that of Washington County; in 1910 it was nearly

[1] Buckley, *Missouri Bur. Geol. and Mines*, IX, 164, 196.
[3] *Ibid.*, p. 3.
[2] *U.S. Geol. Surv., Mineral Resources* (1915), I.
[4] *Twenty-sixth Ann. Rept. Bur. Mines, State of Missouri*.

three times as large. The mines are so distributed that no one center overshadows the rest in size and importance. Flat River, with a population of 5,112 in 1910, is at present the center of greatest activity, and is a typical, hastily built mining town. Bonne Terre (4,500) is the oldest mining town in a field which still is producing satisfactorily. The town has the appearance of prosperity and stability. Elvins (2,071) and Desloge (2,200) are mushroom places. In all, there are at present at least 25,000 people dependent on the mines of the district. The workers are largely foreigners from the east of Europe. Mining has aided the growth of the old city of Farmington and has contributed greatly to its wealth. Because of its established residential character it has been the home of many of the men connected with the mines in superior capacities. Some of its inhabitants have been made prosperous by the sale or lease of land to the mining companies. As a result the city has an air of prosperity and refinement rare in places of its size.

QUARRIES AND ASSOCIATED INDUSTRIES

Next to the lead and zinc mines, quarries are the leading producers of mineral wealth. The quarries that ship out their product fall into two groups: (1) those possessing competitive water rates, and (2) those producing a stone of such quality that it can be shipped considerable distances by rail. To the latter class belong the Carthage quarries and those of the granite region. The Carthage limestone is the best-known and most successfully developed building stone of the state. It is much stronger than the Bedford stone, is hardly surpassed by any limestone in uniformity of color,[1] dresses well, and does not discolor readily. It is quarried by improved methods and has a stable output, 75,000 tons having been shipped in 1912. The stone is shipped not only throughout Missouri but to regions in the Southwest as well which are deficient in structural stone. The stone is used for all exterior work in the new state capitol. The extensive use in Carthage has made that city one of the most beautiful in the state. Ste. Genevieve has the largest quarry in the state. Limestone is produced here by the government for riprap to protect the banks of the Mississippi. Granite quarrying commenced at Graniteville in 1869[2] and a few years later at Syenite and Knob Lick. The industry flourished until very recently, Knob Lick alone shipping out a thousand carloads annually for fifteen years.[3] The decadence of

---

[1] Buckley and Buehler, *Missouri Bur. Geol. and Mines*, Ser. 2, II, 123.

[2] Buckley and Buehler, *op. cit.*, p. 62.

[3] Winslow, *Missouri Geol. Surv., Sheet Rept. No. 4* (1896), p. 112.

the industry was due in the first place to the decrease in the demand for paving blocks;[1] secondly, to the working out of the bodies which were easily accessible and required little machinery; and thirdly, to a lack of initiative and to poor management. At present the quarries are at work only when a contract for stone comes in, an event which seems to occur more and more rarely. The quarry towns of the granite region are all decadent, the remaining population being obliged to eke out an existence by various occupations.

At Crystal City and Festus the St. Peter sandstone outcrops near the Mississippi River. Sand is therefore shipped out cheaply. In 1912, 108,000 tons of sand are reported to have been sent out by rail.[2] Coal is also shipped in at low cost from the nearby Illinois fields and is used to operate a large local glass industry. Sand is quarried also at Pacific from the same formation.

Lime is burned at many different places, most notably at Springfield, Ash Grove, and Pierce City on the west, and at Kimmswick, Ste. Genevieve, and Cape Girardeau on the east.[3] In the border regions nearly pure limestones are available in most localities. The location of lime-kilns is determined therefore primarily by shipping facilities. Cape Girardeau has a cement mill, which utilizes the local limestone and clay, and ships in coal at competitive water rates.

MINOR MINERAL INDUSTRIES

Only one iron smelter remains in operation.[4] This is the furnace at Sligo, which produces charcoal iron. It is able to continue in business because there is demand for this particular kind of iron at a good price, because charcoal is produced at low cost from the timber of the flint hills, and because labor is cheap. The ore comes chiefly from Crawford County, from small open pit mines of the filled sink type. The demand for ore and for timber has resulted in the construction of a number of spurs from the Salem branch of the Frisco Railroad.

The production of tripoli began in 1888 with the manufacture of scouring bricks and of tripoli powder. There are works at Seneca, Racine, and Neosho. The production of tripoli flour has increased from 200 tons in the first year to about 5,000 tons at present. In addition, filters of all sizes are made. The total output in 1912 was worth in

---

[1] Winslow, *Missouri Geol. Surv., Sheet Rept. No. 4* (1896), p. 112.

[2] *Missouri, 1912, 1913, 1914:* Jefferson County.   [3] *Ibid.,* p. 29.

[4] Recently a plant has been built at Midco, Carter County, to produce wood distillate and charcoal iron.

excess of eighty thousand dollars and supplied most of the demands of the country.[1]

Banks of fire clay are worked in many counties, usually intermittently and on a small scale. Their small size makes the use of machinery generally unprofitable, and they are worked as a rule by pick and shovel, commonly by farmers during the winter months. Baryte, or tiff, is produced similarly. Four-fifths of the total annual production of Missouri comes from Washington County and is valued at nearly a hundred thousand dollars.[2]

These minor minerals, produced principally by the farming population, are a mixed blessing to the region. They bring to poor sections a certain amount of money. They also divert attention from farming. The hill farmers especially are glad for a chance to earn a few dollars in cash. They are farmers by necessity and not by choice, and gladly take to digging mineral or to hauling it to market. They become only too willing to turn to such jobs not only in winter but at other seasons. It is only as they realize that their salvation lies in the land, not under it, that the consistent development of the poorer regions is possible.

WATER-POWER DEVELOPMENT

In the interior of the region the water wheel still is to be seen (Plate XXII *b*). Timber is sawed, flour and meal are ground, and wool is carded in the same fashion as when the region was first settled. The old mills are fast disappearing, however, and in their stead have come the gasoline and portable steam engines to furnish the small power needed for most rural industries. Hydroelectric power has been developed at a few places only, in spite of the excellent possibilities. The one large power plant of the Ozarks of Missouri is at Powersite, Taney County, where a dam 53 feet high has been built across the White River, and forms a lake about 23 miles long. The plant in September, 1914, had a capacity of 17,000 horse-power, and expected to develop 28,000.[3] Small plants for lighting and power are in successful operation at Houston, Ava, Ozark, Alley, and Neosho. Water power, if utilized properly, would be sufficient to make good the deficiency of coal and to serve as the basis of well distributed and varied manufacturing interests, not only within the Ozarks, but in the larger cities adjacent to the region.

[1] *Missouri, 1912, 1913, 1914*, pp. 52–54; *U.S. Geol. Surv. Bull.*, pp. 429–35.

[2] *Missouri, 1912, 1913, 1914*, p. 51.

[3] Stevens, *Missouri, the Center State*, I, 116.

MANUFACTURES NOT DEPENDENT ON MINING

Manufactures other than those connected with mining are few, for the most part small, and scattered. Even in the larger cities manufactures are of secondary importance. This is due, not to lack of raw materials or of power, but to the stage of development of the region. Flour milling and woodworking are most extensive. These are dependent almost solely upon advantageously located, cheap raw materials. A second, smaller group is a response primarily to transportation facilities and labor supply. Here belong most of the industries in the Missouri River towns as well as some of those located at the larger railroad centers, such as Springfield and Joplin.

The table below shows the value of manufactures and number of people employed in cities of more than 10,000 in 1909. The rank of Jefferson City is due largely to the convict labor employed at the penitentiary, secondarily to the boot and shoe industry. Because of low taxes and rentals, cheap labor, and competitive freight rates the shoe industry has extended from St. Louis to Missouri River towns, such as

	Value of Product	No. of People Employed
Jefferson City........	$5,446,000	1,572
Springfield...........	5,382,000	2,473
Joplin...............	4,136,000	1,089
Webb City..........	777,000	212

Jefferson City, Hermann, and Washington. In Springfield, Webb City, and Carthage the milling of flour is first in importance. These cities are in an important wheat-growing region and have been manufacturing flour for many years. They are so situated also that they can secure hard wheat cheaply from the West. Springfield has developed a variety of manufactures to supply the demands of the large agricultural section for which it serves as trading center. These are most notably wagons, furniture, saddles, and stoves. The making of saddles and of wagons are among the oldest industries, and apparently originated when Springfield was an outfitting point for travelers and emigrants setting out for the Southwest. Springfield also has a large number of men employed in the railroad car shops. In Joplin lead smelting has remained the leading industry. The small amount of fuel required has enabled the manufacture of lead at Joplin, whereas the zinc ore, because of its large requirements of fuel, is mostly shipped away to be smelted. Washington is the center of the cob-pipe industry, producing the greater part of the world's output. The industry is due to personal initiative, aided by the adaptation of the river bottom lands to the growth of large cobs. At present there are many farmers engaged in raising a special variety of corn with large cobs. Few of these cities have any highly localized advantage for the manufacture of a particular product other than good transportation and labor. Most of those now engaged in manufacture were commercial centers first, and added manufacturing interests later, in a minor way.

CHAPTER XV

TRANSPORTATION AND COMMERCE

WATERWAYS

The Mississippi is still an important highway for the eastern border. Regular service is maintained between St. Louis and local points, usually as far as Cape Girardeau or Commerce. Other boats, operating between St. Louis and the lower Mississippi or the Ohio and Tennessee rivers, make landings at the more important local ports. An important part of the products of the eastern counties is still shipped by water, therefore. On the Missouri, the swift current, the snags and sawyers, and the rapidly local bars have discouraged navigation. For a time there was only local service of very uncertain character. Recently, however, barge service between St. Louis and Kansas City has been resumed.

The Osage and Gasconade rivers are handicapped by their exceedingly devious courses, by the occurrence of large shoals caused by gravel bars, and by small volume in dry seasons. To maintain a satisfactory channel in these streams would require an excessive expense. The distance to which boats go up these rivers depends upon the stage of water. On the Osage River boats ply at irregular intervals, usually not above Tuscumbia, although Warsaw is head of navigation; on the Gasconade, Arlington is nominally at the head of navigation, but a boat rarely passes above Richfountain, in Osage County. Nevertheless, these two streams are of considerable commercial significance because they furnish an outlet to a country, difficultly traversed by land, in which railroad facilities are largely lacking. To the "bottom" farms situated along them the steamboat is the usual means of marketing the crops, which are stored, convenient to the river's bank, until a boat arrives. To those who live at some distance from the river the most irregular schedule of shipping is a very great disadvantage.

Many streams which are not navigable for boats are important for rafting lumber.

RAILROADS

Of the 2,500 miles of railways in the Ozark Highland of Missouri approximately 30 per cent are in the Springfield Plain, nearly as much in the Missouri River Border, about 10 per cent each in the Courtois Hills,

Mississippi River Border, and in the Central Plateau, and the remainder in the St. Francois, White River, and Osage-Gasconade districts. Nearly two-thirds of the total, therefore, is in the narrow border areas of the west and north.

The net is densest by far in the Springfield Plain (see Fig. 43), where the prairie surface has enabled construction of railroads at low cost, and where there are also the greatest profits to be secured in carrying the products of mine and farm. In this region important railroad junctions have been formed at Joplin, because of its mines, and at Springfield.

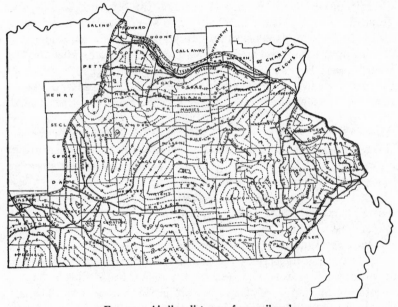

FIG. 43.—Air-line distances from railroads

The latter city is the first railroad center of southern Missouri. It lies approximately at the focal point from which the most important Ozark streams radiate, including several forks of the White and Gasconade rivers and the headwaters of the Spring, Sac, Pomme de Terre, and Niangua rivers. The even-crested watersheds between these streams form the most convenient location for railroads, which consequently intersect at Springfield. The Frisco main line, for example, south of St. Louis is located on the watershed between the Meramec and Bourbois rivers, crosses the Gasconade River (Plate XXIII a), and then follows the great watershed between the Gasconade and Osage to Springfield.

Its Kansas City–Memphis branch is located on the upland between the Pomme de Terre and Sac rivers north of Springfield and south of that city on the divide between the White and Gasconade systems (Plate XXIII b). The main shops and hospital of the Frisco Railroad are at Springfield. There are 2,500 railway employees in the city, constituting nearly a fourth of the wage-earners, and their annual pay-roll was said to aggregate $5,000,000 in 1915.[1]

The Missouri River Border forms an important passageway for trunk lines between the East and the far West. Here are main lines of the Missouri Pacific, the Rock Island, and the Missouri, Kansas, and Texas railroads. The Missouri Pacific and Missouri, Kansas, and Texas utilize the Missouri flood plain, with very low grades, but are subject to flooding by the river, and are in serious danger of washouts when freshets occur in the hills. The larger part of their traffic originates outside of this area, although the productivity of the river valley and its advanced economic development result in heavy local freight. The Rock Island, one of the most recent roads of the state, takes a somewhat more circuitous route between St. Louis and Kansas City by following remnants of the old peneplain, but has thus avoided expense in bridges, embankments, and cuts, as well as upkeep. The only difficult engineering problem which it has confronted has been the crossing of the rough belt adjacent to the Osage River. The roads on the northern border are in general parallel, no important roads penetrate the Ozarks from the Missouri River, and there are therefore no large railroad centers.

On the east, railway construction has been more difficult than in the other border regions, because the drainage is directly to the Mississippi by many small streams and because the region has neither extensive smooth uplands nor large valleys which railroads may follow. The two lines of the Iron Mountain, as well as the Bonne Terre Railroad, have followed valleys wherever they are available. The table[2] (p. 221) shows distances from St. Louis and altitudes on the main line of the Iron Mountain Railroad and indicates the grades encountered. The latest important railroad lines of the region are the St. Louis–Memphis line of the Frisco, and the Cape Girardeau Northern. The former is located at the base of the Mississippi River bluffs, and, like the main line of the Missouri Pacific, has low grades, but many curves and trestles (Plate XIII). It is the only direct line between St. Louis and Memphis west of the river. The Cape Girardeau Northern is built to tap fertile

[1] *Missouri, 1912, 1913, 1914*, p. 578.

[2] *Missouri Geol. Surv.*, VIII, 255.

regions of Hagerstown and Fredericktown soils hitherto unsupplied with rail facilities. In this the railroad has been only partially successful, as it has been meagerly financed and is not well connected with larger systems at present. In considerable part it was not operating in 1918. The Illinois Southern Railroad gives most direct connections with the coal fields of southern Illinois and hauling coal to the St. Francois mining district is its most important business. The only railroad center on the east is Bismarck, which owes its significance solely to the railroad junction. On the margins of the area are Cape Girardeau and Poplar Bluff, both at gateways between the Ozarks and the Mississippi lowlands. At Poplar Bluff the Black River opens a direct route of easy grade into the highland. This is followed by the main line of the Iron Mountain. A branch line of the Frisco, running southwest from Cape Girardeau along the margin of the southeastern lowlands, passes through Poplar

	Miles	Feet above Sea-Level
Irondale.............	73	796
Bismarck............	79	1,025
Iron Mountain.......	85	1,077
Middlebrook.........	87	1,139
Ironton.............	91	919
Tiptop..............	97	1,198
Des Arc.............	119	544
Gad's Hill..........	124	842
Piedmont...........	131	501

Bluff. Another branch railroad has been built from there to the mouth of the Ohio River. Poplar Bluff is therefore well supplied with rail facilities. It is also a rail division point. Cape Girardeau is the leading center of transportation in the southeastern part of Missouri, as it possesses an excellent river harbor, three railroads, and is benefited by the bridge across the Mississippi at Thebes.

The interior region is traversed by three railroads, the St. Louis–Springfield and the Springfield-Memphis lines of the Frisco system, and the White River Route of the Iron Mountain. In addition there are three local branches of the Frisco as well as the Missouri Southern and the Sligo and Eastern lines, all of which are in the Courtois Hills and are built principally to carry timber and ore. These short lines are devious and have heavy grades. In the Central Plateau the construction of railroads is hardly more difficult than in the plains of north Missouri. The main lines of the Frisco, for example, follow watersheds, which in large part are more nearly level than most glacial plains. Similarly, some years ago, a route was surveyed from Belle in Maries County, through Rolla and Licking into Arkansas, on which it is said that not a single bridge and almost no grading would be required. The resources and stage of development of the plateau, however, are such that the number of railroads is small.

The lack of rail facilities is a most serious handicap to the development of the Ozarks. Fig. 43 shows the air-line distance to rail transportation. Considering that the distances by road are greater than linear distances and that railroad stations are on the average at least five miles apart, the actual length of haul from farm to rail shipping-point is considerably more than the distances shown on this map. In the Springfield Plain the actual distance is at least one-third greater, and in the hill districts it may be doubled. In the border regions a farmer, living five miles in a straight line from the railroad, may haul two loads to town in one day only under the most favorable conditions. In the hills he can make only one round trip a day with a loaded wagon. In the second zone not more than one haul per day is possible by wagon, and in the hill sections twice as much time may be required. The first zone therefore is the only one having adequate transportation facilities. Areas located beyond the ten-mile line are seriously handicapped, and in places twenty-five to forty-five miles distant from rail transportation the exportation of farm crops and minerals, and in many cases also of timber, is virtually impossible. The map further understates the difficulty of transportation, as some of the timber and ore railroads are not public carriers, some charge higher freight rates than normal, and some, as the Missouri Southern Railway, have outlets only to the south, whereas the trade of the region is mostly with points to the north.

The sections which are remote from railroads are connected with the outside world by hack (stage) and freight service, usually operated on fairly regular schedule by professional teamsters. The war period has seen the abandonment of certain branch lines, as, for instance, the scrapping of the Ozark Valley Railway. Nor is the outlook for future building of branch railways promising. The promise of the future appears to lie in the substitution of automobile truck and trailer for the present teaming service on the ridge roads and in telferage for the hill sections. One additional major railway line, however, is needed badly, the line surveyed north and south from Rolla, which could be constructed as a ridge-top railroad virtually from the Missouri River to Arkansas, would give a north-south line through the heart of the Ozarks, and would open several large tracts that are now isolated.

ROADS

With few exceptions the main traveled highways of the Ozark region follow the crests of ridges (Plate XXIV *a*).   The exceptions are principally in the Springfield Plain and on the larger prairies of the Central Plateau, where the level surface allows equally facile communication in all directions.   The ridge roads drain well, are never flooded, and for the most part have easy grades.   They are located in most cases on the longest ridges, which require the fewest crossings of valleys. Where a valley is to be crossed the road approaches it by a spur or tributary valley and strikes directly across to the next ridge, within the shortest distance that the slopes of the valley permit.   On a few of the best roads the steepest part of the slope is negotiated by means of warps or serpentine bends, and long hills are supplied with balks which prevent washing and give the teams a chance to rest.   Most roads, however, are entirely innocent of such improvements.   In the hilly sections the main roads are located on the narrow, flinty crests of timbered ridges, the farms lying hidden in the valleys.   These roads are as desolate today as they were a century ago, when Schoolcraft wrote of them: "The traveler can no where go into Washington County, keeping the main roads, without passing over some of the most sterile soil in it.   For the sake of getting good roads, they have been carried along the tops of the most sterile flinty ridges, running in the required direction, and when one deviated too far, it has been left, and another ascended. . . . . The traveler riding along these, is . . . . impressed with the almost unvaried barrenness of the country."[1]

From the ridge roads private roads lead to the farms that are located in the valleys.   If the valleys are sufficiently large they are followed usually by secondary public roads.   Roads in the valleys are impassable at times because of freshets.   The road commonly follows gravel bars marginal to the stream or, if the stream is not large, even the stream bed itself.   After a freshet the valley roads usually need to be cleared of the driftwood that has lodged in them, and also must be relocated here and there to avoid quicksands, undercut banks, and washed-out fords.

The making and care of roads are very simple in the interior counties. A road is made usually by felling timber so that the axle of a wagon will clear the stumps.   The improvement of the road is left to travel.   The soil is thin and is underlain in most places by several feet of residual chert.   When a road is opened, therefore, the soil is speedily worn away, and the roadbed soon becomes a mass of well-packed chert, which forms

[1] *View of the Lead Mines*, p. 52.

an excellent natural macadam (Plate XXIV *b*).   The sharp chert causes tires and horseshoes to wear out rapidly.   Such a road has the slightly roughened surface and the compactness necessary to give good pulling power and drains exceedingly well.   With very little care it remains in excellent condition under average traffic.   For the most part, however, roads receive no attention.   As a result, especially where they lie on hillsides, they are usually in bad repair.   Lacking ditches along their sides, the roads serve as drains for the hillside and soon are gullied, in many cases down to bedrock.   When this happens, a new trail is cleared, soon to be destroyed in the same fashion.   This process may continue until the present road is flanked by older, gullied roads to a width of several hundred feet.   Plates XXV *a*, *b* show roads which have been injured to different degrees by erosion.   As indicated in Plate XXV *b* the damage to hill roads by erosion is greatest in regions of non-cherty soil.

Streams are crossed most commonly by means of fords, which are located at broad shallows, formed by gravel bars (Plate XXVI *a*). Many of these bars are probably residual rather than transported, and do not change their positions.   Because of the stability of these bars, the fords may remain at the same place for many years.   In some cases they have not changed appreciably since the first settlement of the region. They are usually impassable for a number of days in time of freshet and may be dangerous afterward, until the gravel and sand have again become compact.   Ferries are used on the larger streams where fords are wanting.   There are few bridges, in some counties not more than two or three.   The construction of bridges is one of the most serious questions which the hill counties have to face.   In every county there are districts from which a shipping-point can be reached without crossing any troublesome stream.   The residents of such localities usually oppose the appropriation of county funds for bridges.   Other settlements are handicapped seriously by the absence of bridges and are strongly in favor of their construction.   Unfortunately, in many counties bridges are needed at many places, and each location has its supporters, who in turn are antagonized by the partisans of other sites, with the not uncommon result that nothing is done.   Bridge building not rarely is the livest issue in the county politics, and county courts stand or fall by their attitude toward this problem.

In the border regions the main traveled highways are in fair or good condition.   Most of the border counties are beginning to use crushed rock to some extent, stone of excellent quality being generally available for this purpose. More commonly chert from the creek bars is used and makes a cheap and fairly satisfactory surface for roads, deficient, however, in binding qualities. The best roads are in the mining districts, which have not only abundant revenue for the construction of good roads, but can make use of the huge quantities of "chats," the finely crushed limestone from which the ore has been removed. Some of the richer agricultural counties, as Greene and Cooper, have many excellent roads. In some of the older counties, as Cape Girardeau, many roads follow curious and devious courses up and down hill. These are old roads which came to be in this manner. The old homesteads were built mostly on elevations, not infrequently detached from each other. Roads were gradually established from one farmhouse to the next. Although shorter and easier roads could be constructed, many of the old pattern still exist. In the border counties roads are being relocated so as to cross the valleys by long, easy slopes. This necessitates blasting and filling. Such a road is shown in process of construction on Plate XXVI *b*. The cost has prevented the general introduction of this type but it may be considered the permanent form to which roads of the entire region will approach ultimately.

COMMERCIAL CENTERS

In the sections which are deficient in railroad facilities commercial development is most primitive. Exports are largely cattle and lumber, in the handling of which a relatively small number of people are engaged. Because these districts sell little they buy little. Their wants are supplied largely by crossroads stores, which carry the ordinary staples and collect produce. These stores are operated commonly by men who combine storekeeping with other occupations, usually farming. Storekeeper, farmer, postmaster, and barber may be combined in one person. Within half a dozen miles of a railroad few such stores exist. Beyond that distance, however, they become increasingly numerous, as the people find it more and more difficult to get to a town.

Because of larger resources, easier communication, and more advanced development the number and size of commercial centers is greater in the border than in the central regions. In most parts of the Ozarks commercial advantages are not centralized in any locality to any great extent, and as a result there are many small towns rather than a few of considerable size. Of the twenty Ozark cities having a population in 1910 in excess of 2,500, nine are supported primarily by trade and transportation. These are Springfield, Cape Girardeau,

Poplar Bluff, Boonville, Washington, Neosho, West Plains, Frederick-town, and Farmington. Eight are dependent on mining industries, two are important solely as railroad division points, and one chiefly as the seat of the state government.

Springfield (35,201 inhabitants in 1910) is the largest city as well as the leading commercial center of the Ozarks. Its rank is due to its position relative to lines of communication in a fertile section. Because of its excellent shipping facilities it has developed a large wholesale and retail business. It has wholesale grocery, dry-goods, hardware, produce, drug, fruit, and other establishments. It is estimated that a thousand traveling men make their headquarters at Springfield because of its commercial advantages. After Springfield and the cities of the Joplin mining district, Neosho (3,661) is the largest city and the one most important commercially in the Springfield Plain. It is located at the convergence of three creeks, which have been utilized by as many railroads. The city has rail service in five directions and thus has become a commercial center. Most of the other trading centers of the Springfield Plain possess little geographic distinction. In this level region there are few sites that have any marked natural merit, their locations being more or less accidental. The successful cities[1] are either railroad junctions, as Pierce City (2,943), Ash Grove (1,075), and Crane (1,002), or county seats, selected because of central location, as Greenfield (1,434), Mount Vernon (1,161), and Cassville (781), or merely railroad shipping-points more or less central to a prosperous farm region, the settlement usually having been established at an early date, as Sarcoxie (1,311), Marionville (1,272), and Humansville (913). On the northern margin of the area Osceola (1,114) and Warsaw (824) are old ports on the Osage River which have retained part of their importance because two railroads cross at the former place and one terminates at the latter.

In the Missouri River Border most of the important trade centers are on the Missouri River. These places originated where good landings were combined with easy access to the interior. The cities of this class are Jefferson City (11,850), Boonville (4,252), Washington (3,670), Hermann (1,592), Glasgow (1,507), New Haven (855), New Franklin (794), and Chamois (649). Their commerce at present is carried mostly by rail, but they retain the advantage of competitive water rates. Because of floods the sites of these cities are mainly on the hilly upland,

[1] In Missouri a great many places of a few hundred inhabitants are incorporated as cities.

which gives to them a picturesque appearance. On the southern margin of the region a number of important centers have formed on the long watershed followed by the Frisco Railroad. Here is Rolla (2,261), on a narrow upland which forms a passage between the northern border and the Central Plateau. Southeastward and westward of Rolla is a rough hill country, and only through this passage is there easy connection between the northern part of the Central Plateau and the outside world. Rolla is the shipping-point, therefore, for an area extending fully fifty miles to the south. St. James (1,100), Sullivan (934), and Cuba (619) are shipping-points on the Frisco, located on the main divide between the Meramec and Bourbeuse rivers at points where secondary watersheds join the main ridge. Each of the smaller divides forms a strip of prairie a number of miles in length and several miles wide, on which are numerous farms. The territory tributary to each of these cities consists chiefly of one or two "prairies." On the Rock Island Railroad, Owensville (677) is located similarly. This type of location is illustrated west of the Osage River by California (2,154), Eldon (1,999), Versailles (1,598), and Tipton (1,273).

On the eastern border, Cape Girardeau (8,475), possessing rail and water facilities, and serving as a gateway between Ozark Highland and Mississippi lowlands, has kept far ahead of the other cities. Its recent rapid increase, more than 75 per cent in the decade 1900–1910, is due principally to extensive reclamation of fertile farmland by drainage in southeast Missouri, for which it is the chief entrepôt. The southeastern lowlands may be likened to a funnel with the apex pointing north. At this apex Cape Girardeau lies, and through it flows a large part of the trade of this section. Ste. Genevieve (1,967) and St. Mary's (702), like the Missouri River towns, have developed railroad interests to supply the waning river trade. Jackson (2,105) and Perryville (1,708) continue to be good trading centers, principally because they are surrounded by fertile farming districts, and because of their early start and accumulated prosperity. Similarly, in the St. Francois region the old nuclei of settlement retain their pre-eminence in commerce and population, as in the case of Farmington (2,613) and Fredericktown (2,632).

In the Ozark Center a majority of the important trade centers are situated on the upland at the intersection of strips of prairie. On the Frisco Railroad, Lebanon, Marshfield, Richland (884), and Dixon (715) are examples. Lebanon (2,430) is the center of trade for half a dozen counties, for long prairie ridges lead off from there to the east, south, and northwest and form numerous approaches to isolated parts of the

Gasconade and Big Niangua valleys.   Marshfield (1,193) lies where the railroad crosses the Elkland Plateau.   Other cities of this type are Mountain Grove (1,722) and Seymour (590), on the southern line of the Frisco, and Buffalo (820) and Ava (713).   In more dissected regions towns are located preferably at the margins of the river valleys, where converging tributaries give access from various directions.   The danger from floods usually prevents the location of a town immediately upon the floor of the larger valleys.   The site chosen is commonly on the lower slopes of tributaries adjacent to a larger valley.   The exact site is determined in a number of cases by a large spring which affords water and power.   To the valley margin type belong Salem (1,796), Willow Springs (1,401), Doniphan (1,225), Cabool (789), Steelville (773), Hartville (507), Linn Creek (435), and Waynesville (257).   In the White River country the "bench lands" provide ample room and security, as in the case of Galena (353), Branson. and others.

COMMERCIAL RELATIONS OF THE HIGHLAND WITH ST. LOUIS AND KANSAS CITY

The wholesale business of the Ozarks is done mostly with St. Louis and Kansas City, to a much smaller extent with Springfield and Joplin. Of the former two St. Louis is in much the better location.   (1) St. Louis is situated on the northeastern margin, and is therefore on a nearly direct line between the Ozarks and the industrial sections of the north and east.   Goods moving to or from the Ozarks through Kansas City, to the northwest of the Ozarks, make a détour in most cases.   (2) The railroads are so arranged that all counties east and north of a line drawn from Ripley County to Webster County and from there due north have better connections with St. Louis than with Kansas City.   (3) Springfield and Joplin divide a considerable territory with Kansas City but do not interfere with the St. Louis trade.   The greater part of the Ozark region, therefore, with the exception of the western border, trades mostly with St. Louis.

In the competition for the trade of the southwestern states the Ozark Highland is a handicap to St. Louis in favor of Kansas City.   On the north and east the territory tributary to St. Louis is small, due to the competition of Chicago.   The chief direction of expansion for the commerce of St. Louis is to the south and west.   Here, however, the Ozarks interpose a partial barrier, which has tended to aid the growth of Kansas City rather than of St. Louis.   From St. Louis the Frisco Railroad is the only direct line across the Ozarks to the Southwest.   The

Iron Mountain and Cotton Belt railroads, which skirt the southern margin of the Ozarks, are the two other important arteries that connect St. Louis with the Southwest. Kansas City, on the other hand, has the main lines of the Rock Island, Santa Fe, Missouri, Kansas and Texas, and other railways running directly to the southwest. These are built across a nearly level surface at low cost and are maintained at less expense than the roads operating through the Ozarks. Kansas City is also on a direct line between Chicago and a large part of the Southwest and serves as a distributing point for the latter city. It is natural, therefore, to find Kansas City appropriating an increasing share of the southwestern trade.

CHAPTER XVI

THE OZARKS AS RECREATION GROUND

FISHING AND HUNTING

The organized summer- and health-resort business is in its infancy in the Ozark region, which has been too inaccessible in large part and too. little known to attract the ordinary summer traveler. It is largely because of this fact that the region is frequented by many who enjoy hunting, fishing, and camp life. In a number of places large tracts of wild land are kept as game preserves by clubs or individuals. Probably the greatest number of visitors come primarily to fish. The Ozark streams provide bass fishing that is perhaps unsurpassed in the country. Jack salmon, sunfish, and other fish give variety to the sport. In muddy pools bullfrogs, eels, and catfish are taken. Live bait is secured readily from the vast numbers of minnows that feed in the shoals. In addition, at the proper season, there is usually good hunting for quail, squirrels, turkey, opossum, and raccoon. Add to these attractions a camping site on a clean gravel bar, near a spring of clear, cold water, in the midst of the forest solitude, and the conditions are almost ideal for a recreative vacation. In summer and autumn one may discover a camping party in almost any section of the Ozarks, no matter how remote. So long as no disorder occurs these parties are accorded the same freedom of the country which the native enjoys. It should be added that the last few years have seen in some sections a serious depletion of wild life due to the use of automobiles in hunting and fishing expeditions.

Camping vacations are popular, especially with business men from St. Louis and Kansas City. St. Louis has within an hour's ride beautiful Meramec Valley, to which in summer a special week-end train service is operated by both railroads. For those who have more time the upper Gasconade River, especially the Osage and Big Piney forks, and the Niangua River offer splendid camping opportunities. "Float" trips are becoming popular here. At some convenient point the party, usually accompanied by a guide, starts down the river in flat-bottomed boats, which are rowed or poled when desired. The canoe, although well suited to Ozark streams, is almost unknown. The trips are usually taken in very leisurely fashion, numerous stops being made to fish. Camp is pitched on a gravel bar or at a spring. A float may last a day or several weeks, and usually ends at a railroad point, from which the boats return to their starting-place.

Trips of this sort are also popular south of St. Louis. On the St. Francois River it is possible to float from Fredericktown through many miles of rugged igneous knobs to Greenville, Chaonia, or Fisk. On the Black River a float of similar nature may be begun at Centerville and continued to a convenient point on the Iron Mountain Railroad. One of the finest trips for sportsmen is down the Current River, beginning at some point south of Salem and continued to Van Buren or Doniphan.

Kansas City has no such regions near at hand. It has better access, however, than St. Louis to the James and White river valleys, the best of all vacation regions in the Ozarks. This section is frequented especially by people from Kansas City, Springfield, and the Joplin district. One of the best-known institutions of the regions is a float, usually from Galena to Branson or beyond. The Galena-Branson float is about a hundred and twenty-five miles and requires ordinarily about six days. The renting of boats and camp outfits has become a considerable business, and dozens of guides are engaged at one time in making the trip, the parties fishing and camping out on the way. This float is through a region which is not surpassed for scenery in the Middle West and which also affords some of the best fishing in the state.

FAMILY RESORTS

In the less remote parts families from the cities spend their summers. Resort hotels are few, the principal ones being at Leasburg and Bourbon on the Meramec, Jerome on the Gasconade, Hahatonka in Camden County, and Hollister on the White River. Many families, however, take summer boarders. There are numerous summer cottages of Kansas City people on James Fork at Galena and on White River at Hollister and Branson. The dam at Powersite forms a magnificent artificial lake, twenty-three miles long, called Lake Taneycomo. Due to the attractiveness of this lake and the rugged, semi-mountainous scenery which surrounds it, Hollister and Branson have become much-visited summer resorts. At the former place a Y.M.C.A. encampment and a Presbyterian camp have become widely attended institutions. A few St. Louis people have built cottages on the Meramec and Gasconade rivers and in Iron County, and many more board with farmers. The Frisco Railroad has recently met with some success in directing the attention of people of Memphis to the vacation opportunities in the eastern

Ozarks. Outside of the cities lying adjacent to the Ozarks the highland is almost unknown for vacation purposes. Even from St. Louis and Kansas City a much greater number of people leave annually for the eastern and northern resorts than come to the Ozarks. One reason for this undoubtedly is that a vacation in the Ozarks is attended by few of the ordinary amenities of city life and by none of the social allurements with which the established resorts are provided abundantly. Also, the Ozark climate is the climate of the rest of Missouri, with the exception that cottages built on the valley slopes enjoy cool nights. For persons of moderate means, who enjoy bathing, canoeing, fishing, forested hills, bare bluffs and ledges, and pioneer simplicity, the Ozarks are an excellent recreation ground. It costs little to reach any section from St. Louis, Kansas City, or other points in Missouri. The natives are unspoiled as yet, and all commodities, as well as lodging and board, can be secured at very low prices.

Health resorts are almost non-existent. Medicinal springs at De Soto, Boonville, and Paris Springs, Lawrence County, enjoy somewhat more than local repute. At Mount Vernon is the state hospital for tuberculosis. Otherwise the region is without sanitaria or spas.

PROPOSAL OF A STATE PARK

The increased attention which this region is receiving from summer visitors has resulted in a movement for the creation of a state park. The site spoken of most has been at Hahatonka, in Camden County. Here, in the midst of the rugged Osage River hills, is one of the largest springs in the world, which feeds an artificial lake. Here is also a fine natural bridge, as well as much hill and bluff scenery. At this place one of the very few resorts of the Ozarks has been established and has provided an opportunity for people to become acquainted with the beauties of the locality. Not far away are the bluffs and "balds" of the sinuous Big Niangua Valley. The upper Black River, with its "shut-ins," towering porphyry knobs, and unending forested slopes, is also to be considered as the site of a state park. At latest accounts the state was about to initiate its park program by the securing of the old Meramec Springs property, at one of the sources of the Meramec. The difficulty lies not in finding an area that will meet every need of a state park, but in making a beginning by concentrating attention on one of these sites. Few states have the choice of such excellent sites for public recreation, and the state of Missouri should not long delay taking the necessary steps for their preservation. When this happens it is to be hoped that the charm of the Ozarks will become known to a larger group of people, and that other areas will be set aside from time to time for the perpetual recreation of the public. In this manner, at little additional expense, sanctuary could be provided to the vanishing wild life of the Mississippi Valley, even now largely driven out of the agricultural districts of the prairie state, and fast being reduced even in the Ozark forests.

CONCLUSION

In wealth, population, and stage of development the Ozark Highland, considered as a whole, is far inferior to the plains of north Missouri. Accessibility by river and variety of resources, especially the presence of widely scattered lead deposits, made its borders the first part of Missouri to be settled and long gave to these border sections pre-eminence in state affairs. In time, however, the superior acreage and productivity of the prairies of north Missouri enabled them to outstrip the settlements of the highland border. As striking as the contrast between the highland and the rest of the state is that between the bordering and the central regions of the Ozarks. The former have made consistent progress from the earliest period, and are today in a very fair state of development. They have many moderately prosperous farmers and some wealthy ones. Industrial development is beginning. Transportation conditions are at least fairly adequate. These border areas possess the conservatism that comes of several resident generations, but they are far from being backward. The central region, on the other hand, is in a rather primitive condition, due primarily to isolation, in second place to poverty of the country, and not in any large degree to the inherent character of the people. Productive activities here for the most part are little specialized. One man may be alternately crop farmer, stock raiser, tie cutter, miner, and teamster. The Ozark Center again shows strong contrasts between its component parts. Of the interior regions the Central Plateau is more advanced than are the hill sections. These last constitute the area of sparsest population in the state (Fig. 44). The contrast between the various sections is well illustrated by the fact that of the cities and towns with a population in excess of 500 in 1910 seventy-four were in the Ozark border regions (of which thirty-two belonged to the Springfield Plain) and only twenty-four in the interior districts. Of these twenty-four, nineteen were located in the Central Plateau and only five in the three hill sections, which are of considerably larger extent than the plateau area.

The Ozark Highland will never possess the wealth nor the population of adjoining districts. It is quite incorrect, however, to consider it doomed perpetually to poverty and sparse settlement. In this part of the country the esteem of an area has always been determined primarily

234

by its adaptation to field agriculture and by its mineral wealth. Because the Ozarks are much inferior in production of grains to the adjacent prairies the aspiring settler has passed them by. This is too narrow a standard for judging of the merits of a region, yet this is the standard that has been set in the Middle West. The Ozarks possess opportunities, as yet but poorly recognized, which ultimately will bring the region into much better repute than it has at present. The following lines of

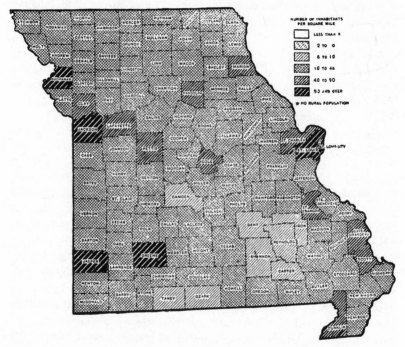

FIG. 44.—Population in 1910 (*Thirteenth Census, Statistical Atlas*)

development, in particular, are forecast. (1) The grain-farming system now in vogue is ill adapted to large sections of the area. The Ozark farmer is in much the same condition as the upland farmer of New England and New York. He cannot make an adequate living at growing corn in competition with his prairie neighbor. Agricultural practice must be readjusted. (*a*) Permanent agriculture will depend primarily on dairying and stock raising. For this type of farming the region is properly constituted. Throughout the highland are large tracts of hill land associated with small, but on the whole well-distributed, tracts of good plowland.   Some of the latter is on uplands, probably more lies in bottoms.   This association of good land for crop growing with cheap land for pasturage is of the greatest advantage to animal husbandry. The cultivable lands are sufficient for the production of most if not all of the grain and hay that may be required for the feeding of stock.   The upland farms especially could be maintained in a much more productive condition by this practice, much of the land having been sadly depleted through the long-continued removal of its crop.   Hill land that cannot be cultivated is considered at present nearly worthless.   A not inconsiderable part of it, however, can be converted into profitable pasturage. It must be remembered that these hillsides are not lacking in plant food. The soil is readily eroded when laid bare, it becomes rather dry in summer, and it lies on difficult slopes.   The chief problem is that of developing pastures which can maintain themselves under deficient moisture conditions of summer and which can stand grazing.   The bluestem and blue grass in the main are not satisfactory Ozark pasture grasses.   Much better results have been secured with orchard grass.   Lespedeza and sweet clover have demonstrated as volunteer growth that they succeed on almost any hillside.   Lespedeza has in fact become a very important factor in grazing in the southeastern counties and has improved the pasturage there very notably in the last few years.   Another interesting possibility is the Bermuda grass of the South, with its almost indestructible turf, which is now successfully established in a number of localities. With these and other pasture plants it may be expected that largely increased values will result for many tracts that now are producing virtually nothing.   The remarkable wealth of springs will also be a large asset in the development of a farm system centering about animal products, as will the mild winters and the nearness of a number of large markets.   In the farm economy of the future it may be possible to assign an important place to sheep, especially for the production of lambs and mutton.   (b) The area has superior adaptations to horticulture.   Its southern part has many localities in which peaches enjoy a high measure of immunity from unseasonable frosts.   Apples are known to do very well and most other fruits of intermediate latitudes may be grown successfully.   For commercial production the time at which these fruits would enter northern markets is favorable.   For a long time to come, however, it is idle to expect any large planting of orchards on rough hills.   The encroachment of the orchard areas will be rather on the areas now used for general farming than on the rough, wooded slopes.   The substitution of orchards for general fields is most likely to take place especially on the rather thin, stony soils of the valley margins. A most serious retarding feature at present is the lack of growers' organizations. Especially in the loess-covered border areas the experimental culture of nut trees should be encouraged. (2) Forestry is unknown locally. After deducting all areas that may be converted to some form of agricultural use there will still be thousands of square miles which should remain in timber. In the Courtois and Osage-Gasconade hill sections this will include tracts of many thousands of acres in one body. The present growth is largely unsatisfactory because of excessive density of stand. Under proper management the Ozarks may support oak forests which will become a permanent resource of national significance, since they may help to preserve our dwindling supply of hardwoods. (3) There is little doubt that Ozark streams and springs, properly developed, can furnish permanent power for more extensive manufactures than are now operated within the state from all sources of power. (4) Although the mineral wealth of the Ozarks does not equal the popular estimation, there are possibilities of the extension of mineral industries. (5) It is to be hoped that the many idyllic spots in which the region abounds may be preserved forever, and that with the continued urban growth in the surrounding areas the Ozarks may become more familiar to the people of the cities. There are few better localities for recreation than may be found in the Ozarks. These are all possibilities worthy of serious consideration. They will be realized only slowly and imperfectly, however, under the existing conditions of scattered individual initiative. The state of Missouri needs a policy of conservation and development for this area, which embraces about one-half of the state. Few matters, indeed, are of more vital concern to the state than this.

By developing along the lines sketched above the Ozark Highland will offer homes to a much larger number of people under much better conditions than at present. Few of them will accumulate large wealth, but, engaged in useful pursuits, they will be strangers to poverty, and they may participate equitably in the progress of the state. By thus becoming the seat of an enlightened and contented population, preserving still the democratic spirit which it now possesses, this region in the future may make its appropriate and sufficient contribution to our national life.

INDEX

INDEX

PLATE I

a, Pilot Knob, a noted porphyry elevation of typically symmetrical form

b, Shut-in portion of St. Francois Valley in St. Francois County, a basin of soft sedimentary rocks, from which the river enters a difficult gorge in igneous rock.

PLATE II

Bostwick

Bostwick

a

b

At a shut-in near Hunt's Farm, Reynolds County

c, Outlier of cherty limestone, probably Potosi, in the Farmington Basin

PLATE III

a, Cedar glade, typical of chert-free limestone areas. Bonne Terre formation, Ste. Genevieve County.

b, Spring at Waynesville, Pulaski County, issuing from base of cliff of Gasconade cherty limestone. Near the top of the cliff is the opening of a cavern and below it are several cavernous openings.

PLATE IV

Frisco Railroad

a, Little Piney Creek near Newburg.   Typical scene of an Ozark stream, showing alternating pools and shoals, bars of chert fragments, and a wagon trace following the stream bed.

b, Chert-floored bed of Roubidoux Creek at Waynesville

PLATE V

a, Cave at Ozark, Missouri

Frisco Railroad

b, Upland scene near Sullivan, Franklin County, showing characteristic even sky line of the Ozarks.

PLATE VI

a, Undissected upland south of Licking, Texas County, in the heart of the Ozarks

b, Abandoned farm on Berryville soil, near Forsyth, Taney County

PLATE VII

a, Intrenched meander of James River above Galena. *A* is an old slip-off slope; *B* a terrace, or "bench," its margin defined by the tree-clad slope.

b, Meander loop on James River at Virgin Bluff. A slip-off slope is well shown beyond the neck of the loop.

PLATE VIII

a, Bluff on Big Piney Fork of Gasconade above Newtown, Pulaski County

b, Bluff on James River below Galena

PLATE IX

a, Field in Howell soil near Ava, Douglas County

b, Pasture and stone fence on Howell soil, near Ava, Douglas County

PLATE X

a, Loess slopes south of Missouri River, Gasconade County

b, Bottom field being undercut by Roubidoux Creek, Pulaski County. The corn (6 to 9 ft. high) is a measure of the depth of the alluvial soil above the level of the creek.

PLATE XI

a, Contrast in stoniness agreeing with contrasted exposure of slope. At right, the excessively stony slope faces south. In the middle distance, at the left, is a north-facing slope with little chert exposed upon it. Near Ava, Douglas County.

Frisco Railroad

b, Big Blue Spring, near Bourbon

PLATE XII

a, Sink hole, near Newtown, Pulaski County. Note the submerged tree trunks. By the blocking of its outlet this sink hole has been converted into a pond.

b, Upland scene in Missouri River Border near Hermann

PLATE XIII

Mississippi River bluffs near McCoy

PLATE XIV

a, Rugged flint hills at Hahatonka, Camden County

Frisco Railroad

b, On the western edge of the Central Plateau, Cedar Gap

PLATE XV

a, Floating out ties at Boss, on Huzzah Creek

Frisco Railroad

b, Clearing land in Howell County

PLATE XVI

a, Clearing south of Vienna, Maries County

Frisco Railroad

b, Cornfields near Lebanon, Laclede County

PLATE XVII

Frisco Railroad

a, Upland pasture near Bourbon, Crawford County

Frisco Railroad

b, Angora goats in Laclede County

PLATE XVIII

a, Horse Show at Licking, Texas County

Frisco Railroad

b, Apple orchard at Lebanon

PLATE XIX

Frisco Railroad

a, Picking peaches in southeastern Missouri

Frisco Railroad

b, Spring house near Sullivan

PLATE XX

a, Log house in Big River Township, St. Francois County

b, Log house and log smokehouse near Galena, Stone County

PLATE XXI

Hill farm in Polk County

PLATE XXII

Frisco Railroad

a, Prairie farm near Sullivan, Franklin County

Frisco Railroad

b, Schlicht Springs Mill, Pulaski County

PLATE XXIII

Frisco Railroad

a, Frisco Railroad approaching the Gasconade Valley from the east by descending Little Piney Creek.

Frisco Railroad

b, Frisco Railroad, Kansas City–Memphis branch, located on divide between Gasconade and White River basins, at Cedar Gap.

PLATE XXIV

Frisco Railroad

a, Road along the crest of a flint ridge near Hahatonka

Frisco Railroad

b, Unimproved chert-surfaced road, characteristic of all parts of the Ozarks which have a cherty soil.

PLATE XXV

a, Gullied road near Hermitage. The gully in the background at the left was the original road. The present road is at the right. Chert washed down from the gully has been spread over the lower slope in the foreground.

b, Road south of Doe Run. The soil has been washed away and the sandstone bed rock exposed. Granite bowlders have rolled down from the upper slopes of the hill which this road ascends.

PLATE XXVI

Frisco Railroad

a, Ford on Spring Branch, White River

Weeks, Linn

b, Road located along valley side, beyond reach of floods. The old road was located in the creek bottom and was often impassable because of floods or wash-outs.